Auditory-Verbal Therapy and Practice

Warren Estabrooks, M.Ed., Dip. Ed. Deaf, Cert. AVT®
Editor

Alexander Graham Bell
ALEXANDER GRAHAM BELL
ASSOCIATION FOR THE DEAF AND HARD OF HEARING
3417 Volta Place, NW, Washington, DC 20007–2778

Library of Congress Control Number: 2006-927-568

ISBN 978-0-88200-223-1

The Alexander Graham Bell Association for the Deaf and Hard of Hearing (AG Bell) is a lifelong resource, support network and advocate for listening, learning, talking, and living independently with hearing loss. Through publications, outreach, training, scholarships, and financial aid, AG Bell promotes the use of spoken language and hearing technology. Headquartered in Washington, D.C., with chapters located in the United States and Canada and a network of international affiliates, AG Bell's global presence provides its members and the public with the support they need—close to home. With over a century of service, AG Bell supports its mission: *Advocating Independence through Listening and Talking!* For more information, contact AG Bell at (202) 337-5220, (202) 337-5221 (TTY), or visit the AG Bell website at www.agbell.org.

Alexander Graham Bell Association for the Deaf and Hard of Hearing, Inc.
3417 Volta Place, NW
Washington, DC 20007-2778, USA
www.agbell.org

Cover and interior design: Susan Westrate
Editorial: Francine Geraci
Manufacturing: Victor Graphics, Inc.
Printed in the United States

10 9 8 7 6 5 4 3

For the pioneers of Auditory-Verbal therapy and practice,

and for those who follow in their footsteps

to bring the gifts of listening and talking

to children who are deaf or

hard of hearing around the world

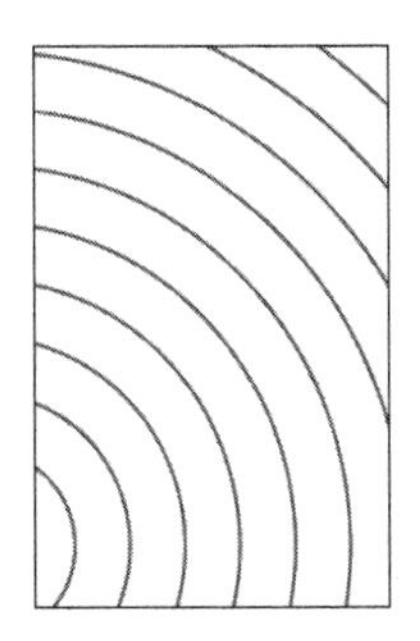

Contents

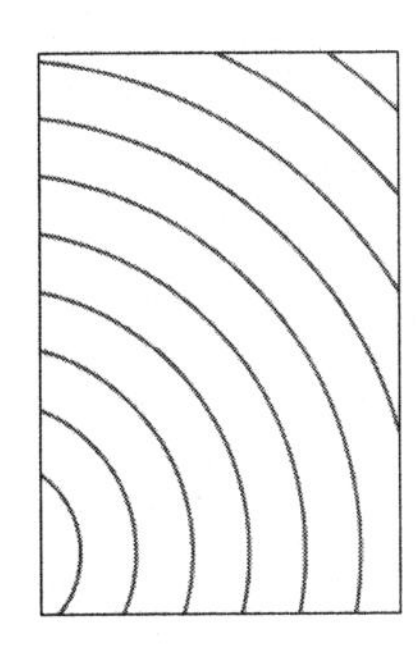

Acknowledgments

Auditory-Verbal Therapy and Practice is the result of a collaborative effort by professionals and parents whose passion and hard work brought this text to life over a period of three years. I express my gratitude to everyone:

- The contributing professional authors;
- The contributing parent authors;
- Mary Woodburn, executive assistant at the Learning to Listen Foundation;
- The professional staff of the Learning to Listen Foundation;
- The staff of the Alexander Graham Bell Association for the Deaf and Hard of Hearing;
- John Craig, president of the Learning to Listen Foundation;
- The board of directors of the Learning to Listen Foundation;
- Teresa Caraway, president of the AG Bell Academy for Listening and Spoken Language®;
- The children and families of the Learning to Listen Foundation;
- Francine Geraci, copy editor of *Auditory-Verbal Therapy and Practice;*
- Pierre-Roch Côté.

Warren Estabrooks
Editor

About the Editor

Warren Estabrooks, M.Ed., Dip. Ed. Deaf, Cert. AVT® is director of the Learning to Listen Foundation (LTLF) in Toronto, Ontario, Canada. He is also an international consultant who lectures worldwide about Auditory-Verbal therapy, auditory (re)habilitation, childhood hearing impairment and cochlear implant habilitation, and is instrumental in global training and development of professionals in related pediatric and adult disciplines.

Estabrooks is a Global Ambassador of the Alexander Graham Bell Association for the Deaf and Hard of Hearing and a founding director of the AG Bell Academy for Listening and Spoken Language®. He is an honorary director of AV Israel and Bundesverein für Auditiv-Verbale Therapie Deutschland e.V. (BVAVT) and a founding director of Auditory-Verbal International, Inc. (AVI). He is registered with the College of Teachers of Ontario and has held the position of assistant professor at the University of Toronto, Faculty of Medicine.

Estabrooks has been honored with the Susann Schmid-Giovannini Award for international excellence in auditory-verbal practice, the Professional of the Year Award from the International Organization for the Education of the Hearing Impaired (IOEHI), the Dr. E.W. Wight Memorial Scholarship, and the Peter R. Newman Humanitarian Award in recognition of his contribution to children who are deaf and their families around the world. He has been acclaimed to the Canadian *Who's Who* (2005) as a Canadian of influence. The Learning to Listen Foundation received the first International Voice of Deafness Award (2003) and has twice been honored as the International Program of the Year from the professional section of AG Bell (INPROSEC).

Estabrooks has made significant contributions to literature, including *Do You Hear That?* (1992), *Hear & Listen! Talk & Sing!* (1994), *Auditory-Verbal Therapy for Parents and Professionals* (1994), *The ABCs of AVT* (1995), *Cochlear Implants For Kids* (1998), *The Baby Is Listening* (2000), *50 FAQs About AVT (50 Frequently Asked Questions About Auditory-Verbal Therapy)* (2001), *Songs for Listening! Songs for Life!* (2003), *The Six-Sound Song* (2003), *Jacob's Journey* (2003), *Listen to This, Volume 1* (2004), *We Learned to Listen* (2005), and *Listen to This, Volume 2* (2006).

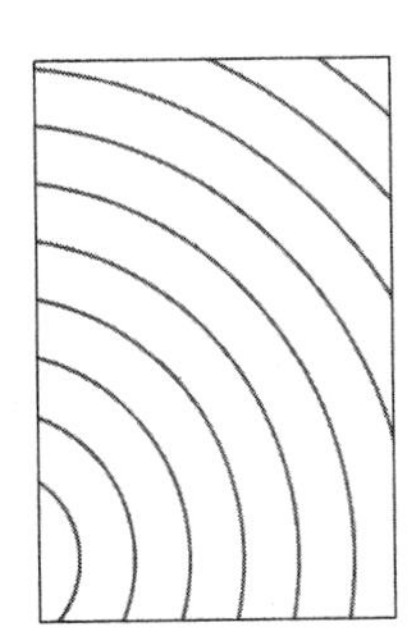

Preface

Auditory-Verbal Therapy and Practice began three years ago as a second edition of *Auditory-Verbal Therapy for Parents and Professionals* (Estabrooks, W. (Ed.), 1994) but it developed into something different. Over the past decade, the technological and educational landscapes for children who are deaf or hard of hearing have changed dramatically. Child-centered early intervention programs have given way to family-centered programs that are evolving in many places. The future of listening and speaking for children who are deaf or hard of hearing will continue to provide miracles that were only dreamed about in the past.

The auditory-verbal movement has grown greatly in many parts of the world, but there is much more to do. As more is revealed about the mystery and magic of hearing, listening, and spoken communication, the formation of global alliances with parents and professionals who are working in a variety of approaches is critical.

Through the Alexander Graham Bell Association for the Deaf and Hard of Hearing and a host of regional, national, and international organizations, parents and professionals will continue to find sources of comfort and courage as they face the challenges of teaching and raising their children who are deaf or hard of hearing.

Auditory-Verbal Therapy and Practice has been a labor of love, a collective effort of individuals who share the knowledge of the pioneers, personal commitment, and a spirit of community in order to help children and their families.

William Henry Channing said it best when expressing the dreams that many of us have for the children who may be influenced through this work:

> *To live content with small means;*
> *To seek elegance rather than luxury*
> *And refinement rather than fashion;*
> *To be worthy, not respectable, and wealthy, not rich;*
> *To study hard, think quietly, talk gently, act frankly;*
> *To listen to stars and birds, babes and sages, with open heart;*
> *To bear all cheerfully, do all bravely, await occasions, hurry never;*
> *In a word, to let the spiritual, unbidden and unconscious, grow up through the common—this is to be my symphony.*

It is my hope that this book will play a significant role in future generations of children who are deaf or hard of hearing and those who love them.

Warren Estabrooks
Toronto, Canada
Summer 2006

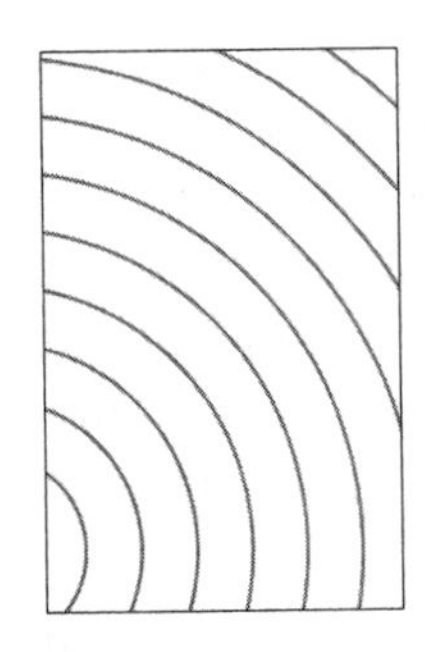

Introduction

Teresa H. Caraway, Ph.D., CCC-SLP, Cert. AVT®

On a bright August morning, 16 team members of the Hearing Enrichment Language Program (HELP) in Oklahoma City, Oklahoma, gathered for a strategic planning retreat. The facilitator asked the team to describe the history and significant events that shaped HELP since its beginning in 1994. Each member was encouraged to share the major steppingstones on the path of his or her journey in teaching children who are deaf or hard of hearing to listen and talk.

The first of these occurred in the spring of 1995, when we were searching for information to improve our professional skills so that we could best serve the two families in HELP who had bravely believed us when we told them that their children could learn to talk. A pamphlet had crossed our desks about a seminar on March 9, 1995, in Dallas, Texas, entitled, "A Little Hearing Can Go a Long Way," being given by Warren Estabrooks. Four of us made the three-hour drive south to Dallas, cautiously hopeful that we might return home with some valuable practical information. Little did we know how that day would be the beginning of a mentorship and friendship that would profoundly change us and the future of children who are deaf or hard of hearing and their families in Oklahoma.

Warren shared his knowledge, passion, and commitment to helping children who are deaf or hard of hearing learn to listen and talk, and we were captivated. Even though we had a significant background in child language development and teaching children who are deaf or hard of hearing, we watched in amazement as he demonstrated how children with profound hearing losses were actually listening, talking, and participating in conversations through audition, using the auditory-verbal approach. Never before had we heard children who were deaf or hard of hearing with speech, language skills, and vocal quality like those of their hearing peers! Never before had we seen children who were deaf or hard of hearing engaged in spoken conversations, developed through listening. Never before had we seen children who were deaf or hard of hearing use listening as a strength!

The four of us bombarded Warren with questions. Could we learn to do Auditory-Verbal therapy? How could we learn more about this approach? Did he think it was possible for us to experience the same outcomes with children and families in Oklahoma? Would he come to Oklahoma City? Could we go to Toronto to learn more? What books or articles could we read? How might we begin?

Warren was encouraging and resoundingly confident that we could learn about Auditory-Verbal therapy. He traveled to Oklahoma, and we traveled to Canada in order to improve our knowledge and skills. He mentored and coached us, and he encouraged us to the next stage of our journey—to sit for the examination to become certified. Consequently, in 1998, two of us became certified Auditory-Verbal therapists.

These steppingstones have created a well-established pathway for children who are deaf or hard of hearing in Oklahoma. Today, HELP serves over 120 children and their families in weekly Auditory-Verbal therapy sessions. Children with profound hearing losses are entering mainstream schools with the speech and language skills equal to those of their hearing peers.

As with many others in this field, all this started with our vision and passion that children in Oklahoma who are deaf or hard of hearing would have the opportunity to learn to listen and talk. Many people share this same vision, and are using it to create similar opportunities for children in many parts of the world. Some of us are parents who step onto the path when a child with hearing loss is born into our family and we search for guidance, hope, and encouragement. Some of us are professionals seeking to improve our knowledge and clinical skills so that we are better able to serve the families who want the best for their children. We are sojourners together on this path. Each of us is searching and learning.

We find encouragement in the knowledge that the pioneers of Auditory-Verbal therapy laid the groundwork upon which we travel. Families who have persevered, and dared to dream that their children who were born deaf could learn to listen and talk through Auditory-Verbal therapy, have offered us all hope, and we all have become empowered. Professionals who have continued to define Auditory-Verbal therapy through research, writing, mentoring, presentations, and programs have given us wisdom from which we have gained strength and patience.

No matter where one finds oneself on the path, this book, *Auditory-Verbal Therapy and Practice,* will be a significant steppingstone in forging ahead as we learn from one another. The future has never been brighter for children with hearing loss. It is possible for them to develop exceptional conversational skills, reading skills, and academic competencies because of early identification and diagnosis of hearing loss through infant hearing screening, advances in hearing technology, medical intervention, and Auditory-Verbal therapy and practice. Within hours of birth, innovative testing procedures can screen an infant's hearing to indicate whether further diagnostic tests are warranted, allowing early identification of hearing loss. Advances in contemporary hearing technology—including digital hearing aids, personal FM systems, sound field FM systems, and cochlear implants—provide improved access to intelligible speech. As a result, intervention begins immediately. As babies are fitted with hearing aids and cochlear implants, greater language enrichment can be maximized during the critical periods of brain neural plasticity (Flexer, 2000; Northern & Downs, 1991).

It is during these critical periods of development that a child's brain is learning rapidly from new experiences. Learning changes the brain because it can rewire itself with each new stimulation, experience, and behavior (Carter, 1999). As a result, the connections in the brain that make learning possible are multiplied and become stronger. As a child with a hearing loss is fitted with appropriate advanced hearing technology, the speech and language of others and environmental sounds become accessible and intelligible, and the opportunity for auditory brain development occurs (Flexer, 2000). This stimulation of the auditory pathways is needed for the brain to organize itself for spoken language (Sharma, 2004). That is why ongoing, aggressive audiological management of a child's hearing loss by a qualified pediatric audiologist and the wearing of hearing aids, cochlear implants, or both during all waking hours are critical.

As children experience new words through audition, the cells in the auditory cortex of the brain are developed so that the children will comprehend all the sounds of speech. In 1995, Hart and Risley at the University of Kansas conducted a study involving 42 families with children who had typical hearing, in which the families recorded all interactions with their children from infancy. The researchers found that children with typical hearing hear an average of 2,153 words per hour, and extrapolated that by 4 years of age a child hears over 46 million words. It has been estimated that a child learns approximately 10 new words each day, or roughly one new word each hour and a half (Howard, 2000).

Therefore, a staggering amount of listening and talking is required for children who are deaf or hard of hearing if they are to keep up with their hearing peers. Listening and spoken language are the foundation of literacy skills and academic competencies. James Britton (1970) said, "Reading and writing float on a sea of talk." It stands to reason, therefore, that children with hearing loss should be swimming in an ocean of spoken language! To do so, they must have access to intelligible speech, be taught to listen, and have opportunities to participate in conversations with adults, older children, and hearing peers. Conversational exchanges provide children the opportunity to learn to listen and interpret what others are saying and, at the same time, to put into words their own thoughts, feelings, and messages (Dougherty, 1999). That is the mission of *Auditory-Verbal Therapy and Practice.*

The journey of helping a child who is deaf or hard of hearing learn to listen and speak through Auditory-Verbal therapy is shared by many, walking side by side, guiding and encouraging one another. Steppingstones direct our footsteps along the auditory-verbal path that has been forged by its pioneers and envisioned by its practitioners. Twists and turns in the path are guaranteed. There are few dull moments, and there are new opportunities at every bend. The possibilities for children who are deaf or hard of hearing to develop exceptional conversational abilities, literacy skills, and academic competencies are incredible today. This wonderful book, *Auditory-Verbal Therapy and Practice*, provides the theory, practice, and current research needed to turn these possibilities into realities for children who are deaf or hard of hearing around the world. Enjoy the journey.

REFERENCES

Britton, J. (1970). *Language and Learning.* Coral Gables, FL: University of Miami Press.

Carter, R. (1999). *Mapping the Mind.* Berkeley and Los Angeles: University of California Press.

Dougherty, P. (1999). *How to Talk to Your Baby: A Guide to Maximizing Your Child's Language and Learning Skills.* New York: Avery.

Flexer, C. (2000). "How are new amplification technologies changing everything that we know about deafness?" In L. Robertson (Ed.), *Literacy Learning in Children Who Are Deaf or Hard of Hearing* (pp. 1–21). Washington, DC: Alexander Graham Bell Association for the Deaf and Hard of Hearing.

Hart, B., & Risley, T. (1995). *Meaningful Differences in Everyday Parenting and Intellectual Development in Young Children.* Baltimore: Brookes.

Howard, P. (2000). *The Owners' Manual for the Brain: Everyday Applications from Mind–Brain Research* (2nd ed.). Austin, TX: Bard Press.

Northern, J.L., & Downs, M.P. (1991). *Hearing in Children* (4th ed.). Baltimore: Williams & Wilkins.

Robertson, L. (2000). *Literacy Learning for Children Who Are Deaf or Hard of Hearing.* Washington, DC: Alexander Graham Bell Association for the Deaf and Hard of Hearing.

Sharma, A., Tobey, E., Dorman, M., Martin, K., Gilley, P., & Kunkel, F. (2004). "Central auditory maturation and babbling development in infants with cochlear implants." *Archives of Otolaryngology, Head and Neck Surgery, 130*(5), 511–516.

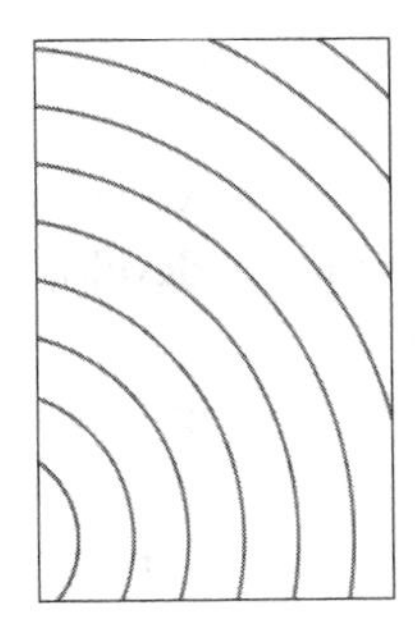

CHAPTER 1

Auditory-Verbal Therapy and Practice

Warren Estabrooks, M.Ed., Dip. Ed. Deaf, Cert. AVT®

Never before have children who are born deaf or hard of hearing, or those who acquire deafness early in life, had such potential to hear, listen, and talk. They can learn to listen to their own voices, the voices of others, and all the sounds of the world around them with greater ease than in the past. With unprecedented advances in hearing technology, and the assistance of professionals who are trained in family-centered education and therapy, most children who are deaf or hard of hearing can learn to communicate efficiently using natural spoken language developed primarily through *listening*.

As universal screening for hearing loss in newborns becomes the standard of care, more parents of children who are deaf or hard of hearing desire family-centered intervention to help their children learn to listen and talk. Early identification and prompt intervention mean that more children can grow up without the speech and language delays that historically have been associated with childhood deafness. With appropriately fitted, state-of-the-art hearing aids, cochlear implants, and other hearing technology, children who are deaf or hard of hearing can benefit significantly from Auditory-Verbal therapy more than ever before.

Auditory-Verbal therapy (AVT) is an early intervention approach for children who are deaf or hard of hearing and their families. AVT focuses on education, guidance, advocacy, family support, and the rigorous application of techniques, strategies, conditions, and procedures that promote optimal acquisition of spoken language through listening.

The primary goals of Auditory-Verbal therapy are to guide parents in helping their children develop intelligible spoken language through listening, and to coach parents in advocating their children's inclusion in mainstream schools. Ultimately, parents gain confidence that their children will have access to the full range of educational, social, and vocational choices.

Even in their early auditory-verbal sessions, working in partnership with an Auditory-Verbal therapist, parents will quickly gain hope and encouragement and will learn that

- hearing aids, cochlear implants, and other hearing technology are critical for the development of listening and spoken communication;

- the ability to hear and listen will facilitate their child's development of spoken communication;
- active participation, both in Auditory-Verbal therapy sessions and everyday activities with their child, will maximize the child's opportunities to develop listening and spoken communication as efficiently as possible;
- the first years of life are critical periods of neurological and linguistic development (Pollack, Goldberg, & Caleffe-Schenck, 1997);
- listening, speech, and language can be acquired in the same way as children with typical hearing, following the same sequences of development;
- the child can attend mainstream schools;
- the family will be coached, guided, and supported by a team of highly qualified professionals.

In AVT, the collective processes involved in hearing and listening become a major force in nurturing the development of the child's personal, social, and academic life. When Auditory-Verbal therapy is carried out with the necessary thoughtfulness, expertise, guidance, and love, many children who are deaf or hard of hearing develop exceptional listening skills and spoken language competence (Ling, 1993; Estabrooks, 2001).

HISTORY OF THE AUDITORY-VERBAL APPROACH[1]

In February 1978, following a colloquium by Daniel Ling, the Larry Jarret Foundation of the Helen Beebe Speech and Hearing Center sponsored a two-day conference in Easton, Pennsylvania, which brought together Daniel Ling, Doreen Pollack, and Helen Beebe. These pioneers attended to support the auditory approach and to combine their independent energies. The meeting was chaired by George Fellendorf, Ph.D., former executive director of the Alexander Graham Bell Association for the Deaf. Shortly after this historic gathering, the International Committee on Auditory-Verbal Communication (ICAVC) was formed.

In 1981, the board of directors of AG Bell invited ICAVC to join them as a "special committee." This relationship continued until October 1986, at which time the Central Committee of ICAVC voted to establish an independent, non-profit organization in order to achieve the goal of increasing the availability and effectiveness of the auditory-verbal approach. ICAVC thereby evolved into Auditory-Verbal International, Inc. (AVI).

The origins of the auditory-verbal approach, however, go much farther back. Victor Urbantschitsch wrote *Auditory Training for Deaf Mutism and Acquired Deafness* in 1895. Urbantschitsch published his work (in German; its translation was completed in 1981 by S. Richard Silverman, Ph.D., Director Emeritus of the Central Institute for the Deaf) about the auditory potential of most children who

---

[1] This section was written by Donald M. Goldberg, Ph.D., CCC-SLP/A, Cert. AVT®, and is adapted from his article in W. Estabrooks (Ed.), *50 FAQs About AVT* (pp. 9–12) (Toronto: Learning to Listen Foundation, 2001).

were deaf. As noted by Silverman, Urbantschitsch's central argument was "that the education and ultimately the emotional and social adjustment of profoundly deaf children could be facilitated by methodical and persistent auditory training (exercises) that exploited any remnant of residual hearing by stimulating what he termed a dormant auditory sense" (p. viii). Similarly, Max Goldstein, founder of the Central Institute for the Deaf in St. Louis in 1914, has been credited with founding the Acoustic Method (1939) and advancing the notion regarding the power of audition. Goldstein worked with Urbantschitsch and was reportedly encouraged "to introduce his method to America and to convince all who would listen that congenitally deaf children could, by his approach, learn to talk intelligibly" (Silverman, in Urbantschitsch, 1981, p. x).

Goldstein, Emil Froeschels, and other Europeans who had fled Nazi Germany arrived in the United States and brought with them the seed that would germinate into today's auditory-verbal philosophy.

The idea that most "deaf" children had some remnant of residual hearing, coupled with the advent of wearable hearing aids in the 1940s, allowed auditory-verbal pioneers to begin exploring the belief that the use of amplified hearing might permit children who are deaf or hard of hearing to learn to listen, to process verbal language, and to speak. Daniel Ling and Agnes ("Nan") Phillips, first in Britain and subsequently at the Montreal Oral School for the Deaf and at McGill University in Montreal, Canada; Doreen Pollack, initially at Columbia Presbyterian Medical Center in New York City and later at the University of Denver and Porter Memorial Hospital in Denver; and Helen Beebe in New York City and Easton, Pennsylvania, are recognized as auditory-verbal pioneers.

Another gifted auditory-verbal clinician was Dr. Ciwa Griffiths in New York and later in California as founder of the Hear Center in Pasadena (Griffiths, 1974). A variety of the colleagues and students of Ling, Pollack, and Beebe, as well as other independent practitioners, also played significant roles in the development of the auditory-verbal approach. They include Susann Schmid-Giovannini in Switzerland; Marian Ernst with Pollack in Colorado; Antoinette Goffredo with Beebe in Easton; Louise Crawford at the Hospital for Sick Children in Toronto, Canada; and Enelda Luttmann in Mexico City, among others.

Helen Beebe, working with Froeschels, a physician, wrote, "Both in home training and in therapy, lip-reading should be avoided as much as possible. Otherwise the child will become dependent upon lip-reading and will not use his hearing" (1953). In Beebe's book, *A Guide to Help the Severely Hard of Hearing Child* (1953), she described her initial work with her first pupil, Mardee. Mardee's deafness was suspected at 15 months. Beebe made use of the Direct Tone Introduction Test, using Urbantschitsch whistles, to confirm the hearing loss (Froeschels & Beebe, 1946). Because of Mardee's small size, it was recommended that she be initially trained with the use of an ear tube. Beebe wrote that the "tube was made out of an ordinary kitchen funnel with a small rubber tube attached to it. At the other end was an ear olive. For short periods of time each day, we would say syllables through the tube. This was done to stimulate her hearing and prepare her for the later use of a hearing aid" (1953, p. 10). When

Mardee was about 2 years old, Beebe continued to explore the "unisensory" training with a primitive hearing aid, and thus Mardee became Beebe's first auditory-verbal student. Beebe noted in 1953, "It is my opinion that when a child has any usable hearing, he should be given a hearing aid for constant use and his hearing should be trained. In this way, he will have a more normal life and most certainly he will have more normal speech" (p. 11).

It is interesting to note that as Beebe and Froeschels began, so too did pioneer Doreen Pollack. Pollack was later to move from New York to Colorado, where she developed a comprehensive "acoupedic" program. The term acoupedics was copyrighted and first described to the professional community in the seminal and classic book, *Educational Audiology for the Limited-Hearing Infant* (1970). In this treatise, Pollack outlined the guiding principles of auditory-verbal practice, which have become the hallmark of the philosophy. Subsequent editions of the Pollack text (1985, 1997) have continued to explain and explore the auditory-verbal philosophy, including the impact on the approach of modern technology, such as improved hearing aids and cochlear implants (Pollack et al., 1997).

With the continued development of new technology, we are indebted to all pioneers of the auditory-verbal approach for their vision regarding the power of hearing and the groundbreaking reality that it is indeed possible for a child who is deaf or hard of hearing to learn to listen and develop spoken language. Thousands of infants and children who are deaf or hard of hearing and their families have benefited immeasurably from their wisdom, knowledge, and nonwavering belief in the "power of hearing."

Today, an exciting development is on the horizon. It has recently been concluded that the rationale for a separate membership organization (AVI, Inc.) needed to be re-evaluated. At a strategic planning meeting in early 2004, tentative decisions were made to focus AVI's efforts on the certification process and to investigate the integration of AVI's organization with the Alexander Graham Bell Association for the Deaf and Hard of Hearing. Immediately following the formal adoption of the revised Principles of Auditory-Verbal Practice, in Toronto, 2005, the Board of Directors of AVI voted to dissolve AVI, Inc., ask for a legally required membership vote to do so, and move forward under the leadership of the Bell Association. The certification process leading to the Cert. AVT® accreditation will continue at AG Bell under the direction and leadership of the Academy Board, with representation by several leaders who have earned the credential of Cert. AVT®.

RATIONALE FOR AUDITORY-VERBAL PRACTICE[2]

The following points provide the historical rationale supporting auditory-verbal practice. (See Chapter 10 of this book for a discussion of current research on Auditory-Verbal therapy.)

- The majority of children who are deaf or hard of hearing have some residual

2 This section was adapted from Donald M. Goldberg, Ph.D., CCC-SLP/A, Cert. AVT®, et al., and is used, with permission, from *The Volta Review*, 95(3), 183–184 (Summer 1993).

hearing. This fact has been known for decades (Bezold & Siebenmann, 1908; Goldstein, 1939).

- When properly aided, children who are deaf or hard of hearing can detect most, if not all, of the speech spectrum (Beebe, 1953; Goldstein, 1939; Johnson, 1975, 1976; Ling, 1989; Ling & Ling, 1978; Pollack, 1970, 1985; Ross & Calvert, 1984).
- Once all available residual hearing is accessed through technology (e.g., binaural hearing aids, acoustically tuned earmolds, FM units, cochlear implants) in order to provide maximum detection of the speech spectrum, then a child will have the opportunity to develop language in a natural way through the auditory modality. That is, a child who is deaf or hard of hearing need not automatically be a visual learner. Hearing, rather than a passive modality that receives information, can be the active agent of cognitive development (Boothroyd, 1982; Goldberg & Lebahn, 1990; Robertson & Flexer, 1990; Ross & Calvert, 1984).
- For the child to benefit from the "critical periods" of neurological and linguistic development, the identification of hearing impairment, use of appropriate amplification and medical technology, and stimulation of hearing must occur as early as possible (Clopton & Winfield, 1976; Johnson & Newport, 1989; Lennenberg, 1967; Marler, 1970; Newport, 1990).
- If hearing is not accessed during the critical language-learning years, a child's ability to use acoustic input meaningfully will deteriorate due to physiological and psychosocial factors (retrograde deterioration of auditory pathways; deficits in attention, practice, and learning) (Evans, Webster, & Cullen, 1983; Merzenich & Kaas, 1982; Patchett, 1977; Robertson & Irvine, 1989; Webster, 1983).
- Current information about normal language development provides the framework and justification for the structure of Auditory-Verbal therapy. That is, infants, toddlers, and children learn language most efficiently through consistent and continual meaningful interactions in a supportive environment with significant caretakers (Kretschmer & Kretschmer, 1978; Lennenberg, 1967; Leonard, 1991; Ling, 1989; MacDonald & Gillette, 1989; Menyuk, 1977; Rhoades & Chisholm, 2000; Ross, 1990).
- As verbal language develops through the auditory input of information, reading skills can also develop (Geers & Moog, 1989; Ling, 1989; Robertson & Flexer, 1990).
- Parents in auditory-verbal programs do not have to learn sign language or Cued Speech. More than 90% of parents of children who are deaf or hard of hearing have normal hearing (Moores, 1987). Studies show that over 90% of parents with normal hearing do not learn sign language beyond a basic preschool level of competency (Luetke-Stahlman & Moeller, 1987).
- If a severe or profound hearing impairment automatically makes an individual neurologically and functionally "different" from people with normal hearing (Furth, 1964; Myklebust & Brutton, 1953), then the auditory-verbal philosophy would not be tenable. The fact is, however, that outcome studies

show that individuals who have been taught since early childhood through the active use of amplified residual hearing are, indeed, independent, speaking, and contributing members of mainstream society (Goldberg & Flexer, 1991, 1997; Ling, 1989; Yoshinaga-Itano & Pollack, 1988).

Auditory-Verbal Philosophy

In 1987, the board of directors of AVI, Inc. adopted the following position statement[2]:

> The auditory-verbal philosophy is a logical and critical set of guiding principles. These principles outline the essential requirements to realize the expectation that young children who are deaf or hard of hearing can be educated to use even minimal amounts of amplified residual hearing. Use of amplified residual hearing in turn permits children who are deaf or hard of hearing to learn to listen, process verbal language and speak.
>
> The goal of auditory-verbal practice is that children who are deaf or hard of hearing can grow up in regular learning and living environments, enabling them to become independent, participating and contributing citizens in mainstream society. The auditory-verbal philosophy supports the basic human right that individuals with all degrees of hearing impairment deserve an opportunity to develop the ability to listen and to use verbal communication within their family and community constellations.

Principles of Auditory-Verbal Practice[3]

On January 11, 2006, the following 10 principles of Auditory-Verbal Practice were adopted by the AG Bell Academy for Listening and Spoken Language. All 10 principles are to be followed by professionals who provide auditory-verbal services.*

1. **Promote early diagnosis of hearing loss in newborns, infants, toddlers, and children, followed by immediate audiologic management and Auditory-Verbal therapy.**
   Prompt detection of hearing loss followed by immediate audiologic management during early infancy is critical. Prolonged auditory deprivation during the first years of life will create significant delays in receptive and expressive language development. Auditory-Verbal therapy is a natural companion to audiologic management in that therapists can guide parents[4] in helping their child maximize his or her newly acquired auditory potential so that receptive and expressive language delays can be prevented.

2. **Recommend immediate assessment and use of appropriate, state-of-the-art hearing technology to obtain maximum benefits of auditory stimulation.**
   Once hearing loss is identified, immediate assessment and use of appropri-

---

[2] Adapted from Pollack, 1985, 1997; incorporated by AVI, July 2005. Adopted by the AG Bell Academy for Listening and Spoken Language, November 2005.

[3] Adapted from Pollack, Goldberg, & Caleffe-Schenck, 1997; Pollack, 1985, 1970. Copyright by the AG Bell Academy for Listening and Spoken Language®, January 2006.

[4] The term "parents" also includes grandparents, relatives, guardians, and any caregivers who interact with the child.

* The author thanks Karen MacIver-Lux for the expansion of the "Principles of Auditory-Verbal Practice."

ately fitted hearing technology is necessary so that the child can begin to receive auditory stimulation. The sounds of the child's environment, particularly speech sounds, must reach the auditory centers of the brain so that growth can take place. Growth and maturation of the auditory pathways and brain centers will help the child develop the listening skills necessary for natural-sounding spoken communication.

Exciting advances in hearing aids and cochlear implant technology have been made in the last decade. Improvements in hearing technology currently address such problems as distance from the speaker, noise interference, directional confusion, frequency distortion, and limited frequency range, among others. As a result, opportunities for incidental language learning have increased, and many children with profound hearing losses can now match hearing peers in language development when compared on the basis of "hearing age."

A suggested protocol for systematic audiologic management was developed by audiologists who are Certified Auditory-Verbal therapists (Appendix A [AVI Audiologic Protocol]).

3. Guide and coach parents to help their child use hearing as the primary sensory modality in developing spoken language without the use of sign language or emphasis on lipreading.

Hearing impairment is a family affair; it can alter family dynamics by changing expectations and the ways in which family members communicate. In order for children to attain success in Auditory-Verbal therapy, parents must become active listeners and effective spoken communicators. Children learn best from their parents, and they will feel encouraged when they see that their parents have confidence in their listening skills with hearing aids, cochlear implants, or both. As well, listening (rather than watching) helps children develop natural-sounding speech. Lipreading does not encourage the development of the auditory feedback loop system, which helps children monitor their own speech. Sign language is used by those who are deaf or hard of hearing and who have chosen vision as their primary mode of receiving and communicating information. Parents who have chosen Auditory-Verbal therapy have made the commitment to provide the most productive and positive experiences to stimulate verbal communication through listening.

4. Guide and coach parents to become the primary facilitators of their child's listening and spoken language development through active, consistent participation in individualized Auditory-Verbal therapy.

Auditory-Verbal therapists are committed to guiding, counseling, and supporting parents, caregivers, and all family members. Auditory-Verbal therapists provide one-to-one Auditory-Verbal therapy sessions to maximize individual development of both the child as a listening and verbal communicator and the parents as the primary models. Individualized sessions permit more effective diagnostic auditory-verbal treatment, greater attention to the uniqueness of the child and parents, and better outcomes. During auditory-verbal sessions, the therapist demonstrates to parents how targets in *audition, speech, language, cognition,* and *communication* can be integrated into natural play with their child. Suggestions are given for effective carryover activities in the child's daily environment to maximize progress in the most efficient ways. The therapist demonstrates the science and art of auditory-verbal development through the creative use of techniques, strategies, and procedures to help incorporate the targets of the session into carryover activities at home. The auditory-verbal goals of each session will be generalized in all daily routines.

5. **Guide and coach parents to create environments that support listening for the acquisition of spoken language throughout the child's daily activities.**
   Auditory-Verbal therapists help parents create ideal listening environments that make the reception of speech through listening as easy as possible. Taking into consideration the child's unique listening needs, the Auditory-Verbal therapist facilitates the child's listening and spoken communication development using a range of techniques and strategies. Parents are expected to practice these during the session and then incorporate them into daily activities. Parents must learn to manage their environment so that the child can become a full participant in daily interactions with peers, family, and community members. When the child is able, he or she will manage the listening environment, just as those with typical hearing do.

6. **Guide and coach parents to help their child integrate listening and spoken language into all aspects of the child's life.**
   Even with today's hearing technology, children who are deaf or hard of hearing need help and encouragement to integrate listening and spoken language into their total development. Once parents learn to capitalize on auditory experiences in the most meaningful ways, they will experience their child as one who can hear and actively listen. As the family continues to value listening, the child will value listening and will then integrate listening into his or her personality. The child will begin to perceive himself or herself as a child "who hears." The ultimate goal is for the child to be a well-adjusted, well-integrated person who uses listening and speaking to interact successfully with others at home and at school, in the community and in the world.

7. **Guide and coach parents to use natural developmental patterns of audition, speech, language, cognition, and communication.**
   Auditory-Verbal therapists develop individualized treatment plans based on natural developmental patterns in listening, speaking, language, cognition, and communication. Therapist and parent will help the children develop skills in these areas comparable to those of their hearing peers. Thus, the

Auditory-Verbal therapist guides the parents in targets that are appropriate for the child considering his or her hearing, chronological age, and current level of skills. New skills build upon previously learned skills, and targets will be established accordingly to help the children experience success as quickly as possible in learning spoken language through listening.

8. **Guide and coach parents to help their child self-monitor spoken language through listening.**
In the early stages of therapy, parents are encouraged to imitate their child's vocalizations to help the child establish an auditory-feedback loop system, and to encourage the child to listen to his or her own verbalizations and attempts at communication. Then, parents model appropriate speech or language models, and the child is encouraged to listen to and verbally match these models, eventually learning to modify his or her own speech. Effective listening and voice modulation prepare the child for independent verbal communication with minimal need for clarification or interpretation.

9. **Administer ongoing formal and informal diagnostic assessments to develop individualized Auditory-Verbal treatment plans, to monitor progress, and to evaluate the effectiveness of the plans for the child and family.**
In order to monitor the progress of the child and family after establishing an auditory-verbal treatment plan, the therapist must administer formal and informal diagnostic assessments. Every therapy session is diagnostic in that the child's auditory functioning and use of communication in meaningful contexts are observed and recorded. Based on these observations, the Auditory-Verbal therapist can introduce new targets within the session to help stimulate growth in areas of audition, speech, language, cognition, and communication. The child's development is also evaluated through the use of standardized tests, which are typically administered once every 6 months. The Auditory-Verbal therapist uses a battery of tests modeled on children who have hearing within normal limits to assess listening and auditory skills; speech articulation; receptive and expressive vocabulary; and development of cognition and receptive and expressive language. A detailed account of tests and assessments can be found in *50 FAQs About AVT* (Estabrooks, 2001, pp. 156-161).

10. **Promote education in regular classrooms with typical hearing peers and with appropriate support services from early childhood onwards.**
Appropriate support services need to reflect mainstreaming preparation for parents, classroom teachers, resource teachers, consultants, and teachers with specialized professional duties for the child. This team can determine whether placement in the mainstream classroom is indeed the best educational and social environment for the child to realize his or her potential. Sometimes success in the mainstream classroom is not forthcoming, and a change in placement is necessary. The (educational) audiologist,

working in collaboration with the parents, teachers, and Auditory-Verbal therapist, helps to create a "safety net" that ensures the child's developmental needs are met in the mainstream school environment. The role of the audiologist cannot be overstated, as it is upon this professional that the work of the rest of the team relies.

AUDITORY-VERBAL PROFESSIONALS

Auditory-Verbal therapists are qualified educators of the deaf and hard of hearing, audiologists, and/or speech-language pathologists who have chosen a career supporting the guiding principles of auditory-verbal practice. They must complete a process of certification determined by the Certification Council of the Academy for Listening and Spoken Language (Alexander Graham Bell Association for the Deaf and Hard of Hearing).

Auditory-Verbal therapists receive additional specialized training and intensive monitoring, and are required to pass both a theoretical and a practical examination to obtain the accreditation known as Certified Auditory-Verbal Therapist (Cert. AVT®). Continuing education is a requisite for maintaining this designation. Certified Auditory-Verbal therapists are bound by ethical principles and practices under a professional code of ethics for auditory-verbal practice (Appendix B [Code of Ethics]).

Partnerships with Other Professionals

The Auditory-Verbal therapist, in partnership with the child's parents, forms a team with other professionals to address the child's needs. The ideal team regards the child as part of a system of extended-family members and of various social networks within the community. The team supports family-focused work, respects parents and caregivers as responsible decision makers, and listens attentively to the needs of the family so that plans can be prioritized based on the family's culture.

The Auditory-Verbal therapist most often works with the child's audiologist, family physician, otolaryngologist (ENT), teachers, and family members. In addition, the following professionals augment the comprehensive service delivery model for many families who choose Auditory-Verbal therapy: social worker, physiotherapist, speech-language pathologist or other early intervention specialists, clinical geneticist (Appendix C [Genetic Counseling]), and occupational therapist (Appendix D [Sensory Integration]). These professionals, although not specific to Auditory-Verbal therapy, have proven to be invaluable resources to the family, and their support, understanding, and encouragement are important to the team.

LISTENING TO SPOKEN LANGUAGE

Children who are deaf or hard of hearing need to learn speech and language in the same ways as children with typical hearing. Thus, excellent perception of spoken language is critical for children who are deaf or hard of hearing in order to learn auditory self-monitoring of speech. In Auditory-Verbal practice, the hearing management team, in which the parents and Auditory-Verbal therapist are the key stakeholders, ensures that the child has auditory access to all the sounds of speech through hearing technology so that development of spoken language through listening can be as easy as possible. Figure 1.1 delineates the critical features of speech available at frequencies from 250 Hz through 4000 Hz. This knowledge permits the Auditory-Verbal therapist and the parent to determine, in part, the child's auditory potential and to mark changes in auditory and spoken behaviors.

LEARNING SPOKEN LANGUAGE THROUGH LISTENING

To help very young children to hear, listen, and talk, Auditory-Verbal therapists use Learning to Listen Sounds (Estabrooks, 2001), sounds from the Six-Sound Test (Appendix E), noisemakers, music, books, and age-appropriate toys. Parents learn to create meaningful listening experiences so that the child's newly acquired auditory potential is used optimally. Regardless of their chronological age, children who are deaf or hard of hearing need the same listening, learning, and language foundations as children who can hear. The

Figure 1.1 Speech Information
Availability at 250-4000 Hz (+/– one-half octave)

250 Hz	500 Hz	1000 Hz	2000 Hz	4000 Hz
• 1st formant of vowels /u/ and /I/ • Fundamental frequency of females and children's voices • Nasal murmur associated with the phonemes /m/, /n/, and /N/ • Male voice harmonics • Voicing cues • Prosody • Suprasegmentals patterns (stress, rate, inflection, intonation)	• 1st formants of most vowels • Harmonics of all voices (male, female, child) • Voicing cues • Nasality cues • Suprasegmentals • Some plosive bursts associated with /b/ and /d/	• Important acoustic cues for manner • 2nd formants of back and central vowels • Important consonant-vowel and vowel-consonant transition information • Nasality cues • Some plosive bursts • Voicing cues • Suprasegmentals	• Important acoustic cues for place of articulation • 2nd and 3rd formant information for front vowels • Consonant-vowel and vowel-consonant transition information • Acoustic information for the liquids /r/ and /l/ • Plosive bursts • Affricate bursts • Fricative turbulence	• Key frequency for /s/ and /z/ audibility (critical for language learning) - plurals - idioms - possessives - auxiliaries - 3rd person - singular verb forms - questions - copulas - past perfect • Consonant quality

Source: Adapted from Ling et al. (1996).

developmental approach to auditory-verbal communication (Pollack et al., 1997) identifies distinct yet overlapping stages (Figure 1.2).

Learning to Listen Sounds

Learning to Listen (LTL) Sounds and Songs (Figure 1.3) are chosen for their specific acoustic properties in that many consist of vowels and diphthongs that have first formants (lowest bands of energy), which are audible to most children with low-frequency hearing (Figure 1.4).

Other LTL Sounds are consonant sounds that contain bursts of energy clustered in the mid- and high-frequency ranges (Estabrooks & Marlowe, 2000) (Figure 1.5). By observing the baby's response to each of these sounds, the Auditory-Verbal therapist can gain valuable information about the baby's auditory potential across the speech spectrum using hearing aids, a cochlear implant, or both. Most babies, if provided with optimal hearing technology, find these sounds easy to hear, enjoyable to listen to, and subsequently easy to say and sing.

Listening Environments

Auditory-Verbal therapy encourages the maximum use of hearing in order to learn language, and stresses listening rather than watching. Therapy therefore needs to be carried out in the best possible acoustic conditions. The listening environment is enhanced by:

- the parent or therapist sitting beside the child, on the side of the better ear;
- speaking close to the child's hearing aid or cochlear implant microphone;
- speaking in a quiet voice at regular volume;

Figure 1.2 Stages of Listening and Talking

Listening		Talking
	Birth	
auditory awareness	↓	crying
attention		cooing
localization		smiling
discrimination		laughing
auditory feedback		vocalizing
monitoring of voices		babbling, lalling
sequencing		imitating
auditory processing		blowing, whispering
understanding		jargon
		first words
		word combinations
		sentences
		conversation
higher-level understanding		nearly perfect grammar
	Age 6	

Source: Adapted from Pollack et al. (1997).

Figure 1.3 Learning to Listen Sounds and Songs

Sound	Activity/Toy	Song
ah	airplane	The Airplane
oo	train	The Train
bu, bu	bubbles	Bubbles
bu, bu	bus	The Bus
beep/brr	car, truck	The Car
p, p, p	boat, popping toys	The Boat
t, t, t	clock	The Clock
ow/ouch	fall down, cut	Ouch!
owowowow	ambulance	The Ambulance
WOW	any surprise	WOW!
hee, hee	monkey	Monkey in a Tree
ha, ha, ha,	clown, laughter	Funny Little Clown
g/go	running	Running, Running
ho, ho, ho	Santa Claus	Santa Claus
ya hoo!	Cowboy	The Cowboy
whee	slide	The Slide
whee	Chinese yoyo	My Blue Yoyo
mama	baby doll	Baby Doll
hi!	mirror	The Mirror
meow	kitty cat	Kitty Cat
ruff, ruff, bow wow	dog	The Dog
moo, neigh	cow, horse	The Farm
baa, oink	sheep, pig	Living on the Farm
quack	duck	Six Little Ducks
tongue clack	horse	Clip, Clop
hoo hoo	owl	Mr. Owl
hop, hop	rabbit	The Rabbit
whistle	birdie	The Birds
cock-a-doodle	rooster	The Rooster
caw, caw	crow	Big Black Crow
round and around	windmill	The Windmill
round and around	top	The Spinning Top
round and around	wheels	Wheels
mmm	any good thing	Mmmmm Good
n	"no"	No No!
d	toy shovel	Dig Dig
s	snake	The Snake
sh	sleeping games	Someone's Sleeping
la	rocking the baby	Rock the Baby
u, u, up	any "up" activity	Pick Me Up

Source: Adapted from Estabrooks & Birkenshaw-Fleming (1994).

- minimizing background noise;
- using speech that is repetitive and rich in melody, expression, and rhythm;
- using acoustic highlighting techniques (Figure 1.6) to enhance the audibility of spoken language.

Figure 1.4 Vowel Frequency Bands (Hz)

Position	Vowel		1st Formant	2nd Formant
Back	who	u	430	1170
	would	ʊ	540	1410
	know	o	760	1250
	more	ç	840	1060
Middle	of	A	1030	1370
	art	a	1020	1750
	must	√	850	1590
	learn	œ	580	1740
Front	and	æ	1010	2320
	then	E	690	2610
	take	e	610	2680
	his	I	530	2730
	ease	i	370	3200

Source: Adapted from Ling (1989).

AUDITORY-VERBAL THERAPY SESSIONS

Auditory-Verbal therapy sessions are generally conducted jointly by the Auditory-Verbal therapist and the parent(s) (Chapters 5 and 6). The child learns to listen to his or her own voice, the voices of others, and the sounds of the environment in order to communicate effectively and naturally through spoken language by following a specific auditory-verbal treatment plan (Ernst, 2001).

Most auditory-verbal programs offer weekly therapy sessions, lasting for an hour or an hour and a half each, although some private programs and independent therapists provide therapy more often. No hard data exist to suggest that more than one therapy session per week is advantageous; measurable benefit would depend on a range of variables.

The parent(s) and caregivers need to apply the targets from each session in natural contexts throughout the day. Through motivation and guidance, they acquire the confidence to implement techniques and strategies to reach specific goals in audition, speech, language, cognition, and communication development, following the hierarchy of listening skills (Chapter 4). The charting of progress may also be facilitated by using the Listening Skills Scale for AVT (LSSAVT) (Figure 1.7).

In each session, the Auditory-Verbal therapist demonstrates, the parent and child practice, and the interaction is discussed. (Detailed lesson plans are given in Chapters 5 and 6.) The Auditory-Verbal therapist outlines specific goals to work towards at home and suggests ways through which they may be achieved. Goals for parents of infants and toddlers may include drawing attention to sounds in the environment; helping the child develop the Learning to Listen Sounds and Songs; encouraging the child's lalling, babbling, and jargoning; helping the child develop early vocabulary; beginning small conversations; developing the child's conditioned responses to the Six-Sound Test (Appendix E); and understanding the child's audiogram (Chapter 2).

Figure 1.5 Consonant Frequency Bands (Hz)

Consonant	1st Formant	2nd Formant	3rd Formant	4th Formant
/p/			1500-2000	
/b/	300-400		2000-2500	
/t/			2500-3500	
/d/	300-400		2500-3000	
/k/			2000-2500	
/g/	200-300		1500-2500	
/m/	250-350	1000-1500	2500-3500	
/n/	250-350	1000-1500	2000-3000	
/N/	250-350			4500-6000
/f/				4000-5000
/v/	300-400			3500-4500
/s/				5000-6000
/z/	200-300			4000-5000
/S/			1500-2000	4500-5500
/Z/	200-300			4000-4500
/T/				6000
/D/	200-300			5000
/dZ /			1500-2000	
/h/	1500-2000			
/r/	600-800	1000-1500	1800-2400	
/l/	250-400		2000-3000	

Source: Adapted from Ling et al. (1996).

Goals for older children may include developing speech and auditory skills in the presence of noise; helping the child to enhance his or her voice quality; developing better articulation of consonants; conversational repair strategies; paraphrasing; storytelling and re-telling; higher-level auditory and cognitive skills; and learning school-based subject material.

The goals for each session are directly linked to the developmental stage and hearing age of each child and are incorporated in structured activities, in ordinary daily routines, in songs, and, most importantly, in play.

Auditory-Verbal Techniques, Strategies, and Procedures

A variety of techniques, strategies, and procedures are used in each session and throughout the day to ensure the maximum development of spoken conversation through listening. These may include

- acoustic highlighting;
- auditory closure;
- using a singsong voice;
- establishing attention through speech;
- developing both eye and ear contact;
- encouraging one person at a time to speak;

Figure 1.6 Acoustic Highlighting

Acoustic highlighting includes a variety of techniques for enhancing the audibility of a spoken message. These may include rewording; rephrasing; pausing; waiting; whispering; singing; and emphasizing specific suprasegmentals, segmental features, or both.

Variables Influencing the Type/Degree of Acoustic Highlighting

Variable	Most Audible ⟶		Least Audible
Background Noise	Absence		Presence (Type and/or intensity)
Distance/Location	Proximity to microphone of hearing aid or cochlear implant		Increased speaker distance
Repetition	Repetition(s) required		Spoken message presented only once
Length	Short utterance		Long utterance
Complexity	Simple utterance		Complex utterance
Rate	Slow rate of utterance		Individual rates of utterance
Suprasegmentals	Speech with emphasis on specific pitch, intensity, and/or duration cues		Little or no specific acoustic emphasis provided
Segmentals	Specific contrasting of acoustic features (place, manner, and/or voicing cues)		Little or no specific acoustic emphasis provided
Target Position	End of word, phrase, sentence, or whole message	Middle	Beginning of word, phrase, sentence, or whole message
Set	Closed		Open
Speaker Familiarity	Familiar voice(s)		Unfamiliar voice(s)

Source: Daniel (1987).

- captivating the child's attention through sound;
- modeling the correct use of linguistic patterns;
- expanding language;
- using a natural speaking model;
- rewording;
- asking, "What did you hear?";
- providing alternatives;
- pausing;
- repeating;
- repeating a previous strategy;
- waiting;
- rephrasing;
- labeling by category;
- asking for or providing a definition;
- changing the task from open set to closed set;
- providing rhyming words;
- suggesting opposites;
- providing a visual clue and putting the stimulus back into hearing;
- moving or leaning closer to the child;

Figure 1.7 Listening Skills Scale for Auditory-Verbal Therapy (LSSAVT)

Level I: Pre-Verbal

- ❑ Quiets when wearing hearing aids.
- ❑ Noisy without hearing aids.

Quiets, stills, or smiles upon hearing
❑ a loud sound; ❑ a quiet sound.

- ❑ Responds to noisemaking toys.
- ❑ Responds to environmental sounds (doorbell telephone, knocking, barking, car horns, airplanes, others).
- ❑ Explores environment for new sounds (bangs spoon on table, bangs blocks).
- ❑ Quiets, stills, or smiles to singing, humming, or music.
- ❑ Quiets, stills, or smiles when spoken to.
- ❑ Tries to localize sounds, usually by head turning.
- ❑ Indicates something heard (by pointing to hearing aids and/or looking puzzled).

Turns to
❑ loud speech; ❑ quiet speech; ❑ whispered speech.

- ❑ Turns when called from a distance.
- ❑ Reacts when noises suddenly stop.
- ❑ Looks from one speaker to another.
- ❑ Attends by listening for a few minutes.

Level II: Verbal

- ❑ Turns to name when called from
  ❑ 3 ft; ❑ 6 ft; ❑ 9 ft; ❑ far away.
- ❑ Stops activity to "no."

Matches suprasegmental features:

- ❑ Duration
- ❑ Pitch
- ❑ Intensity

- ❑ Learning to Listen Sounds:
  ________________ ________________
  ________________ ________________
- ❑ Words varying in number of syllables (umbrella, car, ice cream, rhinoceros, hippopotamus):
  ________________ ________________
  ________________ ________________
- ❑ Familiar expressions (Don't touch! Let's go home! Mm, that's good!):
  ________________ ________________
  ________________ ________________
- ❑ One syllable words (different vowels and consonants; limited choice) (hat, comb, ball, shoe).
- ❑ Phrases based on known words (in the car, to the store, up the stairs).
- ❑ One syllable words with different vowels but same initial or final consonant (bat, boat, bee, ball, bug, bin).
- ❑ Similar phrases (a big purple truck, a small purple truck).
- ❑ Words with same vowel but different consonants (blue, shoe, two; cow, pow, bow, now).
- ❑ Memory for two items; ❑ three items; ❑ four items.
- ❑ Minor differences in sentences (in/on; the/a; he/she).
- ❑ Memory for phrases.
- ❑ Memory for short sentences.

Level III: Comprehension

A. Closed Set → Open Set

- ❑ Familiar expressions.
  ❑ Single directions; ❑ two directions;
  ❑ three directions.
- ❑ Two critical elements (e.g., the big house, the green ball).
- ❑ Three critical elements (e.g., flowers on the table).
- ❑ Four critical elements (e.g., purple car on the road).
- ❑ Multi-element directions.

B. Sequencing

- ❑ Sequence a series of multi-element directions.
- ❑ Make identification based on several related descriptions.
- ❑ Sequencing
  ❑ two events; ❑ three events; ❑ four+ events.
- ❑ Recall details in a story, lesson or event:
  ❑ two details; ❑ three details; ❑ four details.
- ❑ Understand main idea of
  ❑ a story; ❑ a lesson; ❑ a conversation.

C. Conversation

- ❑ Answer questions requiring comprehension of main idea of a short conversation.
- ❑ Paraphrase ❑ stories; ❑ conversations.
- ❑ Spontaneous, pragmatically correct conversation skills.

Level IV: Figure ground

All above skills need to be developed in various acoustic environments through the following hierarchy:

A. Quiet → Regular Noise → Noisy Environment

- ❑ Next to the sound source.
- ❑ 5-6 ft from source.
- ❑ Across the room.

B. In the presence of:

- ❑ Fan-type noise.
- ❑ Classroom-type noise.
- ❑ Cafeteria-type noise.
- ❑ Four-speaker babble.

C. In the presence of:

- ❑ Increased distances.
- ❑ Various background noises.

Sources: Phillips (1977); Erber (1982); Office of the Los Angeles County Superintendent of Schools (1976); Edwards & Estabrooks (1994).

- directing the child to listen closely;
- looking expectantly at the child;
- asking the parent to model the correct response or question;
- repeating part of the message containing the correct answer;
- the Hand Cue (Figure 1.8).

PARENT PARTICIPATION

Most babies who are deaf or hard of hearing are born to parents with typical hearing. The diagnosis is usually alarming and generates shock, confusion, anger, despair, and frustration. Along with the well-documented grieving process comes conflicting, albeit well-meaning, advice from professionals, family, and friends. At this critical time, parents of the newly diagnosed child possess little, if any, knowledge about hearing impairment and find themselves thrust headlong into another career! Taking any action that will affect their child's future is difficult at the best of times; it is especially so when trying to cope with the diagnosis of deafness.

Most parents want to do something immediately to alleviate their concerns about their perceived inability to communicate effectively with their child. It is the right of all parents to make well-informed choices on behalf of their child and family. Unfortunately, "well-informed choices" is a relative term and varies in interpretation.

Professionals in the field of hearing health care and education are charged with the responsibility of providing parents and other family members with sufficient information and counseling to help them affirm their sense of control as the primary case managers.

Auditory-verbal professionals embrace the knowledge that children learn language most easily when actively engaged in relaxed, meaningful interactions

Figure 1.8 The Hand Cue

The Hand Cue is used in varying degrees in many Auditory-Verbal therapy programs in order to emphasize the use of audition in the acquisition of spoken language.

The Hand Cue may consist of:

- the therapist, parent, or caregiver covering his or her mouth briefly, from time to time, when the child is looking directly at the adult's face. When the child is playfully engaged and not looking, it is unnecessary. The adult, however, must be close to the microphone of the child's hearing aid or cochlear implant;
- the adult moving his or her hand towards the child, in a nurturing way, as a prompt for vocal imitation or as a signal for verbal turn-taking;
- the adult talking through a stuffed animal, a toy, a picture, or a book, placed in front of the speaker's mouth.

The Hand Cue signals the child to listen intently. It must be used only when necessary, in that some of its uses distort, smear, or eliminate the sound arriving at the microphone. As children come to rely on their hearing, the use of the Hand Cue is diminished (Estabrooks, 1994). Once the child has "integrated hearing into his or her personality" (Pollack, 1985), the Hand Cue is rarely used.

with supportive parents and caregivers (Kretschmer & Kretschmer, 1978; Ling, 1989; Ross, 1990; Estabrooks, 1994). In auditory-verbal practice, parents will observe, participate, and practice in order to learn to

- model techniques for stimulating speech, language, and communication activities at home;
- plan strategies to integrate listening, speech, language, and communication into daily routines and experiences;
- communicate as partners in the therapy process;
- inform the therapist of the child's interests and abilities;
- interpret the meaning of the child's early communication;
- develop appropriate behavior management techniques;
- record and discuss progress;
- interpret short-term and long-term goals;
- develop confidence in parent–child interaction;
- make informed decisions;
- advocate on behalf of the child (Estabrooks, 1994).

VARIABLES AFFECTING PROGRESS

Each family and each child are unique, with a specific living and learning style (Luterman, 1991). Listening and communication development vary from child

Figure 1.9 PARENTS

- **Patience:** The child needs to learn how to use the sound that is now available. The implant team needs time to work with the child and arrive at the optimal program in the speech processor. Ongoing MAPping at regular and frequent intervals will assist in this process. Parental feedback to the implant team is essential. Be patient.
- **Access:** The cochlear implant gives the child access to the speech signal at audible levels, possibly for the first time. However, only through consistent use of the device and ongoing therapy does this new hearing potential become functional.
- **Relevance:** Targets and activities must be selected that are relevant and interesting to the child. As the processor is designed to code speech, use spoken language as the stimuli whenever possible. When using environmental sounds, select those that occur as a natural consequence of an activity.
- **Expectations:** High, but realistic expectations for your child are critical. We assume the child can now hear! We must provide many opportunities for the child to hear and respond to speech. Naturally occurring situations are the best means of stimulating listening and language learning. To develop these skills, we like to make the most of activities such as getting dressed, cooking, and cleaning the house.
- **Nurture:** Provide an abundance of affection, remembering that this little person is a child first and a recipient of a cochlear implant second.
- **Time:** Learning to listen does not happen overnight. Learning speech and language through listening is an ongoing process. We need to be consistent.
- **Success:** With the energy and love parents put into this process, successful listening experiences will become an integral part of daily life.

Source: Zara (1998).

to child and from family to family. Progress, of course, depends upon a number of variables, including

- age at diagnosis;
- cause of hearing impairment;
- degree of hearing impairment;
- effectiveness of amplification devices or a cochlear implant;
- effectiveness of audiological management;
- hearing potential of the child;
- health of the child;
- emotional state of the family;
- level of participation of the family (Figure 1.9);
- skills of the therapist;
- skills of the parents or caregiver;
- child's learning style;
- child's intelligence.

CONCLUSION

Professionals and parents engaged in auditory-verbal work embrace the current hearing technology, which drives changes in the clinical landscape for children who are deaf or hard of hearing. Today's sensory devices are far more sophisticated, user-friendly, and effective than in previous times, and the range of support services is much broader. There is far greater understanding of child development, of personal, social, and educational issues, and of the family system. Even families who choose other communication approaches are interested in the techniques, strategies, and procedures of auditory-verbal practice. Most parents want their children to be able to hear, listen, and talk.

The pioneers of auditory-verbal practice set the stage; the current auditory-verbal community continues to raise standards so that outcomes of Auditory-Verbal therapy for children, teenagers, and adults around the world will exceed our current expectations.

Recent scientific advances in amplification and cochlear implant technology continue to provide enormous potential listening opportunities worldwide for children and adults who are deaf or hard of hearing. As an applied science with objectively measured goals, auditory-verbal practice is their natural companion.

REFERENCES

Beebe, H. (1953). *A Guide to Help the Severely Hard of Hearing Child.* Basel/New York: Karger.

Bezold, F.R., & Siebenmann, F.R. (1908). *Textbook of Otology for Physicians and Students.* Chicago: E.H. Colegrove.

Boothroyd, A. (1982). *Hearing Impairments in Young Children.* Englewood Cliffs, NJ: Prentice Hall.

Clopton, B., & Winfield, J.A. (1976). "Effect of early exposure to patterned sound on unit activity in rat inferior colliculus." *Journal of Neurophysiology, 39,* 1081–1089.

Daniel, L. (1987). "Effects of acoustic exaggeration on the imitation of selected suprasegmental patterns by profoundly hearing-impaired children." Unpublished research.

Edwards, C., & Estabrooks, W. (1994). "Learning through listening: A hierarchy." In W. Estabrooks (Ed.), *Auditory-Verbal Therapy for Parents and Professionals* (pp. 55–74). Washington, DC: Alexander Graham Bell Association for the Deaf.

Erber, N. (1982). *Auditory Training.* Washington, DC: Alexander Graham Bell Association for the Deaf.

Ernst, M. (2001). "What is an auditory-verbal treatment plan?" In W. Estabrooks, *50 FAQs About AVT* (pp. 90–93). Toronto: Learning to Listen Foundation.

Estabrooks, W. (Ed.). (1994). *Auditory-Verbal Therapy for Parents and Professionals.* Washington, DC: Alexander Graham Bell Association for the Deaf.

Estabrooks, W. (Ed.). (1998). *Cochlear Implants for Kids.* Washington, DC: Alexander Graham Bell Association for the Deaf.

Estabrooks, W. (Ed.). (2001). *50 FAQs About AVT.* Toronto: Learning to Listen Foundation.

Estabrooks, W., & Birkenshaw-Fleming, L. (Eds.). (2003). *Songs for Listening! Songs For Life!* Washington, DC: Alexander Graham Bell Association for the Deaf and Hard of Hearing.

Evans, W., Webster, D., & Cullen, J. (1983). "Auditory brainstem responses in neonatally sound deprived CBA/Jmice." *Hearing Research, 10,* 269–277.

Froeschels, E., & Beebe, H. (1946). "Testing the hearing of newborn infants." *Archives of Otolaryngology, 44,* 710–714.

Furth, H. (1964). "Research with the deaf: Implications for language and cognition." *Psychological Bulletin, 62*(2), 145–162.

Geers, A., & Moog, J. (1989). "Factors predictive of the development of literacy in profoundly hearing-impaired adolescents." *The Volta Review, 91,* 69–86.

Goldberg, D.M., et al. (1993, Summer). "Rationale for auditory-verbal practice." *The Volta Review, 95*(3), 183–184.

Goldberg, D.M., & Flexer, C. (1991, June). "Where are they now? Survey of auditory-verbal graduates." Presentation at the Auditory-Verbal International Conference, *Listening Is the Future—The Time Is Now—The Future Is Hear,* Easton, PA.

Goldberg, D.M., & Flexer, C. (1997). "Outcome survey of auditory-verbal graduates: A study of clinical efficacy. *Journal of the American Academy of Auditology, 4,* 189–200.

Goldberg, D.M., & Lebahn, C. (1990, July). "Performance of auditory-verbal children in the TAC." Poster session presented in the Biennial Convention of the Alexander Graham Bell Association for the Deaf, Washington, DC.

Goldstein, M. (1939). *The Acoustic Method.* St. Louis: Laryngoscope Press.

Griffiths, C. (Ed.). (1974). *Proceedings of the International Conference on Auditory Techniques.* Springfield, IL: Charles C. Thomas.

Johnson, D. (1975). "Communication characteristics of NTID students." *Journal of the Academy of Rehabilitative Audiology, 8,* 17–32.

Johnson, D. (1976). "Communication characteristic of a young deaf adult population: Techniques for evaluating their communication skills." *American Annals of the Deaf, 121*(4), 409–424.

Johnson, J., & Newport, E. (1989). "Critical period effects in second language learning: The influence of maturational state on the acquisition of English as a second language." *Cognitive Psychology, 21,* 60–90.

Kretschmer, R.R., & Kretschmer, L. (1978). *Language Development and Intervention with the Hearing Impaired.* Baltimore: University Park Press.

Lennenberg, E. (1967). *Biologic Foundations of Language.* New York: Wiley.

Leonard, L.B. (1991). "New trends in the study of early language acquisition." *ASHA, 33,* 43–44.

Ling, D. (1976). *Speech and the Hearing-Impaired Child: Theory and Practice.* Washington, DC: Alexander Graham Bell Association for the Deaf.

Ling, D. (1989). *Foundations of Spoken Language for Hearing-Impaired Children.* Washington, DC: Alexander Graham Bell Association for the Deaf.

Ling, D. (2003). "The Six-Sound Test." In W. Estabrooks & L. Birkenshaw-Fleming (Eds.), *Songs for Listening! Songs For Life!* (pp. 227–229). Washington, DC: Alexander Graham Bell Association for the Deaf and Hard of Hearing.

Ling, D. (2005). "The Six-Sound Test." *The Listener* (Special Silver Anniversary Edition), 72–74.

Ling, D., & Ling, A.D. (1978). *Aural Habilitation.* Washington, DC: Alexander Graham Bell Association for the Deaf.

Ling, D., et al. (1996). *Acoustics, Audition and Speech Reception.* Video. McLean, VA: Auditory-Verbal International.

Luetke-Stahlman, B., & Moeller, M.P. (1987, June). "Are parents trained to sign proficiently to their deaf children?" Presentation to the Academy of Rehabilitative Audiology Summer Institute, Mount Summit, PA.

Luterman, D. (1991). *When Your Child Is Deaf.* Timonium, MD: York Press.

MacDonald, J., & Gillette, Y. (1989). *Becoming Partners with Children: From Play to Conversation.* Chicago: Riverside Publishing.

Marler, P.R. (1970). "A comparative approach to vocal learning: Song development in white-crowned sparrows." *Journal of Comparative and Physiological Psychology Monographs, 71*(2, Part 2), 1–25.

Menyuk, P. (1977). "Effects of hearing loss on language acquisition in the babbling stage." In B.F. Jaffe (Ed.), *Hearing Loss in Children.* Baltimore: University Park Press.

Moores, D. (1987). *Educating the Deaf: Psychology, Principles, and Practices* (3rd ed.). Boston: Houghton Mifflin.

Myklebust, H., & Brutton, M. (1953). "A study of visual perception in deaf children." *Acta Oto-Laryngologica, Supplementum,* 105.

Newport, R. (1990). "Maturational constraints on language learning." *Cognitive Science, 14,* 11–28.

Office of the Los Angeles Country Superintendent of Schools. (1976). *Auditory Skills Curriculum.* North Hollywoood, CA: Foreworks, Inc.

Patchett, T.A. (1977). "Auditory discrimination in albino rats as a function of auditory restriction at different ages." *Developmental Psychology, 13,* 168–169.

Phillips, A.L. (1977). *Schedules of Development in Audition, Speech, Language, and Communication for Hearing-Impaired Infants and Their Parents.* Washington, DC: Alexander Graham Bell Association for the Deaf.

Pollack, D. (1970). *Educational Audiology for the Limited-Hearing Infant.* Springfield, IL: Charles C. Thomas.

Pollack, D. (1985). *Educational Audiology for the Limited-Hearing Infant and Preschooler* (2nd ed.). Springfield, IL: Charles C. Thomas.

Pollack, D., Goldberg, D., & Caleffe-Schenck, N. (1997). *Educational Audiology for the Limited-Hearing Infant and Preschooler: An Auditory-Verbal Program.* Springfield, IL: Charles C. Thomas.

Rhoades, E., & Chisholm, T.H. (2000). "Global language progress with an auditory-verbal approach for children who are deaf or hard of hearing." *The Volta Review, 102*(1), 5–24.

Robertson, L., & Flexer, C. (1990). "The reading development of auditory-verbal hearing-impaired children." Poster session presented at the Biennial Convention of the Alexander Graham Bell Association for the Deaf, Washington, DC.

Robertson, D., & Irvine, D. (1989). "Plasticity of frequency organization in auditory cortex of guinea pigs with partial unilateral deafness." *Journal of Comparative Neurology, 282,* 456–471.

Ross, M. (Ed.). (1990). *Hearing-Impaired Children in the Mainstream.* Parkton, MD: York Press.

Ross, M., & Calvert, D. (1984). "Semantics of deafness revisited: Total Communication and the use and misuse of residual hearing." *Audiology, 9,* 127–145.

Urbantschitsch, V. (1982). Auditory Training for Deaf Mutism and Acquired Deafness (S.R. Silverman, Trans.). Washington, DC: Alexander Graham Bell Association for the Deaf. (Original work published 1895).

Webster, D. (1983). "A critical period during postnatal auditory development of mice." *International Journal of Pediatric Otorhinolaryngology, 6,* 107–118.

Yoshinaga-Itano, C., & Pollack, D. (1988). *A Description of Children in the Acoupedic Method and a Retrospective Study of the Acoupedic Method.* Denver: The Listen Foundation.

Zara, C. (1998). "PARENTS." In W. Estabrooks (Ed.), *Cochlear Implants for Kids.* Washington, DC: Alexander Graham Bell Association for the Deaf.

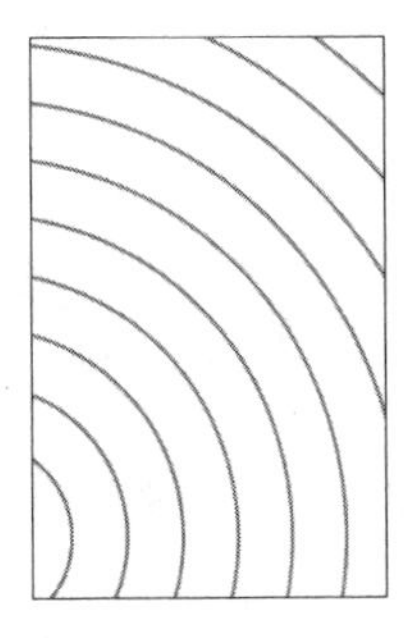

CHAPTER 2

Audiology: Back to Basics

Carolyne Edwards, M.Cl.Sc., M.B.A.

Interpretation of the results of audiological assessment has long been the realm of audiologists alone. Yet the understanding and application of audiological information by the therapist and parents are crucial to the optimal development of listening, speech, and language skills in the child who is deaf or hard of hearing. Auditory threshold and discrimination measures have direct implications for speech perception and the subsequent development of speech production. It is the perception of speech that leads to recognition, comprehension, and, ultimately, language expression with family members and peers.

This chapter provides a basic description of conventional audiological procedures and the relevance of this information for the key players in the child's auditory-verbal program—the parents, the child, and the therapist.

THE OVERALL PICTURE

Audiological assessment addresses a broad spectrum of auditory issues. While the pure-tone audiogram often attracts more attention than other audiological procedures, it is only one piece of the audiological picture. A comprehensive audiological assessment in a clinical setting will evaluate the following areas:

Pathology

- Provision of information about auditory function that will contribute to the medical diagnosis of auditory pathology, such as cause of hearing loss and/or presence of fluid buildup in the middle ear (otitis media)

Acuity

- Description of current hearing levels
- Description of the child's auditory potential for perception of speech and monitoring of the environment

Listening

- Description of the child's current listening skills
- Observation of the child's attitude towards listening, communication, and social interaction

- Measurement of changes in the child's listening skills over time
- Electroacoustical evaluation of hearing aids and FM system

Communication
- Recommendation for alternative teaching and/or communication strategies when auditory limitations are present
- Observation of the communication strategies the child is currently using and additional strategies that would enhance the child's comprehension of speech
- Determination of the amplification strategies that will enhance the child's communication

Children and parents/family
- Evaluation of the parents' and child's acceptance of the hearing loss and the child's overall sense of self-worth
- Determination of the need for additional counseling

The therapist or the parents may be interested in particular areas of assessment or a review of all the areas noted above.

Implications

- Inform the audiologist of any areas in which you have a particular interest, based on your observations or current concerns.

Ask the Audiologist
- Which areas have you focused on today?
- How will today's information affect the child's program?

AUDIOLOGICAL PROCEDURES

The following review of audiological tests will provide parents and therapists with a common ground for discussion of results with the audiologist.

Pure-Tone Audiogram

The pure-tone audiogram (Figure 2.1) is a graph indicating the softest level in each ear at which the child can hear a range of pitches important for comprehension of speech. The purpose of the audiogram is to compare the child's results to a graph of normal hearing to determine

- the presence or absence of hearing loss;
- type of hearing loss;
- degree of hearing loss;
- shape of hearing loss;
- differences between ears.

A *threshold* is the softest level at which a child hears a sound 50% of the time. The type of sound used in testing varies with the means of presentation. Pure-tone

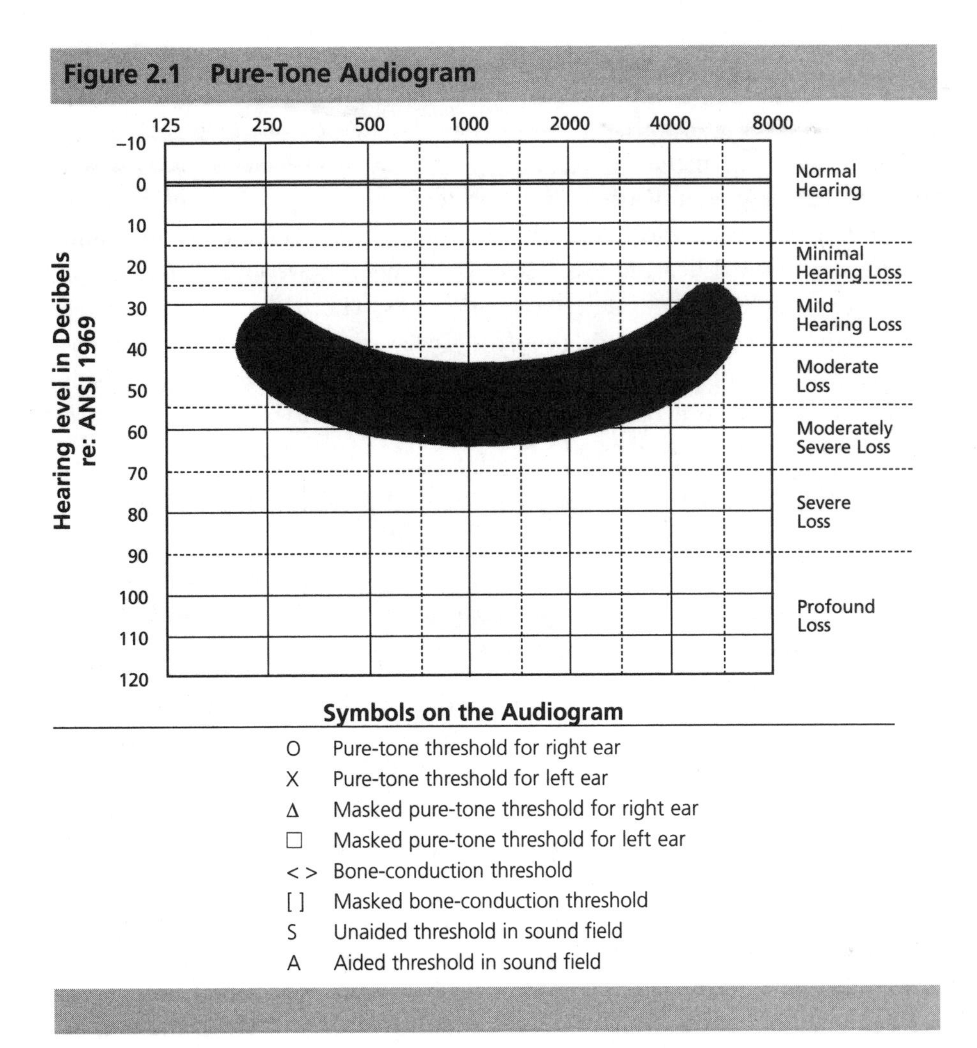

Figure 2.1 Pure-Tone Audiogram

stimuli are typically presented through headphones or insert phones at octave frequencies of 250, 500, 1000, 2000, 4000, and 8000 Hz in each ear. Narrow-band noise or warble-tone stimuli from 250 to 6000 Hz are used during sound field testing in unaided or aided condition.

Thresholds are measured in *decibels* (dB), the unit of sound intensity. On the audiogram, intensities range from the softest level (–10 dB) to the loudest level (120 dB). Zero dB does not imply the absence of sound; rather, it represents the softest level at which the average young adult with normal hearing can detect sound, although some individuals are able to detect sound at levels of –5 or –10 dB HL.

Thresholds are tested at *frequencies* between 125 Hz and 8000 Hz. Hearing levels can differ from one frequency to the next, resulting in audiograms with a flat, rising, falling, trough, or cookie-bite configuration from the low to the high frequencies. The shape of the hearing loss can suggest some of the auditory perceptual difficulties that the child might encounter.

Frequencies at 500, 1000, and 2000 Hz are called the speech frequencies because 70% of all vowel and consonant energy is concentrated in this region. Thus the *pure-tone average* (PTA), which represents the overall hearing level for each ear, is also calculated as the average of the thresholds at 500, 1000, and 2000 Hz. The degree of hearing loss is based on the interpretation of the pure-tone average for each ear. For example, a pure-tone average of 25 dB would represent a minimal hearing loss. There is a danger, however, in looking only at the pure-tone average to describe hearing loss. The PTA cannot accurately estimate the effect of the hearing loss on speech recognition when the audiogram is steeply sloping or rising, and there is no predictable relationship between PTA and word recognition ability for children with severe and profound hearing loss.

Example: Two children were seen for audiological assessment. The first child had a PTA of 95 dB in both ears and a word discrimination score of 72%. The second child had a PTA of 95 dB in both ears and a word discrimination score of 24%. Both children had profound bilateral hearing loss, yet had very different speech recognition abilities.

Testing is completed by *air conduction* and *bone conduction.* Sound presented through headphones or insert phones is conducted by air to the eardrum, whose motion then stimulates the ossicular chain, the oval window, the fluid within the cochlea (inner ear), and subsequently the hair cells in the inner ear. Bone-conducted sound occurs when a vibrator is placed on the mastoid bone behind the ear and the sound vibrates through the skull, which in turn causes the fluid in the cochlea to vibrate, stimulating the hair cells within the inner ear. Thus, bone-conducted sound bypasses any obstruction or damage to the outer or middle ear. Comparison of the results of thresholds obtained by air- and bone-conduction testing differentiates among conductive, sensorineural, or mixed hearing loss.

Normal hearing is present when air- and bone-conduction thresholds are 15 dB or better (–10 to 15 dB) at all frequencies and there is a gap of 10 dB or less between air- and bone-conduction thresholds.

A *conductive hearing loss* is caused by damage or obstruction in the outer or middle ear. Bone-conduction thresholds are within normal limits and a gap of 15 dB or more exists between air- and bone-conduction thresholds.

A *sensorineural hearing loss* is caused by damage or obstruction in the inner ear or auditory nerve. Bone-conduction thresholds are poorer than 15 dB and air- and bone-conduction thresholds are similar or identical.

A *mixed hearing loss* is caused by a combination of damage or obstruction in the outer/middle ear and the inner ear/auditory nerve. In this case, bone-conduction thresholds are poorer than 15 dB and there is a gap of 15 dB or more between air- and bone-conduction thresholds. Recurrent otitis media in conjunction with a sensorineural hearing loss is the most common cause of mixed hearing loss in children.

Implications

- Infants and young children may not respond at threshold levels when tested. Instead, their responses may be described as minimal response levels (MRLs), suggesting that hearing levels may be better than indicated on the audiogram at some later date.
- Although there is variability within each category of hearing loss, the degree of loss conveys some information about potential auditory, speech, and language difficulties.
- The type of hearing loss also has implications for listening skills programs. The child who has congenital conductive hearing loss will not experience the auditory perceptual distortion of speech sounds that the child with mixed or sensorineural hearing loss does, and thus does not require a specific focus on phoneme discrimination and identification skills.

Ask the Audiologist

- What is the child's overall degree of hearing loss?
- Does the child hear better at some frequencies than others? If so, which frequencies?
- Which frequencies is the child unable to hear, if any?
- Which ear has more hearing? At which frequencies?
- Is there any indication of middle ear dysfunction on today's testing?
- Do today's results reflect the child's optimal hearing levels?
- Has there been any change in hearing levels since the last assessment?

Aided Thresholds

Aided narrow-band noise (NBN) or warble-tone (WT) thresholds are obtained when sounds are presented through speakers while the child is wearing a hearing aid. The softest level at which the child detects these sounds 50% of the time is recorded on the audiogram at frequencies between 250 and 6000 Hz.

Results of aided testing can provide information on audibility of various speech features, and therefore suggest auditory potential for detection and identification of speech features. The interpretation of aided thresholds is grounded in the acoustic properties of speech. It is beyond the scope of this chapter to review the principles of speech science; the reader can refer to Ling (1976, 1989) for detailed information.

Implications

The following guidelines summarize predictions for auditory potential based on aided thresholds. However, these are generalizations derived from the frequency spectrum of speech; the therapist must also consider the intensity of that particular feature of speech. A child must have sufficient audibility at each frequency in order to make use of that information. Only through ongoing assessment of auditory perceptual skills will the therapist determine the child's capacity to utilize acoustic cues at various frequencies. (Note that it may be easier for a child to identify certain vowels or consonants with male speakers, who have lower formant frequency transitions than female speakers or other young children.)

Aided thresholds permitting audibility within the speech spectrum at 250–4000 Hz suggest the following auditory potential:

- Detection of all suprasegmentals (duration, loudness, and pitch characteristics of speech) and segmentals (vowel and consonant characteristics);*
- Identification of all suprasegmental features;
- Identification of all vowels;
- Recognition of voicing, manner, and place characteristics of consonants;
- Identification of selected consonants;
- Detection and identification of most environmental sounds.

When aided thresholds restrict audibility within the speech spectrum to frequencies between 250–2000 Hz, the child may have the following difficulties:

- Identification of front vowels;
- Detection of high-frequency consonants such as s, f, and voiceless "th";
- Identification of place characteristics of consonants.

When the child is able to detect frequencies only from 250–1000 Hz within the speech spectrum, the following difficulties may result:

- Identification of mid and front vowels;
- Detection of mid- and high-frequency consonants;
- Identification of some manner characteristics of consonants;
- Identification of place characteristics of consonants;
- Identification of some environmental sounds.

Audible hearing within the speech spectrum only at 250 and 500 Hz may create these difficulties:

- Detection of some back and mid vowels;
- Identification of back, mid, or front vowels;
- Detection of the mid- and high-frequency consonants;
- Categorization of voicing, manner, or place of consonant production;
- Detection of some environmental sounds;
- Identification of environmental sounds.

Ask the Audiologist

- Does the child have the ability to detect and identify suprasegmental features (duration, loudness, and pitch)?
- Which vowel sounds does the child have the auditory potential to detect?
- Which vowels does the child have the auditory potential to recognize/identify?

* Children with severe and profound sensorineural hearing loss will have great variability in recognition of segmental characteristics.

- Which vowels might the child hear as similar, and thus need visual clues to distinguish one from the other?
- Which consonant sounds does the child have the auditory ability to detect?
- Which consonant sounds would be difficult to detect in isolation?
- Which consonant features (voicing, manner, place) does the child have the potential to recognize?

Ling's Six-Sound Test and the GASP 1 Test

The Six-Sound Test is a detection task of six speech sounds—m, oo, ah, ee, sh, and s (/m/, /u/, /a/, /i/, /ʃ/, and /s/) presented at normal conversational level (Ling, 1976, 1989, 2005). Each of the sounds represents critical information in a different frequency range of the speech spectrum. The results can be used in a variety of ways:

- To predict ability to recognize various speech features;
- To monitor any decrease in hearing levels due to middle ear dysfunction;
- To measure any decrease in aided performance from day to day;
- To measure effects of distance from the speaker on the audibility of various speech features (from 6 inches away to 24 feet);
- To observe changes in audibility between hearing aids and hearing aids in combination with an FM system;
- To observe differences in audibility with different FM microphones. Comparisons can be made between omni-directional, directional, boom, and/or pass-around microphones. Each of these has different auditory characteristics and uses; consult with the audiologist to select the appropriate microphone option for the FM transmitter.

The *Glendonald Auditory Screening Procedure: Test 1* (GASP 1 Test) is an expansion of the Six-Sound Test (Erber, 1982). The speech sounds in the detection task include 10 vowels and 12 consonants (nasals, laterals, and voiced and unvoiced fricatives) presented at normal conversational level. Erber describes several additional purposes for this test, including

- evaluation of audibility of speech spectrum of therapist's and parents' voices, by having the therapist and parent present the speech sounds to the child;
- evaluation of any strategies to enhance audibility of the phoneme tested, such as talking closer to the microphone of the child's hearing aid, using an FM system, changing the type of microphone on the FM system, or intentionally distorting the speech sound by directing the breathstream directly across the microphone opening.

The Six-Sound and GASP 1 tests can both also be used as identification tasks in which the child is asked to repeat the sound heard. Repetition of the correct sound indicates the child's ability to utilize the speech spectrum information for identification purposes.

Implications

- If the child detects all sounds, he or she has the potential to detect the full range of the speech spectrum.
- If the child detects m, oo, ah, ee, and sh (/m/, /u/, /a/, /i/, /ʃ/), auditory potential is similar to aided thresholds within the speech spectrum at 250–2000 Hz.
- Detection of the three vowels and /m/ suggests potential similar to aided thresholds within the speech spectrum at 250–1000 Hz.
- Detection of only one or two of the vowels suggests limited ability to detect vowels and consonants.

Ask the Audiologist

- Which speech sounds can the child detect?
- Does the child have the auditory potential to
  - detect all vowels?
  - identify the back, central, and/or front vowels?
  - detect all consonants?
  - identify voicing, manner, and/or place features for consonants?
- Which speech sounds are most sensitive to changes in middle ear function?
- At what distance does the child lose audibility of a specific speech sound?
- What amplification strategies are recommended to enhance audibility of particular speech sounds?

Impedance Audiometry

Impedance audiometry is a test battery consisting of tympanometry, static compliance, and acoustic reflex tests. Tympanometry is an objective test used to determine normal or abnormal middle ear function based on measurement of middle ear pressure and tympanic mobility. Of the three subtests within impedance audiometry, tympanometry is the test of most interest to the therapist and parents. A tone is introduced through a probe tip placed in the child's ear canal. The measurement of the intensity of the sound reflected back from the eardrum as air pressure in the ear canal is varied provides information on the status of the middle ear. The following terms are used to describe middle ear dysfunction.

- *Negative middle ear pressure and normal tympanic mobility* reflects retraction of the eardrum and yet normal mobility within the middle ear system; the physical sensation is similar to the pressure experienced during airplane takeoff and landing. This dysfunction is often seen when young children have congestion.
- *Negative middle ear pressure and reduced tympanic mobility* reflects a stiff middle ear system due to conditions commonly seen in young children such as wax buildup, extreme negative middle ear pressure, or fluid buildup in the middle ear.

- *Extremely high tympanic mobility* reflects a highly mobile middle ear system due to conditions such as ossicular discontinuity or flaccid eardrum.

The transient nature of fluid buildup in the middle ear space plays havoc with auditory learning for children who are deaf or hard of hearing. Hearing levels can decrease by 5–40 dB in the presence of temporary middle ear dysfunction. The fatigue that often accompanies the need to listen more intently owing to a temporary decrease in hearing levels is rarely discussed. Parents and therapists need to be sensitive to children's need for auditory "rest and relaxation" during periods of middle ear dysfunction and adjust amplification in response to depressed hearing levels.

Implications

- For children who have sensorineural hearing loss, the additional presence of fluctuating loss due to middle ear dysfunction can be devastating. Therapists and parents should be aware that interruptions in auditory learning can occur during episodes of fluid buildup in the middle ear.
- The majority of episodes of middle ear dysfunction have no symptoms other than a decrease in hearing levels. It is important that parents and therapists be alert to any changes in hearing sensitivity.
- Children with chronic histories of middle ear dysfunction need to have routine tympanometry, preferably every 1–3 months, to monitor both the status of the middle ear and current hearing levels.

Example: A child with a profound bilateral sensorineural hearing loss arrives at the clinic. The parent has been concerned about the child's poorer responses to sound at home during the past week. The parent wonders if the child's hearing has shifted, if the hearing aid is working properly, if the child has fluid buildup, or if it is simply an "off" week. Results of tympanometry show a flat tympanogram in both ears and a resulting decrease in hearing levels of about 15 dB. For this child, this decrease is enough to lose audibility of normal conversational speech at 2000 and 4000 Hz, thus losing ability to monitor all of the mid and high frequencies in the child's own speech. The parent's only clue to the change in hearing levels in the past week was increased feedback (whistling) from the hearing aid despite no change in volume setting. Increased feedback can occur in the presence of decreased tympanic mobility and fluid buildup.

Ask the Audiologist

- Is there any indication of middle ear dysfunction today that would affect pure-tone thresholds?
- How often does the child experience middle ear dysfunction?
- When should the child return for a re-check of middle ear function?
- Should the volume setting on the hearing aid be adjusted during periods of middle ear dysfunction?

- For children with chronic middle ear dysfunction who are using programmable hearing aids, can another program be designated for those periods when hearing levels are depressed by middle ear dysfunction?

Auditory Brainstem Response

Auditory brainstem response (ABR) is an electrophysiological test to evaluate auditory function. It is used to assess hearing acuity when measurements from behavioral audiological procedures cannot be reliably obtained. Sound is presented through earphones or through a bone-conduction oscillator. Electrodes attached to the scalp and at the earlobe measure the electrical activity generated by the neurons in the auditory (eighth) nerve and brainstem for the first 10 milliseconds after a sound is presented. Clicks centered around the frequency region of 2000–4000 Hz or brief frequency-specific tone bursts are presented many times, and the responses at each stimulus intensity are recorded. A computer averages the electrical response over numerous presentations. The ABR threshold is the lowest level at which the response is visible.

Unlike the pure-tone audiogram, in which frequencies from 250–8000 Hz may be tested, results of ABR testing reflect responses at selected frequencies. Therefore, it may be possible for a child to show no response on ABR testing using click stimuli yet later indicate some measurable hearing at lower frequencies on a pure-tone audiogram. The maximum intensity level used in ABR is typically less than the maximum level used in behavioral testing with headphones. Thus, it is also possible to indicate no response on ABR testing and yet show thresholds at 105–120 dB at the higher frequencies on the pure-tone audiogram. Whereas pure-tone thresholds are obtained using 5 dB intervals, ABR is usually obtained using 20 dB changes in presentation level. Thus, results of ABR testing provide the degree of hearing loss at selected frequencies, but do not have the specificity of pure-tone thresholds.

Implications

- ABR provides information on the degree of hearing loss in each ear, and the presence or absence of a conductive component, without the necessity of active participation by the child.
- ABR provides less specific information regarding frequency sensitivity and thresholds than behavioral audiometry, and therefore is not a substitute for behavioral testing.
- No response on ABR does not necessarily mean no measurable hearing. It means no measurable hearing at the maximum intensity tested in that frequency region.
- ABR is a diagnostic test completed at the initial assessment; it is not used to monitor hearing levels unless behavioral testing is not possible.

> *Ask the Audiologist*
>
> - What degree of hearing loss does the child have in either ear?
> - What is the shape or slope of the hearing loss?
> - Is there any indication of a conductive component?
> - Do other behavioral observations agree with the ABR findings?
> - Are there any discrepancies between the results of ABR and other audiological tests?

Otoacoustic Emissions

Evoked otoacoustic emissions (EOAEs) are another electrophysiological measure of hearing sensitivity. Otoacoustic emissions are low-level sounds generated in the cochlea that can be recorded in the external ear canal using a sensitive microphone. EOAEs occur following acoustic stimulation with clicks or short-duration tones. A microphone is inserted into a soft rubber or foam tip and placed in the child's ear canal. Sounds are presented through miniature earphones, and response tracings are averaged and recorded.

The main types of EOAEs are transient evoked otoacoustic emissions (TEOAEs) and distortion product otoacoustic emissions (DPOAEs), and both can be used to evaluate the status of the cochlea. Like ABR, TEOAE and DPOAE testing do not require the child's cooperation. In fact, because it is noninvasive, there is minimal preparation required of the child. However, middle ear function must be normal in order to obtain an accurate test.

Implications

- As a diagnostic measure, EOAE testing permits the audiologist to differentiate between sensory and neural hearing loss. Reduction in otoacoustic emissions reflects sensory loss due to damage to the cochlea, and abnormal evoked potentials on ABR reflect neural loss due to damage to the auditory nerve and brainstem.
- EOAE testing is used as a hearing screening measure in newborn screening protocols.

> *Ask the Audiologist*
>
> - (Screening tool) Is there evidence of hearing loss?
> - (Diagnostic tool) What is the nature of the sensorineural hearing loss?

CONVENTIONAL SPEECH AUDIOMETRY

Speech audiometry refers to a number of standardized tests using speech material. Sounds are presented using headphones, loudspeakers, or both, depending on the purpose of the test. Some of the more common speech tests used in the clinic are discussed here.

Speech Awareness Threshold

The speech awareness threshold (SAT), sometimes called the speech detection threshold, is the softest level at which one can detect the presence of speech 50% of the time. It provides a measure of the minimum loudness level necessary for the child to detect speech, and suggests the loudness level necessary for detection and possible identification of speech features. For complete detection of the intensity range of speech sounds from the quietest consonant (voiceless "th" or /θ/) to the loudest vowel ("ah" or /a/), speech must be delivered 30 dB above threshold (Ling, 1989). As in other threshold measures, the preschool child may be conditioned through visual or play audiometry, or, at a later age, simply instructed to raise a hand when the sound is heard.

Implications

- The SAT is the gauge for the loudness levels that can be detected in training—whispered (30 dB), quiet (40 dB), normal (50 dB), and loud (65 dB). Note that dB levels are approximations.
- The SAT is also an indicator of potential audibility of the speech spectrum. The range between the softest consonant and the loudest vowel is 30 dB. Thus, the speech signal needs to be 30 dB louder than the SAT in order to obtain complete audibility. For children who have a profound hearing loss, use of an FM system in therapy and in the classroom is an effective means to increase the audibility of the speech spectrum.
- The SAT reflects the optimal level at which the child detects speech—that is, under ideal, one-to-one, quiet listening conditions when the child anticipates a sound. The child's response level in noisier environments will necessarily be reduced.

Example: A child establishes an SAT of 40 dB. In ideal listening situations, the child can detect the presence of quiet, normal, and loud conversational speech. If listening in less than optimal situations (at a distance; in background noise), the child may detect only normal or loud speech levels, and thus not detect the complete range of speech sounds. The child may respond spontaneously to speech only when it is presented at loud conversational levels. That does not mean the child will detect the full frequency spectrum of speech at each loudness level; in fact, the child may hear only part of the speech spectrum.

Ask the Audiologist

- What is the intensity level of speech that the child is just beginning to detect?
- What loudness level would the child be able to detect in a lesson situation?
- What level of voice would the child find difficult or impossible to detect in a lesson situation?
- What level of voice would the child detect spontaneously in the everyday environment?

Speech Reception Threshold

The speech reception threshold (SRT), sometimes called the spondee threshold, is the softest level at which the child can repeat familiar two-syllable words (spondees), or point to pictures or objects representing them, 50% of the time. Spondees have equal stress on both syllables, such as "hot dog," "ice cream," or "baseball." The SRT provides a reliability check on the pure-tone thresholds. If the child is responding accurately, one would expect to see agreement between the SRT and the pure-tone average.

Implications

- The first indication of the child's emerging ability to identify speech sounds and words on formal testing is the child's ability to establish an SRT.
- The ability to establish an SRT is primarily based on the child's ability to differentiate vowels. A child with poor consonant identification skills often has little or no difficulty establishing an SRT.
- The SRT will typically be about 5–10 dB greater than the SAT. A listener requires more intensity to identify words than simply to detect the presence of speech.
- Like the SAT, the SRT indicates the optimal level for identification of speech. For example, listeners with typical hearing require speech at approximately 30 dB above the SRT in order to achieve 100% discrimination scores.

Ask the Audiologist

- Can the child understand familiar words through hearing only?
- What is the softest level at which the child can identify words?
- In the everyday environment where background noise is present, what is the softest level at which the child can identify a small group of words?
- What is the optimal level for recognition of speech for this child?
- Can we achieve this optimal level with the child's current hearing aids? At what distance?
- Can we achieve this optimal level with the use of an FM system coupled to the child's hearing aids?

Word Discrimination Testing

Word discrimination tests measure the child's ability to recognize monosyllabic words under ideal and typical listening conditions. Ideal conditions include presentation levels 25–30 dB above the SRT without any background noise. Typical conditions may include presenting speech at quiet or normal conversational levels with and without background noise. The child is asked to repeat a list of 25 or 50 words, and the word discrimination score (WDS) is calculated as a percentage reflecting the number of words correct (example: 16/25 = 64%). Word discrimination ability improves during the preschool and early school years, and then stabilizes as the child reaches his or her maximum auditory potential.

Word lists such as the PBK, W-22, or NU-6 refer to *open-set word repetition tasks* in which the child has no contextual clues. The child must identify both the vowel and consonant sounds in each word in order to obtain a correct word score. Phoneme scoring in which each sound in the word is scored (three sounds per word) provides a better estimate of the child's degree of difficulty with specific speech sounds.

A *pictured word discrimination task,* such as the NU-CHIPS or the WIPI, is designed for children of three years and older. Four or six words are pictured on each page of a 25- or 50-page booklet, and the child is asked to point to one of the pictures on each page. Since the words on each page use the same vowel but vary the initial or final consonant (or both), this is actually a consonant recognition task from a closed-set or multiple-choice format.

The *Early Speech Perception Battery* (Moog & Geers, 1990) includes a *closed-set identification task* of single words for young children *using objects.*

There are varying interpretations for the WDS. For example, a score of 90–100% may be described as excellent word discrimination ability and 50–60% as poor word discrimination ability. It is important to remember that the score reflects discrimination ability for a specific task—single words, which is the most difficult recognition task possible. If the child were asked to repeat sentence material, the word score would increase significantly because of the increased contextual and syntactic clues inherent in sentence material.

Although WDS is referred to as a discrimination test in the audiological world, it is actually a recognition or identification task in the context of auditory skill development. Based on auditory skill levels, *discrimination* is the ability to perceive similarities or differences among two or more sounds. *Recognition* or *identification* is the ability to repeat or point to the picture of the sound heard.

Implications

- Closed- and open-set discrimination test scores cannot be directly compared. Closed-set tasks are typically easier than open-set tasks. It is therefore important to know which discrimination test has been administered in order to interpret the results.
- Word discrimination scores can underestimate the child's recognition of speech, particularly for children with high-frequency precipitous or steeply sloping hearing loss. Sentence recognition tests provide additional information.

Ask the Audiologist

- Are there any speech sounds that the child cannot hear?
- What is the child's ability to recognize single words:
  - in a multiple-choice format?
  - in an open-set format?
- What types of identification errors did the child make:
  - vowels?
  - consonant voicing?

- manner of consonant production?
- place of consonant production?
- Which modalities does the child rely on most for identification of words under ideal conditions:
  - listening only?
  - speechreading only?
  - combined listening and speechreading?
- What effect does the presence of background noise have on the child's identification of words?

Figure 2.2 provides a simple and quick summary for parents and educators of standard audiological tests.

Figure 2.2 Summary Chart of Standard Audiological Tests

Assessment Technique	Measurement	Determines
Pure-Tone Audiogram	Hearing sensitivity	• Degree of loss • Type of loss • Shape of loss • Ear differences
Aided Thresholds Six-Sound Test GASP 1	Hearing sensitivity wearing hearing aids	• Potential for dectection and identification of speech features • Potential for detection and identification of environmental sounds • Aided benefit
Impedance Audiometry	Middle ear function	• Need for medical intervention • Possible reason fora temporary shift in hearing levels • Need to adjust hearing aid volume setting • Gross prediction of degree of hearing loss
Speech Awareness Threshold	Hearing sensitivity	• Minimal audibility for speech detection • Prediction of optimal intensity for speech recognition
Speech Reception Threshold	Hearing sensitivity for speech recognition	• Ability to recognize vowels within words • Minimal audibility and prediction of optimal intensity levels for speech recognition • Reliability of pure-tone thresholds
Word Discrimination Score	Identification of speech	• Ability to identify vowels and consonants • Differences in word recognition ability between ears

ADDITIONAL TESTS

A wide variety of additional tests are used in audiological assessment with young children. The following list provides a sampling of the diverse tools now available.

GASP 2

The *Glendonald Auditory Screening Procedure: Test 2* (GASP 2) is a recognition test that assesses the child's ability to identify words based on differences in stress patterns among familiar one-, two-, and three-syllable words, and based on vowel and consonant differences (Erber, 1982). A closed set of words is presented, and the child is asked to point to a picture of the word heard. This test is an intermediate step between the SAT and the SRT, and the ability to recognize some words on the GASP 2 often signals emerging word recognition skills.

The *Early Speech Perception Battery* (Moog & Geers, 1990) for young children incorporated this pattern perception and/or simple word identification task, using objects rather than picture stimuli.

Ask the Audiologist

- Is the child able to recognize differences among stress patterns of one-, two-, and three-syllable words? If not, are there any stress patterns that he or she identifies correctly?
- Are there any words that the child identifies correctly within each stress pattern category?

MAC 8: Same–Different Test

This subtest from the *Minimal Auditory Capabilities (MAC) Battery* (Owens, Kessler, Telleen, & Schubert, 1981) assesses the child's ability to discriminate differences between pairs of spondees (two-syllable words with equal stress on both syllables). Two words are presented, and the child is asked if the word pairs are the same two words or two different words. This is primarily a vowel discrimination task. It is useful to assess this skill when a child is able to differentiate among stress patterns on the GASP 2, but not yet able to identify vowel differences when given an SRT.

Ask the Audiologist

- Can the child discriminate any differences between the speech spectrum of two words?

Test of Auditory Comprehension

The *Test of Auditory Comprehension* (TAC) is a battery of 10 subtests of increasing auditory difficulty, ranging from discrimination of speech versus nonspeech sounds to answering questions about a story presented in background noise. All the subtests use a multiple-choice format and can be used with children from the ages of 4–17 years. Norms are provided by age and degree of hearing loss based on pure-tone average. The results of the testing are linked to objectives and activities in the accompanying *Auditory Skills Curriculum* (Office of the Los Angeles County Superintendent of Schools, 1976).

Implications

- The ability to identify words on subtest 4 is a precursor to the ability to identify words on the WIPI picture identification test. TAC 4 is a recognition task based on differences in syllable pattern, vowels, and consonants, whereas the WIPI uses words contrasting only in the consonants.
- Subtests 5 and 6 are useful to assess the child's ability to listen and identify words within phrases rather than words in isolation.
- Subtests 7 through 10 are the only standardized tests of comprehension, and more closely represent the auditory demands of the classroom. However, the multiple-choice answer format and picture cues used on the TAC still create a considerably easier listening task than that experienced in the everyday classroom.

Ask the Audiologist

- Is the child able to recognize words and phrases from a closed set of responses?
- Can the child comprehend a short or a long story and answer questions about the story?
- Can the child comprehend a story presented in background noise?

Sentence Tests

The purpose of sentence repetition tasks is to assess the child's ability to use contextual clues for identification of speech. Although single word repetition is the most commonly used speech recognition task, it is also the most difficult because of the lack of context. It is therefore not always representative of the auditory challenges presented in the child's everyday environment.

A variety of sentence tests are available. The child's task is to repeat the entire sentence or, in the case of the *Speech Perception in Noise Test* (SPIN), to repeat the last word in the sentence. The sentences may be presented in quiet or in noise, and with or without speechreading cues.

Ask the Audiologist

- Is the child able to identify sentence material?
- Does the addition of speechreading cues improve his or her recognition of sentence material significantly?
- What is the child's ability to recognize sentence material presented in background noise?

Sound Effects Recognition Test

The *Sound Effects Recognition Test* (SERT) was originally designed to measure auditory skills in preschoolers or young children with limited speech recognition capability (Finitzo-Hieber, Matkin, & Cherow-Skalka, 1980). Thirty different environmental sounds are presented, ranging from the sound of a dog barking to the sound of a doorbell, and the child is asked to select the correct sound from a closed set of four pictures per item. Recognition of familiar sounds is one of the first indicators of auditory perceptual ability that the child may demonstrate during audiological assessment and is useful as an interim measure of auditory skill development. Children who recognize most of the environmental sounds on this test often later develop some vowel identification skills, as measured by the speech reception threshold (SRT).

Ask the Audiologist

- Can the child recognize differences in the frequency spectrum of environmental sounds?

Assessment Tools in Auditory Curricula

Assessment tools are also included in a number of auditory skills curricula. Examples include:

- *Speech Perception Instructional Curriculum and Evaluation* (SPICE) (Moog, Biedenstein, & Davidson, 1995);
- *Developmental Approach to Successful Listening II* (DASL) (Stout & Windle, 1992);
- *Miami Cochlear Implant Auditory and Tactile Skills Curriculum* (CHATS) (Vergara & Miskiel, 1994);
- *Test of Auditory Comprehension* (TAC), mentioned earlier, which is directly tied to the *Auditory Skills Curriculum* (Office of the Los Angeles County of Superintendent of Schools, 1976) and the *Auditory Schools Curriculum Preschool Supplement.*

ELECTROACOUSTICAL EVALUATION

The electroacoustical characteristics of the amplification systems used by the child must be assessed routinely to ensure satisfactory functioning. The audiologist evaluates:

- gain (intensity across various frequencies);
- frequency response (the bass, mid, and treble response);
- saturation sound pressure level (the maximum intensity produced by the hearing aid at various frequencies);
- equivalent input noise level (the internal noise produced by the hearing aid);
- distortion levels (the clarity of the sound produced by the hearing aid).

With young children, it is desirable to obtain electroacoustical evaluation every 3 months, *or any time there is a decrease in auditory responsiveness or clarity of speech.* When a child is using an FM system in combination with personal hearing aids, the FM system should be evaluated separately and then in combination with the hearing aids to determine the optimal response from the electroacoustical interactions of the hearing aid–FM system.

Probe-Microphone Real-Ear Measurement

Acoustical performance of the hearing aid fitting can also be measured in the child's ear canal using probe-microphone real-ear measurement. While electroacoustical evaluation traditionally evaluates the sound characteristics of the hearing aid alone in an artificial test chamber simulating the ear, real-ear measurement assesses the sound characteristics of the hearing aid coupled to the earmold in the child's ear canal.

The instrumentation uses an external microphone sitting outside the ear, connected to a soft silicone tube. The tube is inserted into the ear canal to measure the difference in acoustic response between the unaided and aided condition. A loudspeaker generates a known intensity across a number of frequencies. The external microphone measures the changes in intensity detected through the tube sitting in the ear canal close to the eardrum, first without and then with the hearing aid. Because greater differences are noted between electroacoustical and probe-microphone measurement techniques for children than adults, the procedure adds vital information about hearing aid fitting for children.

Probe-microphone measurement is used to determine:

- gain, frequency response, and saturation sound pressure level of the hearing aid in the child's ear (the term "insertion gain" is used to refer to the gain measured in the child's ear canal);
- audibility of the speech spectrum for the child wearing the hearing aids with or without the FM system;
- effect of the shape of the child's ear canal on the hearing aid response;
- effects of altering the volume setting or internal hearing aid controls on the insertion gain and/or saturation sound pressure level;
- effects of various earmold modifications on the hearing aid response;
- differences in acoustical response among selected hearing aid responses.

Hearing aid fitting protocols using probe-microphone measurement provide a means of selecting and fitting hearing aids for children that is more reliable, provides more accurate and comprehensive data across frequencies, and requires less cooperation from the child than traditional aided sound field testing. The procedure can be done with infants as well as young children.

Implications

- The use of electroacoustical and probe-microphone measurements in the selection and fitting of hearing aids is essential to ensure that the desired hearing aid characteristics are actually present when the hearing aid and earmold are worn in the child's ear.

- An alteration in the gain or frequency response, either electroacoustically or acoustically through a modification in the earmold, can affect speech perception and production. Any deterioration in the child's responses to sound or speech quality should be followed with an immediate check of hearing aid and earmold performance.

  Example: The parents of a young preschooler who had a sloping severe to borderline profound sensorineural hearing loss had tracked their child's auditory and speech development carefully over the past year. Their child was able to identify all vowel sounds and produce vowels accurately in everyday speech. One day, the parents noticed the child was not able to differentiate between "oo"(/u/) and "ee" (/i/). After the child's sound confusion persisted for several days, they called the audiology clinic. Electroacoustical and real-ear measurement of aided function showed that the shape of the canal of the new earmold had reduced the high-frequency information sufficiently that discrimination between "oo" and "ee" was impossible. Modifications to the new earmold restored the child's high-frequency perception, and speech production returned to previous levels.

Ask the Audiologist

- Are the hearing aids and/or FM system working appropriately?
- Are there any modifications to hearing aid settings or earmold characteristics that would enhance audibility or perception of speech?
- Do the hearing aid characteristics need to be altered when coupled to the FM system?
- Should the child use a different program when wearing the FM system with a programmable hearing aid?
- Which volume setting on the FM system will optimize performance between the hearing aid and the FM system?
- Which FM accessories would enhance the child's audibility of speech in various listening environments (e.g., use of boom microphone, pass-around microphone, patch cords to audio or audiovisual equipment)?

CONCLUSION

Once the child and family walk into the audiology clinic, a myriad of auditory skills can be explored. Often, lack of familiarity with audiological terminology and assessment procedures can distance parents and therapists from the audiologist. The information and questions for the audiologist listed in this chapter provide parents and therapists with the basis for mutual sharing of concerns. It is then possible for all key players on the team to contribute to determining the directions of the audiological assessment.

REFERENCES

Erber, N. (1982). *Auditory Training.* Washington, DC: Alexander Graham Bell Association for the Deaf.

Finitzo-Hieber, T., Matkin, N., & Cherow-Skalka, E. (1980). "A sound effects recognition test for the pediatric audiological evaluation." *Ear and Hearing, 2,* 271–276.

Ling, D. (1976). *Speech and the Hearing Impaired Child.* Washington, DC: Alexander Graham Bell Association for the Deaf.

Ling, D. (1989). *Foundations of Spoken Language for Hearing Impaired Children.* Washington, DC: Alexander Graham Bell Association for the Deaf.

Ling, D. (2005). "The Six-Sound Test." *The Listener* (Special Silver Anniversary Edition), 72–74.

Moog, J., Biedenstein, J., & Davidson, L. (1995). *Speech Perception Instructional Curriculum and Evaluation.* St. Louis: Central Institute for the Deaf.

Moog, J., & Geers, A. (1990). *The Early Speech Perception Battery: Standard and Low Verbal.* St. Louis: Central Institute for the Deaf.

Office of the Los Angeles County Superintendent of Schools. (1976). *Auditory Skills Curriculum.* North Hollywood: Foreworks.

Owens, E., Kessler, D., Telleen, C., & Schubert, E. (1981). *The Minimal Auditory Capabilities Battery.* St. Louis: Auditec.

Stout, G.G., & Windle, J.V.E. (1992). *Developmental Approach to Successful Listening II.* Houston: Houston School for Deaf Children.

Vergara, K., & Miskiel, L.W. (1994). *The Miami Cochlear Implant Auditory and Tactile Skills Curriculum.* Miami: Intelligent Hearing Systems.

SELECTED AUDIOLOGICAL ABBREVIATIONS

BOA: behavioral observation audiometry; method of assessment used with young children in which sound is presented and the child's behavioral responses are observed

CNA: could not average; person did not have measurable hearing at one or more frequencies used to calculate the pure-tone average (PTA)

CNT: could not test

CPA: conditioned play audiometry; method of assessment used with children with cognitive age of 2–5 years in which sound is presented and child is taught to perform some play activity each time he or she hears the sound

DNT: did not test

EOAEs: evoked otoacoustics emissions; electrophysiological measure of hearing sensitivity; includes transient evoked otoacoustics emissions (TEOAEs) and distortion product otoacoustic emissions (DPOAEs)

MCL: most comfortable level

NBN: narrow-band noise; noise bands centered at frequencies of 250–8000 Hz used in masking, unaided, and aided sound field testing

NR: no response; no measurable hearing when signal presented at the limits of the audiometer

PTA: pure-tone average; average of the pure-tone thresholds at 500, 1000, and 2000 Hz in each ear

PTA = –10 to 15 dB:	Normal hearing
PTA = 15 to 25 dB:	Minimal hearing loss
PTA = 26 to 40 dB:	Mild hearing loss
PTA = 41 to 55 dB:	Moderate hearing loss
PTA = 56 to 70 dB:	Moderately severe hearing loss
PTA = 71 to 90 dB:	Severe hearing loss
PTA ≥ 91 dB:	Profound hearing loss
PTA ≥ 15 dB in one ear:	Unilateral hearing loss

SAT: speech awareness threshold, sometimes called speech detection threshold; the faintest level at which the child can detect the presence of speech 50% of the time

SDS: speech discrimination scores; percentage scores obtained using words, phrases, or sentences

SF: sound field; refers to the way sound is presented to the child (e.g., through speakers in a soundproof suite) in unaided and aided testing; results always reflect hearing in the better ear

SRT: speech reception threshold; the faintest level at which the child can repeat familiar two-syllable words (or point to pictures of them) 50% of the time

VRA: visual reinforcement audiometry; method of assessment in which the child is conditioned to look at a toy each time he or she hears the sound; used with children with cognitive ages of 6–8 months to 3 years

WDS: word discrimination score; the percentage score obtained by repeating unrelated one-syllable words (or pointing to pictures of them) in a 25- or 50-item list; interpretations of the scores vary, e.g.:

90–100%:	Excellent word discrimination ability
75–89%:	Slight difficulty
60–74%:	Moderate difficulty
50–60%:	Poor word discrimination ability

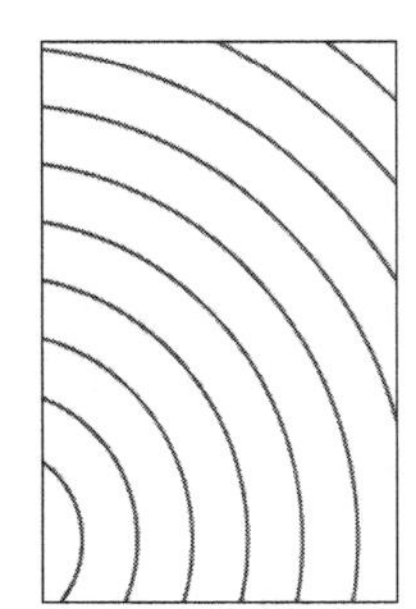

CHAPTER 3

The Cochlear Implant and Auditory-Verbal Therapy

Anne Beiter, M.S., FAAA, CCC-A, SLP
Warren Estabrooks, M.Ed., Dip. Ed. Deaf, Cert. AVT®

The word *deaf* means different things to different people, including educators, healthcare professionals, and parents. The accepted definition of a profound hearing loss, however, is one of 90 dB or greater through the speech frequencies of 500–2000 Hz. Some individuals with severe to profound hearing loss do not receive enough acoustic information about spoken speech and language through hearing aids to make the auditory channel effective for communication purposes.

Learning language has historically been very challenging for a child with a severe or profound hearing loss, and a number of philosophies and methods for teaching children who are deaf or hard of hearing have been tried, explored, and criticized for decades. Changes in therapy and deaf education are occurring now that enable more and more children to take advantage of a relatively new technology—the cochlear implant. This hearing technology offers many children who are deaf or hard of hearing the opportunity to use auditory information to its maximum to develop spoken communication effectively. Many children receive new auditory potential when they receive a cochlear implant.

The cochlear implant, a high-tech biomedical prosthesis that provides hearing sensation via electrical stimulation to the auditory centres of the brain, has become the technology of choice for those individuals who cannot benefit from hearing aids. It continues to be the most significant achievement in scientific hearing technology to assist children and adults who have severe to profound hearing impairments since the advent of hearing aids and tactile devices (Estabrooks, 1998). Cochlear implants are designed to provide sound to adults and children who have significant hearing loss and who receive limited auditory information though amplified hearing. The cochlear implant converts sounds into electrical currents that stimulate the remaining auditory nerve endings in the damaged inner ear or cochlea, and generate sensations of hearing. Most adults and children who are deaf or hard of hearing have residual auditory nerve fibers that can be stimulated electrically.

In the 1980s and early 1990s, only individuals with profound hearing loss were candidates for cochlear implantation. However, today's technology has improved to the point that children and adults with some useful hearing may be implant candidates.

HISTORY OF COCHLEAR IMPLANTS

Although the effects of electrical stimulation on hearing were being studied as early as the 19th century, it was not until the 1960s and 1970s that research groups in the United States, Europe, and Australia were actively studying electrical stimulation in humans. In the United States, Drs. William House, Blair Simmons, and Robin Michelson had active cochlear implant research programs, and Professor Graeme Clark in Australia conducted fundamental research in experimental animal and, later, human subjects. These pioneers implanted the first wearable devices designed for long-term stimulation in the 1970s. Professor Clark implanted several deaf adult patients with a multi-channel device in 1978 and 1979. The professional literature provides a number of excellent reviews of the modern history of cochlear implantation (Clark, 2003; House & Berliner, 1991; Luxford & Brackmann, 1985; Mecklenburg & Lehnhardt, 1991).

The United States Food and Drug Administration (FDA) and the Canadian Ministry of Health regulate the use of medical devices and drugs. Medical devices that are implanted in the body must be examined carefully to determine (a) that they pose no safety hazard to the public and (b) whether they are useful for the specific group for whom they are intended. Before a device is approved for general use in the population, it must be studied in a scientific manner. Thus, manufacturers working in conjunction with medical institutions conduct clinical trials in order to obtain the body of information that will be reviewed by the relevant governmental agencies to judge the safety and effectiveness of a specific medical device.

Late in 1985, the FDA granted approval for commercial use of the Nucleus® 22 Channel Cochlear Implant in adults with profound sensorineural hearing loss. In 1990, this device was approved for use in children aged 2 through 17 years with profound hearing loss. Since then, more types of cochlear implants have been approved for use in the United States and Canada; the technology has improved dramatically, providing even more hearing benefit to adults and children. Thus, the approved indications for use have expanded considerably. Today, children aged as young as 12 months may receive a cochlear implant, and both adults and children may be candidates even if they receive some benefit from hearing aids.

Current Cochlear Implant Systems

Today, cochlear implant systems from three manufacturers are available in the United States and Canada. The MED-EL Corporation, with headquarters in Austria, recently introduced the Pulsar ci^{100} cochlear implant. Advanced Bionics®, a Boston Scientific company, produces the HiResolution Bionic Ear System. Cochlear Americas, the US-based subsidiary of Cochlear Ltd. from Australia, introduced the new Nucleus® Freedom™ system in Spring 2005. All three systems use sophisticated digital electronics.

HOW A COCHLEAR IMPLANT WORKS

All cochlear implant systems consist of an internal portion—the implant itself—that is surgically placed in the inner ear (cochlea), and the external components, which are worn on the body. The Nucleus® 3 and Nucleus Freedom™ systems have a range of implants so that the implant surgeon has options to suit each patient's medical indications. MED-EL also offers several straight electrode array options. Currently, Cochlear is the only manufacturer offering a curved array; this allows the electrodes to be placed near the core of the cochlea. The latest implant, the Nucleus® Freedom™ with Contour Advance Electrode, has a self-curling 22-electrode array that approximates the curvature of the human cochlea. Prior to insertion, a thin stylet holds the pre-curved array in a semi-straight position. This allows the surgeon to place the array in the cochlea gently and easily. As the surgeon inserts the electrode and removes the stylet, the array curves towards the inner core of the cochlea, where the auditory nerve endings reside. Each electrode on the array is connected to the receiver/stimulator package by a separate insulated wire. The surgeon places this package under the skin in a surgically created seat in the mastoid bone, which is located behind the ear. Typically, surgery lasts about two to two and a half hours and is performed under general anesthesia. A thorough review of surgical and safety considerations in children can be found in the literature (Clark, 2003; Clark, Cohen, & Shepherd, 1991; Clark, Pyman, & Webb, 1997).

The external components of a cochlear implant system are designed to pick up sound in the environment and to analyze and convert it into electrical signals that are sent to the cochlear implant located under the skin. This process happens in several stages (Figure 3.1). An ear-level microphone picks up the sound and changes it into electrical energy that is a direct representation of the acoustic signal. This signal is sent to the speech processor, which can be either a behind-the-ear processor or a small body-worn device, depending upon the needs of the individual. The speech processor analyzes and digitizes this signal and changes it to a specific code. The processor sends the coded information to the transmitting coil, which is worn on the outside of the head, directly over the cochlear implant. It is held in place by a pair of magnets, one magnet in the transmitting coil and a companion within the implant. The transmitting coil sends the stream of digital code and power across the skin on a radio frequency to the receiver/stimulator, which is located in the cochlear implant.

The receiver/stimulator contains an integrated circuit that decodes the digital signals and sends correct amounts of electrical current to the electrodes placed within the inner ear. This electrical current directly stimulates the auditory nerve fibers, thus bypassing damaged or missing structures in the inner ear that can no longer change mechanical energy into the electrical stimulus needed to generate a response in the hearing nerve. When the electrodes stimulate the remaining auditory nerve fibers, the resulting neural activity is sent through the auditory nerve to the brain, where it is interpreted as sound.

Figure 3.1 How a Cochlear Implant Works

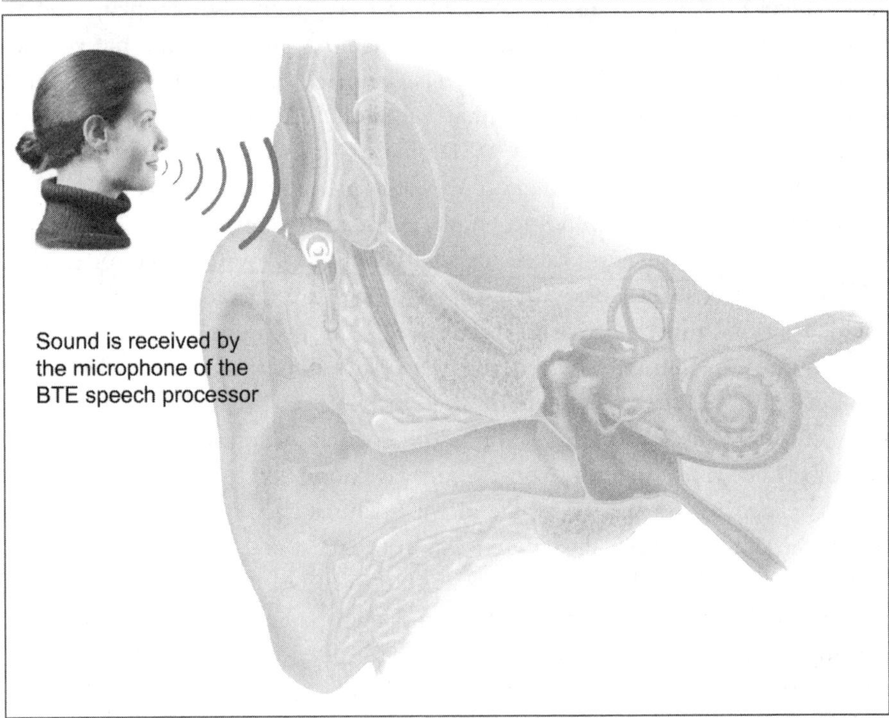

3A

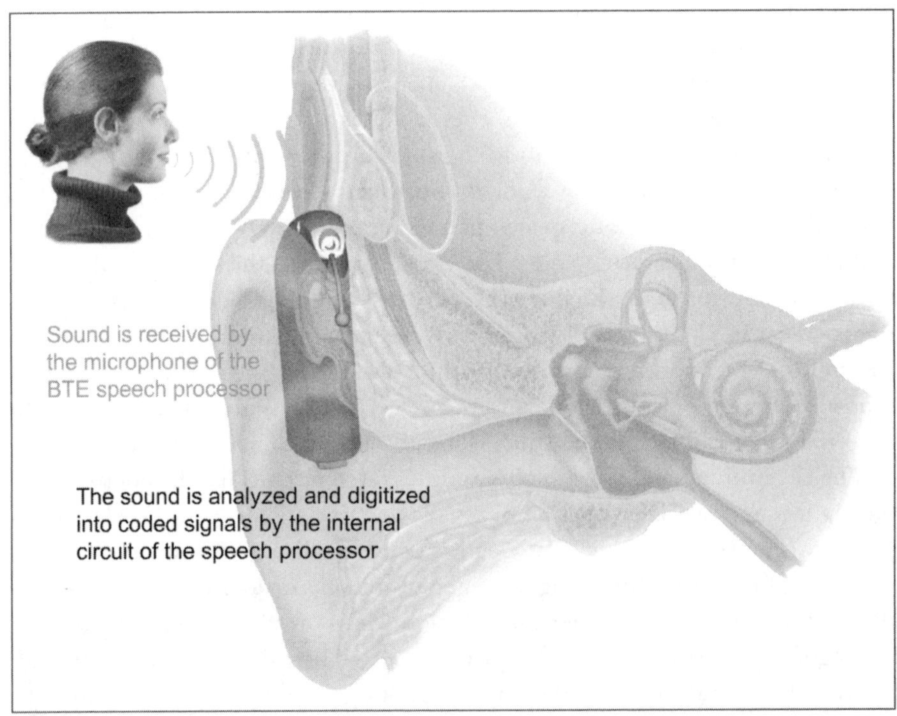

3B

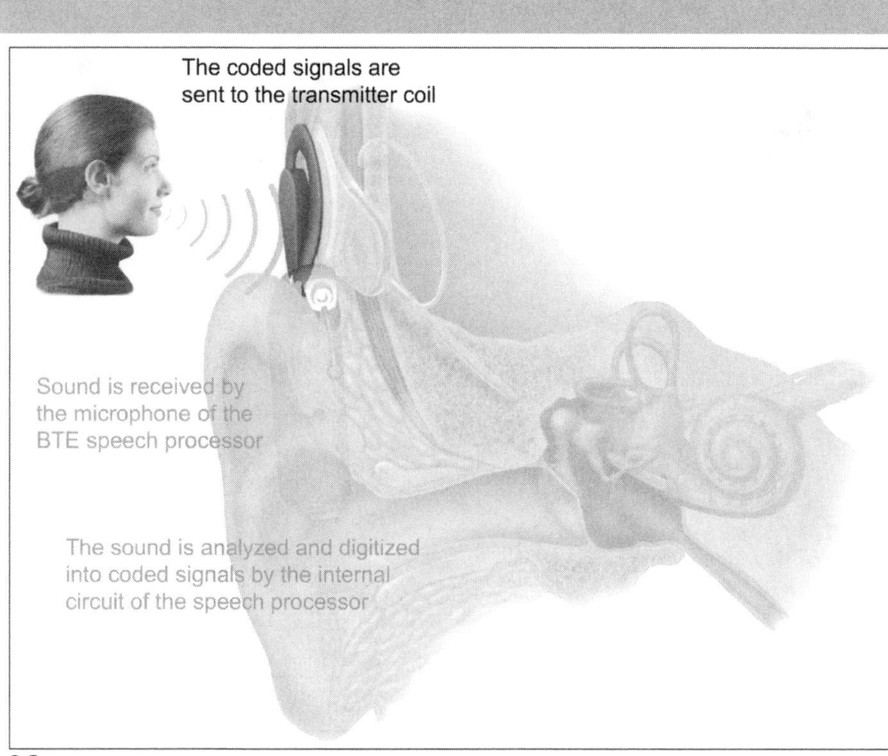

3C

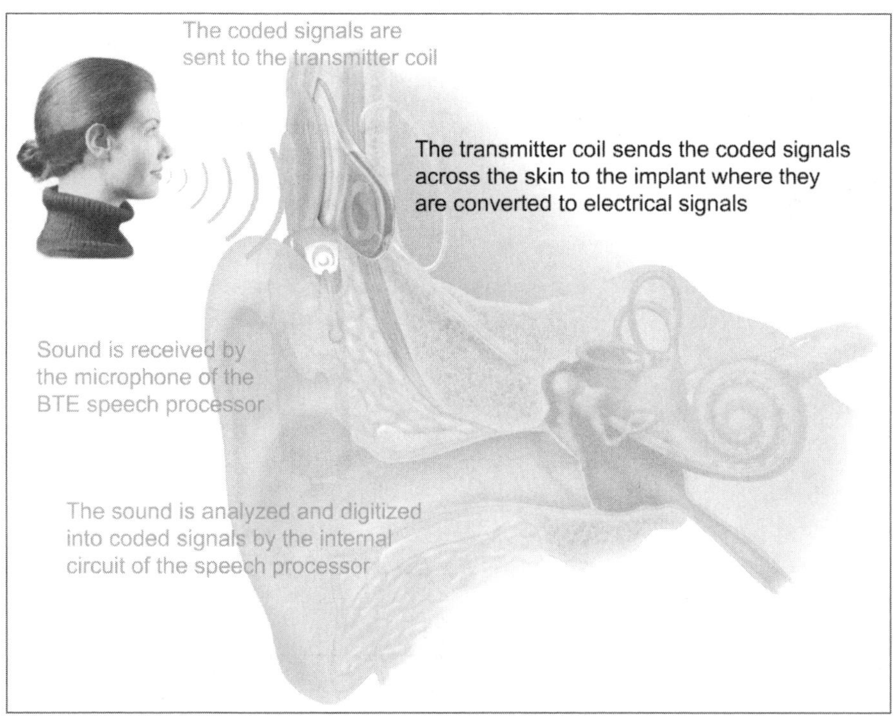

3D

Continued

Figure 3.1 How a Cochlear Implant Works *(Continued)*

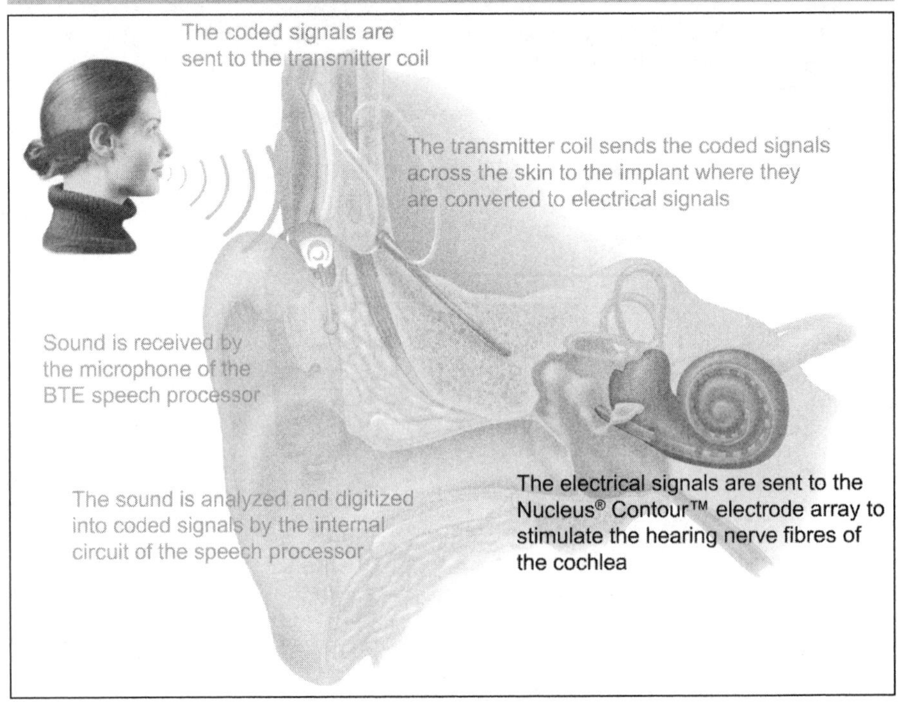

3E

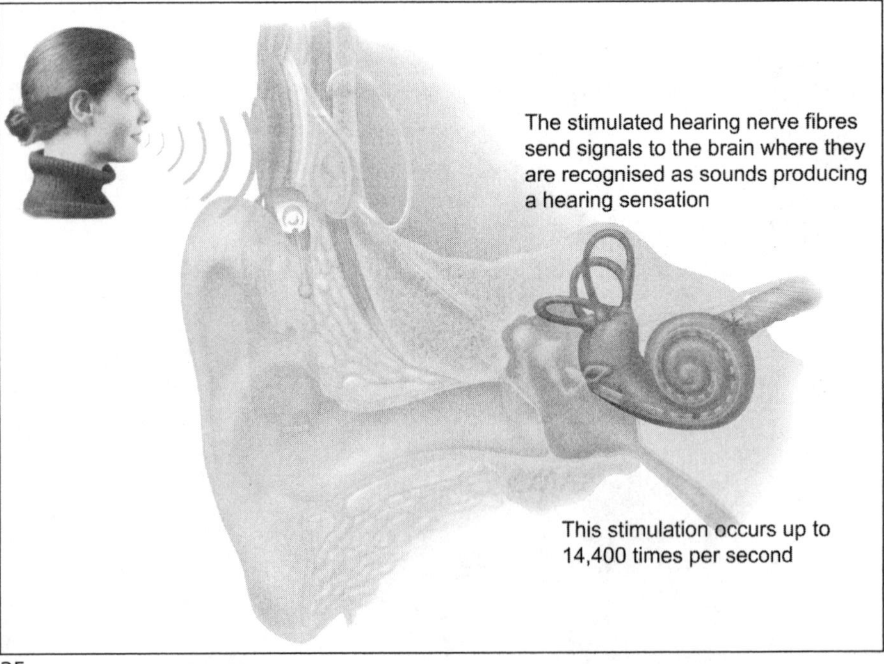

3F

Regardless of the brand of implant system, the speech processor must be programmed (MAPped) to the individual requirements of each recipient. Specifically, the audiologist determines the amount of electrical current needed for a child to discern a soft sound and the amount of electrical current required for him or her to hear a comfortably loud sound. This information is obtained for each of the electrodes and is stored in the speech processor's memory as part of the child's individualized programs or MAPs. Information about these electrical current requirements for hearing is sent across the skin as part of the instructions to the cochlear implant. Thus, each person receives the amount of current that is right for him or her to perceive sounds that vary in loudness in the environment.

The age and attention span of the child, as well as previous experiences with sound, affect how much a child can participate in programming the speech processor. Infants and young children often provide only limited behavioral information about the hearing process. All three manufacturers now have implant systems and software that directly measure the physiological activity of the auditory nerve to electrical signals. This provides the audiologist quick and easy access to electrophysiological information about the hearing nerves' responses as each of the electrodes in the inner ear is stimulated. The audiologist may use this software in the operating room after the device is in place, or in the clinic during a regular programming appointment. The audiologist uses these physiological responses along with any behavioral information to create a series of individualized programs for the child to begin the listening experience. This objective information gives the audiologist and the family confidence that the child is receiving electrical stimulation that is audible. The speech processors hold multiple programs so that parents can move from one MAP to the next as instructed by the audiologist.

USE OF THE COCHLEAR IMPLANT IN CHILDREN

The evaluation of infants and children who may be candidates for a cochlear implant necessitates a team approach, involving professionals from the fields of otolaryngology, audiology, auditory habilitation, Auditory-Verbal therapy, speech-language pathology, education, and psychology. Other disciplines may join the team, depending upon the circumstances and needs of the individual child. The family plays a critical role on the team and contributes important information about how the child uses hearing and other modalities in daily life for communication. The child's family also provides the child's major support structure, including advocacy for the services they believe are necessary for their child to make optimal use of residual hearing. The team professionals are charged with the responsibility of fully informing the family regarding the details of cochlear implants, the associated procedures, and long-term commitments and expectations.

The parents of a child who is a cochlear implant candidate make the final decision, in conjunction with professionals, on whether to proceed. Talking with other families who have made the decision and have experiences to share is helpful. In the case of an adolescent, the parents and other team members include the teenager in the decision-making process. The adolescent's wishes, views, and expectations need to be considered carefully. Misunderstandings and unrealistic expectations need to be resolved prior to implantation.

In addition to measuring the child's residual hearing sensitivity, the audiologist must evaluate the current amplification to ensure that it is appropriate. In some cases, new hearing aids will be needed before the child's auditory, speech, and language abilities can be evaluated. Medical, psycho-social, and educational evaluations must also be completed. The current recommended pediatric selection criteria include:

For children 12–24 months of age:
- Profound bilateral sensorineural hearing loss

For children 2 years through 17 years of age:
- Severe to profound bilateral sensorineural hearing loss

For all children:
- No radiological or medical contraindications
- Limited benefit from amplification as demonstrated by lack of progress in basic auditory skills in conjunction with aggressive auditory intervention; for older children, this is demonstrated using formal tests of speech perception
- Enrollment in an educational program that emphasizes the full-time use of hearing and oral language for communication
- Psychological suitability
- Appropriate family expectations and support.

With the advent of early identification of hearing loss followed by early and aggressive intervention, cochlear implantation in infants and young children is an option to provide early access to sound. This gives children the opportunity to detect, discriminate, identify, and comprehend spoken language so that they can process speech and language through hearing. Thus, many children with cochlear implants will be ready to attend their local school alongside their hearing peers. Pre- and postoperative comparison studies show that children with cochlear implants make significant improvements in speech perception, production, and language development. In general, children enrolled in auditory/oral education programs perform better than children from Total Communication backgrounds. Long-term data also support implantation earlier rather than later to minimize the length of auditory deprivation and the significant delays in speech and language associated with hearing loss (Nicholas & Geers, 2004; Holt, Svirsky, Neuburger, & Miyamoto, 2004; Bergeson, Pisoni, & Davis, 2003; Dowell & Cowan 1997; Geers, Brenner, & Davidson, 2003; Geers, Nicholas, & Sedney, 2003; Staller, Parkison, Arcaroli, & Arndt, 2002; Tobey, Geers, Brenner, Altuna, & Gabbert, 2003).

Many variables affect postoperative outcomes with a cochlear implant, and it is impossible to predict the amount of benefit any child will receive from the device. Although a child may be a good candidate for implantation, there is no guarantee that he or she will ultimately process general conversation through hearing alone. However, the cochlear implant makes the auditory and oral language learning process much easier given a strong habilitation program and long-term audiological followup care (Geers & Brenner, 2004; Barker, Dettman, & Dowell, 1997; Dowell & Cowan, 1997; Galvin, Sarant, & Cowan, 1997).

Owing to improvements in implant technology, as well as the significant benefits demonstrated with unilateral implantation, more adults and children who do not benefit from a hearing aid in the opposite ear are receiving bilateral cochlear implants, either in sequential surgeries or, in some cases, simultaneously. Bilateral implants may improve hearing abilities, especially in noisy and complex listening situations, and potentially make the development of oral communication easier for young children. Recently, Cochlear Americas conducted a pediatric sequential bilateral study to evaluate the incremental benefit of a second implant to speech perception and localization. Thirty children participated in the study; they ranged in age from 3 to 13 years at the time of their second implantation. Data collected to date suggest that children who received their second cochlear implant before the age of 8 years, with a relatively short time between implants (less than 5 years, on average), did well with bilateral implants. On the other hand, children who were over 8 years old, with 6 years or more of unilateral listening, on average, when they received their second implant, showed much less benefit (Parkinson, personal communication, October 2005).

Another study conducted in Germany (Kuhn-Inacker, Shehata-Dieler, Muller, & Helms, 2004) found that bilateral implants improved children's general communication abilities as well as their skills for listening in noise compared to the unilateral condition. These researchers emphasized the importance of an intensive habilitation program to maximize benefit from bilateral implants. Additional studies looking at the benefits of bilateral cochlear implantation in children are ongoing at centers around the world.

AUDITORY-VERBAL THERAPY

A decade ago, about 25% of the caseload at the Learning to Listen Foundation were families who had children with cochlear implant technology. Today, that figure stands at approximately 75%. Ten years ago, the children received their operations at a number of medical centers, and each of those had a prescriptive program for postactivation followup. Now, most of our children receive their implants through the cochlear implant program for children in Toronto, and the Learning to Listen Foundation follows the individual treatment plan that is developed for each child based on existing knowledge of Auditory-Verbal therapy, child development, and the skills gained through working in partnership with today's families.

To provide an optimal treatment program, the Auditory-Verbal therapist coaches and guides the parents as they provide auditory experiences, structured auditory skills development, and carryover activities for play in order to generalize goals in listening, speech, language, communication, and thinking skills. The parent remains the primary case manager and is supported by a team of professionals.

Many parents of children with cochlear implants who choose Auditory-Verbal therapy as the approach for language learning exhibit characteristics similar to those of parents who have children who wear hearing aids. These parents

- advocated for and sought aggressive audiologic management in collaboration with the professional auditory management team;
- sought excellent sources of medical intervention and hearing technology;
- helped their child understand the meaning of sounds with their primary emphasis on spoken language development through listening;
- became the primary model in helping their children learn to listen and talk;
- observed, waited, and listened (Manolson, 1985) to help their child respond effectively to the world;
- assisted their child to integrate as much as possible into the school of choice and into the community.

AUDITORY-VERBAL THERAPY AND THE COCHLEAR IMPLANT

Auditory-Verbal therapy continues to receive great attention from families of children who have cochlear implants and the professionals who guide them. To help children maximize the use of the newly acquired auditory potential that a cochlear implant can provide, many implant teams recommend Auditory-Verbal therapy both pre- and post-implantation. These same teams may also recommend the inclusion of auditory-verbal techniques, strategies, and procedures, even if the child is using another mode of communication. Such recommendations are very encouraging, as cochlear implant technology is designed to improve the reception of speech and the sounds of the environment. The marriage of an aggressive auditory learning program with the technology is critical for optimal outcomes in speech and language development.

There is no single diagnostic moment when the Auditory-Verbal therapist or other habilitation professional recommends that parents investigate the possibility of a cochlear implant for their child. It is a process. The decision to implant is generally made following an aggressive audiological workup that includes a determination of the child's auditory potential with hearing aids.

As each child is unique, the process for assessing auditory potential may take as long as 6 months, depending on age at diagnosis and the initial hearing aid fitting. Auditory performance in structured lesson-type activities and in play must be charted and analyzed by the habilitative specialists, the audiologists, and the parents. All members of the child's care team can assist in determining whether the child receives sufficient auditory information with amplified hearing for the development of spoken language through listening, or whether an alternative intervention program should be considered.

THE CHILDREN

All children at the Learning to Listen Foundation who have received cochlear implants have made significant progress in speech and language acquisition, auditory processing, and conversational competence. "Significant," however, is a relative term. The professional needs to document the habilitation process and the child's achievements according to the auditory-verbal treatment plan. Progress must be charted to ensure that the degree and speed of development accords with the plan. Since children at the Learning to Listen Foundation today receive a maximum of 4 years of Auditory-Verbal therapy after activation of the cochlear implant, we must race to close the gap between the child's hearing age and the chronological age.

The ultimate goal is for children to process spoken conversation in a variety of natural acoustic environments and those featuring a significant amount of ambient noise, because that is the real-world environment in which children live. But some children may not be able to achieve that goal. Progress can mean anything between simple detection and the ability to converse fluently.

Cochlear implant professionals know that many variables affect the rate and proficiency of spoken language development, cognition, and communication through auditory pathways (Ling, 1990). As auditory-verbal professionals, we are cautioned to guard carefully the expectations that are established and expected both by and for parents and their children. One of the greatest challenges for children who are deaf or hard of hearing is that many professionals set the bar far too low. Given current levels of knowledge and technology, it is appropriate to raise the bar, diligently follow our code of ethics, and establish ourselves as sympathetic and driven coaches so that the race is won in the shortest amount of time.

The following stories were written over a decade ago by the parents of children who received a cochlear implant (Estabrooks, 1994). Now, these families have generously offered an update of their children's progress.

ERIC

Angela Sieloff

Our drive to the hospital was an emotional one. Mike and I were relieved that our son Eric was in good hands, anxious about his prognosis, and exhausted. It had been a long day. It was an early September evening, and our 19-month-old son had been airlifted to Children's Hospital in London, Ontario after being diagnosed with pneumococcal meningitis. Fifteen days later, he was discharged, and our lives had changed forever. Nerve damage had affected Eric's right eye and his oral motor abilities. He could not open his eyelid nor control the movement of his eye. He could not eat solid food. He could not roll over. He could not sit up or walk. He also had, we were told, at least a moderate to severe hearing loss.

We spent the first weekend after Eric's discharge in the local library, borrowing every book we could find on deafness. Luckily, one of the books we happened

Eric Sieloff (right) and family, 1994

upon was *Learning to Listen* (Vaughan, 1981), a book about deaf children learning to communicate through the auditory-verbal approach. This book, written by Toronto-area mothers about their children, inspired and challenged us to consider this approach for Eric.

We surrounded ourselves with people who could offer us support and professional help. We joined the local chapter of VOICE for Hearing-Impaired Children and found an excellent audiologist who took the time to explain things to us. We worked with a home visiting teacher from the regional school for the deaf, a speech pathologist, an occupational therapist, and a physiotherapist. Slowly, Eric's physical condition began to improve. He was able to open his right eye and had some control over its movement. He progressed through baby food and junior food to table food. He sat up, crawled, and began to walk along the furniture. As his physical condition improved, it became noticeable that sound was not part of his environment.

Eric was fitted with his first set of hearing aids 4 weeks after his discharge from hospital. Subsequent hearing tests indicated a left-hand corner audiogram, consistent with a profound bilateral sensorineural hearing loss. This resulted in a change to more powerful hearing aids shortly thereafter. Despite our efforts at auditory stimulation, the only sound to which Eric responded was the popping of a balloon behind his back. We were concerned about his lack of progress and wondered if our goal of oral communication was realistic.

At the suggestion of Eric's speech pathologist, we investigated the Auditory-Verbal therapy program at the Learning to Listen Foundation in January. We appreciated the clinical staff's dedication and extensive background in working with young children who are deaf or hard of hearing and their families. Despite the significant time commitment involved, we were excited about the prospect of working with knowledgeable and experienced professionals. Eric was enrolled in the program, and we began therapy a week later.

The routine began! Each Wednesday afternoon, I packed up our baby along with Eric, who still wasn't walking, and drove the two-and-half hours to Toronto, where we stayed with my mother overnight. This allowed us to have therapy on Thursday mornings. At home, we had a sit-down lesson with Eric for an hour each day—not always an easy task with a 2-year-old. The rest of the day, we talked and read books constantly. By mid-March, however, it became apparent that Eric was not progressing. He became very quiet. His vocabulary decreased to about five words, and the pronunciation of these was deteriorating. He began to show signs of frustration at his inability to communicate his wants and needs.

It was at this point that we seriously considered a cochlear implant. We collected newspaper articles, technical papers, and literature from the Cochlear Corporation to learn about the implant and the potential risks and benefits. We spoke to parents of other children who had received implants to learn from their experiences. We applied to two local implant centers in Toronto and London and to a center in New York City. We were offered and accepted an assessment date 5 weeks later at the New York University Medical Center. During the course of this assessment, we discovered that Eric's CT scan showed signs of significant ossification in both ears. This is a scarring process that results in new bone growth and is not uncommon after meningitis. It was recommended to us that Eric receive an implant as soon as possible to maximize the possibility of having a full electrode insertion. Despite our obvious concerns and anxieties, we booked the surgery.

Eric got his implant at the age of 27 months, just over 7 months after losing his hearing. The surgeon spoke with us immediately following the operation. Eric's ossification was, in fact, quite advanced and, despite the surgeon's drilling through the new bone growth, only 12 of 22 electrodes could be inserted. I cried—I'd been so sure that finally something was going to work out for Eric. Yet, with only a partial insertion and his oral motor weakness, we had no idea to what degree his oral communication potential would be limited. Eric bounced back quickly after the surgery and was discharged 2 days later.

We returned to New York 4 weeks later for his initial stimulation, with modest expectations in order to avoid disappointment. Only 10 of 12 electrodes were stimulated during that first 3-day session, but when Eric's processor was turned on to allow him to hear the sounds around him, he cried. He had forgotten what sound was. The first evening after his initial stimulation, Eric was able to detect the sound of a squeaky alligator toy consistently. We were overjoyed! The second evening, while in our 30th floor hotel room, he heard a fire truck go by with its siren wailing. He was terrified and ran to his daddy. We didn't know whether to comfort him or congratulate him. We knew we were on our way, and what a trip it was to be!

At 3 weeks poststimulation, Eric could detect the sounds of the Six-Sound Test, could consistently identify the Learning to Listen Sounds given a closed set of two choices, and had learned nine new words. At 5 weeks, he had a receptive vocabulary of 50 words that he could discriminate through hearing only, and was learning new words at a rate of about one per day. He could identify the telephone ringing and was responding to his name about 30% of the time. At 7.5 weeks he reached 100 words, and we celebrated.

At the time I am writing this, in 1994, Eric has had his implant for almost 5 months. We've lost track of his vocabulary, but think it's about 350 words. He sometimes puts three and four words together and manages to communicate fairly complex ideas. He knows his colors and the names of all the family members, and we're currently working on counting. He shows appreciation for music and often entertains us with his version of singing and dancing. His pronunciation is improving steadily, and friends and family can understand some of what he says. We don't know how long he'll maintain this rate of progress, and we sometimes wonder about long-term issues of the implant, such as device failure and unanticipated side effects. As we see Eric progress and achieve new milestones, however, we're thankful that we chose the auditory-verbal approach and the cochlear implant for our son.

When I returned to part-time work after almost a year off, our schedule changed somewhat and became more hectic than ever. During the days I worked, Eric and his younger brother were at day care, where Eric was receiving an hour of one-on-one time each day with a resource teacher. We use weekly objective sheets, videotapes of the weekly therapy sessions, a daily journal, and monthly meetings to manage his auditory-verbal experiences at the day care. We now drive to Toronto on Sundays and have therapy on Monday mornings. Every 6–8 weeks, we drive to New York for MAPping of the speech processor. We still do a 1-hour sit-down lesson with Eric each day, and we still talk, and talk, and talk. It's easier now because Eric talks back.

Eric has recently become fascinated with dinosaurs. This morning on the way into the day care, we realized that his favorite dinosaur had been left at home. In discussing this grave matter, my husband, Mike, orally spelled out "d-i-n-o-s-a-u-r" to avoid tipping Eric off. We suddenly realized the irony of the situation—we were spelling a word to prevent our deaf son from hearing it! And we laughed.

Update

When Eric was discharged from the hospital in 1994 at the age of 18 months, deaf and unable to roll over unassisted, we often wished for a crystal ball. Would the future be bleak or bright? Had we found a crystal ball, we would have seen a 13-year-old boy who is academically successful, a great downhill skier, and a young musician who plays the piano. Knowing this would have made the journey so much easier.

Over the 10 years that followed, we focused on helping Eric develop adaptive strategies to maximize his potential and reduce the many obstacles to success in a hearing world. In the early years, this meant seeking out support and professional services, often necessitating long drives and many hours of therapy. Lately, the focus has been on maximizing educational success, as we firmly believe that a solid education is the great equalizer for children who are deaf. In the years to come, the responsibility for navigating obstacles and finding a path to success will increasingly be Eric's; teaching him to self-advocate will be key.

Academically, Eric has always done well. When challenged to work and study hard, he earns excellent grades. He is stronger in quantitative subject areas such as math and sciences than in language arts and social studies. He is an avid reader, although at times he is challenged to express well-reasoned written opinions and arguments. To provide added practice in language arts, he is enrolled in the Kumon® reading program.

Eric Sieloff and family today

Eric consistently uses his personal FM system at school, and his teachers have successfully adapted to having him in class. His itinerant teacher has been instrumental in this success. Two areas we continue to deal with are split classes and morning announcements. Because our elementary school was small, split grades were necessary in 3rd, 4th, and 7th grades. Eric has always been placed in the majority split with at least a couple of close friends. We still haven't figured out a good way to deal with the issue of morning announcements made over the school's public address system. Although we are doubtful, Eric is convinced he hears most of what's being said and, consequently, he is reluctant to try alternative strategies.

At home, Eric uses closed-captioned TV at all times. He is beginning to enjoy popular music, and uses the Internet to download lyrics to favorite songs. He follows the lyrics by using a battery-powered CD player plugged into his cochlear implant's speech processor. Telephone use with familiar speakers such as parents and grandparents is relatively easy, and lengthy conversations are not uncommon. Even though classmates call with questions about homework assignments, Eric doesn't particularly enjoy using the phone with unfamiliar listeners. Despite experimentation with an amplified telephone and phone adapter, Eric prefers to use a cordless phone that has the added benefit of allowing him to retreat to a quiet corner of the house when taking a call. Many years ago, we purchased a personal transmitter/receiver and have used this low-cost FM system for ski lessons and summer camp activities. To round out the technology, now that Eric is periodically at home alone, we have installed an audible and visible smoke detector alarm in his bedroom that is connected to the other smoke detectors in the house.

At the age of 8, Eric started piano lessons. Because he has very poor pitch perception, he has learned to play differently than his younger brother. Eric is an excellent reader of music and detects errors not by hearing a wrong note, but by detecting a fingering or hand-position error on the keyboard. He has performed flawlessly at many local recitals, much to the delight of his parents and grandparents. He passed his 4th grade music exam with honors. In 2004, Eric added drum lessons to his extracurricular activities, with the rationale that this would be far more accessible to a "deaf musician" than any other instrument. The school band now has a drummer!

We continue to struggle with the quality of Eric's speech. In addition to deafness, the meningitis resulted in dysarthria (permanent oral motor weakness). "Nothing that 10 years of speech therapy can't fix," we used to say. Well, it has been more than 10 years now, and although Eric can speak very clearly when encouraged, this ability does not consistently transfer into everyday usage. Our hope is that with increasing maturity, Eric's motivation to speak clearly *consistently* will increase as well.

Another area of concern is his social skills. Eric has few close friends of his own age and is more at ease with neighborhood boys younger than himself. He has rarely been invited to birthday parties. This may be due to his deafness, his inconsistent intelligibility, or his maturity lagging behind that of his peer group. Recess time in 5th grade was particularly difficult, as he was not included in games and didn't have the self-confidence to join in on his own. This resulted in many teary-eyed dinner conversations. Thankfully, this phase passed, and Eric's participation in school activities has greatly improved.

In 2004, Eric was involved in the enrichment program, intramural basketball and volleyball, the chess club, and the Lego™ Robot Club. Thankfully, he has never been teased. Probably this is because he was in a small school with the same students since kindergarten.

To take advantage of career opportunities, we moved from our rural community in southwestern Ontario to Houston, Texas. The decision was not taken lightly, and it is remarkable that we find ourselves having severed ties with the nurturing environment that supported our family during the difficult years following Eric's deafness. It is also a measure of Eric's progress that we felt we would—*he* would—be able to make the change successfully. So far, so good.

Back in September 1992, after Eric's discharge from hospital following his bout of meningitis, we were told that he could not hear and would never talk. We were devastated but not deterred; our fight began. With determination and help from various sources—including the Robarts School in London, the Sarnia Rotary Children's Place, VOICE for Hearing-Impaired Children, the Learning to Listen Foundation, the cochlear implant programs at New York University Medical Centre, the Hospital for Sick Children in Toronto, and the staff at Erroll Village Public School—Eric has indeed learned to listen and speak. Although his future will be shaped by his deafness, we are optimistic that his success will not limited by it. If only we had a crystal ball!

Eric is currently living with his family in Houston, Texas. In 2006, he was in 9th grade in a high school of 4,000 students. He is very active in the marching band, where he plays marimba. He also plays piano and snare drum. Academically, he is an excellent student, and takes advanced mathematics and language arts.

DARA

Shirley and Julian Keller

On April 24, 1986, our family was blessed with a perfect little girl, Dara. She had two older brothers, Jeremy and Josh, and we felt that she made our family complete. Dara was cute, good-natured, slept well, and was an absolute pleasure. She was alert and beautiful—all the things babies are supposed to be.

For over 8 months, things went well, and then it happened. Dara's father, Julian, wanted to take a picture of her and a baby cousin. When their names were called, only Dara's cousin responded. After repeated efforts to get Dara's attention, we realized that there was something wrong with our perfect daughter.

We visited several doctors, who clapped their hands or jingled keys behind Dara. They all acknowledged that there was a problem and that further investigation was necessary. We already knew there was a problem, but we were certain, in this technological era, that it could be fixed. Wasn't there an operation or something? We did not want our daughter isolated in a world of silence. We wanted her to have all the opportunities her brothers had.

Dara Keller (center) and family, 1994

Six weeks later, Dara was fitted with binaural hearing aids, and we met with the clinical staff of the Learning to Listen Foundation. It was explained to us that most children who are deaf or hard of hearing have residual hearing; with amplification from the proper hearing aids, they can learn to use this hearing to process language in order to talk. There were no promises or guarantees—only guidance and hard work.

We began to realize what an awesome task lay ahead of us. Hearing aids are not like glasses; they do not immediately correct hearing loss. Dara had a left-corner audiogram, and the hearing aids could do only so much. They would provide sound, but it would be distorted and unclear. How could she learn to talk if she could not hear perfectly and what she did hear was distorted?

Over the next several months, lessons began, parent sharing meetings were attended, books were read, and the attempt to squeeze a response to sound from Dara was begun in earnest.

All the now-familiar Learning to Listen Sounds were repeated over and over again. Finally, one day, Dara saw a dog on television, raced over, and said "Woof!" It was a start! Soon after that, she said "Bu, bu, bu" when she saw a bus. It was a long time until we stopped thinking "bu, bu, bu" every time we saw a bus on the street—with or without Dara in the car.

For the next few years, Auditory-Verbal therapy continued; Dara constantly made progress, but her speech was very poor and many of the different sounds she made sounded similar. Nobody understood her except the immediate family and her Auditory-Verbal therapist—and even we did not always comprehend. Occasionally, Dara would throw a temper tantrum through frustration.

We decided to look into the possibility of a cochlear implant. Dara underwent a battery of tests: language, communication, psychological, audiological, and speech. She was a candidate, and received her cochlear implant at New York University Medical Center on July 26, 1990, at the age of 4 years and 3 months.

The surgery was successful, and Dara started along a new path of milestones, setbacks, and miracles. She could now hear the microwave, doorbell, telephone, dogs barking, cats meowing, birds singing, leaves rustling, and cars honking. She could even hear whispers, and she would whisper back.

She continued Auditory-Verbal therapy every week and, at the age of 5, began speech therapy with a speech-language pathologist. These sessions helped improve her articulation, fluency, and intonation, and consequently, her intelligibility. Previously, Dara did not think twice about dropping syllables, consonants, or even words while conversing.

In 1994, Dara was 7 years old and attending the same local public school as her brother, where she received excellent itinerant help in her classroom for 6 hours per week. She was learning French, participated in music, had many friends, and did quite well on the telephone with the help of a speaker phone with volume control. She also had a small speaking role in a made-for-television movie starring Jennifer Beals and James Wilder.

She loves to read, always goes through a pile of books at bedtime, and was above her grade level in reading skills. This is probably due to her Auditory-Verbal therapy, intelligence, and our closed-captioned television, which we have used since she was 6. One evening, Dara's father went into her room at 10:00 p.m. to tell our night-owl daughter to turn off her light and put away her books. Her response was, "But Daddy, don't you want me to learn?"

To Our Daughter

We are glad you love to learn, which is what we tried to instill in you—far beyond the vocabulary, language, and speech. You are still deaf, and that is a part of you, as is your sweet smile, sharp tongue, and sense of humor. We still have anxious moments worrying about your future, and we realize there is still a long road ahead. With your tenacity and courage, we believe that nothing is beyond your reach.

To Other Parents

When Dara's father and I discovered that she had a hearing loss, we were devastated. If the devil had offered me her hearing in exchange for my soul, I would gladly have made the deal and considered it a bargain. Over the years, my attitude about many things has changed. Dara and her older brothers, Jeremy and Josh, have taught me so much about life that I sometimes feel as if I opened my eyes only after Dara's diagnosis.

In the beginning, I was in Never-Never Land; I could not relate to my peers when they discussed everyday problems. I was also in awe of many parents who had chosen the auditory-verbal approach for their children. They seemed so strong and sure of themselves and, while I never doubted that this was the right route for our family, I did question my own abilities.

I remember lying awake at night, wishing Dara had more hearing with which to work. I also remember staring at her audiogram, paralyzed with fear, wondering how she could ever learn to talk with such a profound hearing loss. Well, today [in 1994] I feel that no one else could have done what we did together. How could I have changed so much?

Acceptance freed me to do my best without compromising the high standards we have always expected. Following the auditory-verbal guiding principles did not offer quick results, but it made the most sense for us and seemed the least restrictive way to learn to communicate.

I have made a list of 10 important points that transformed me from insecurity and powerlessness into a woman who is far from perfect, but secure in the knowledge that I did the best I could do. Acceptance of all these things has helped me become secure and peaceful in the knowledge that I am continuing to do the best I can, and so is Dara! As a parent, I accept the fact that:

- *Mistakes will be made.* Suddenly, you will have to rely on the judgments of professionals, some of whom have never seen an infant with a hearing loss, and so they may simply dismiss your concerns. Even though this may delay getting adequate help for months, do not let anger eat away at you. Your child may not have received proper amplification immediately, but he or she was still constantly learning and practicing other important life skills. Make sure, however, that you never abdicate the responsibility of your child's care to a professional. Surround yourself with the best professionals; seek out as much information as possible through reading, speaking to adults and children who are deaf or hard of hearing and their parents, and follow up on any concerns.
- *You must give your child lots of time to listen.* Try not to rush him or her into talking. Your child is behind in communication, language and speech skills—how could it be otherwise? Set short-term and long-term goals and accept the fact that progress may be very slow.
- *You are not superhuman.* Lean on family, friends, and religion when necessary. If you need more help, seek it. You will help your child more if you are psychologically healthy. Get baby-sitters on occasion and, if you cannot afford it, trade baby-sitting nights with a friend.
- *Children often learn in spurts.* There is a lot of anxiety wrapped up in teaching a child who is deaf or hard of hearing to learn to hear, listen, and speak. Hearing children often experience learning plateaus, but we do not notice them as readily because we know that if they do not learn their colors, alphabet, or numbers this week, then they will learn them next week, or the next. With children who are deaf or hard of hearing, panic can easily set in if the child is regressing or has reached a plateau. Take heart; a child is always learning! In Auditory-Verbal therapy we often teach specific vocabulary and language and follow planned steps in communication. In reality, the child is always absorbing information.
- *You are not wasting your time.* You may wonder whether you are doing the right thing. What if the auditory-verbal approach does not work and you have to start over again? Do not worry! Auditory-Verbal therapy may be your first

choice. It does work for many children, but even if your child does have to learn another mode of communication, nothing is lost. All you have done is teach language. All modes of communication require language.

- *Our children will always miss out on information because no matter how much you teach them and no matter how good their hearing aids or cochlear implants are, they simply cannot hear everything.* Many will not hear public address (PA) announcements at school, teaching assignments, test scheduling, and even friends in group situations. Not everyone will always take the time to repeat things clearly or make eye contact. Teach your child to cope with these situations. You will not always be there to interpret for your child.
- *Usually, one caregiver carries the majority of teaching responsibility.* This is an unfair fact of life, but often this caregiver becomes so good at teaching that it becomes second nature.
- *Your child has special needs at school.* When your child is mainstreamed, a slow realization evolves that many "normal" children have special needs; a child who is learning English as a Second Language (ESL) is behind in certain aspects of English and is accepting help as needed. Chinese, Spanish, or Russian-speaking children learn by being surrounded by English-speaking students who help them grow socially, emotionally, and academically. They also help in acquiring oral and written language skills. A child who is deaf or hard of hearing learns the same way.
- *Not everyone will agree with what you are doing.* Friends, relatives, strangers, professionals, and other parents may feel obligated to point out the fact that you are performing a disservice to your child. If you feel that the auditory-verbal approach is the correct one for your child, remember that you are following it because you feel that it is the least restrictive of the choices for your child and your family.
- *Your responsibility is to your child and family first.* It is important to help other parents, organizations, and research, but do not forget that your primary responsibility is to your child. Pace yourself and balance your needs as well as your child's.

Update

What a difference a decade makes!

Before, I worried about 1st grade. Now, I worry about university.

Before, I worried about her learning to listen and speak. Now, I know she speaks and rarely listens. She is a teenager, after all.

Before, I worried about her catching up to her hearing peers. Now, in some ways, they have to catch up to her.

Before, all I saw was her deafness, and it paralyzed me with fear and dread. Now, I see a beautiful and eloquent young woman who is not perfect, but has as many options for the future as her brothers.

Our journey has not always been easy, but it was the right path to take. When Dara's Auditory-Verbal therapist asked me to keep a diary of her lessons, I did. I was not sure why it was important, but I was just grateful that an experienced professional gave me guidance. It kept me organized and focused. It also helped me survive her many plateaus, setbacks, and regressions.

Dara Keller today

Initially, I thought of Dara as a computer. I would input information and once she retained it, I thought I could go on to the next thing. Unfortunately, people are more complicated than machines. She would often know something one day (by George, she's got it!) and forget it the next. All children learn this way, but all children are not analyzed, measured, tested, and prodded the way Dara was.

When I felt overwhelmed and anxious, Dara's Auditory-Verbal therapist, who doubled as my psychiatrist, told me to look in my diary to compare what she knew at that point with what she did not know 6 months before.

In that way, I could measure her transition from "Aaaaaah, bu-bu-bu, woof-woof..." to "Look behind you; what's in the box?" to "Do you remember what you dreamt about last night?"

Yesterday, we debated nature versus nurture. She thought that the effects of environment were more important than our genetic predisposition. I remember thinking the same way—before I had children. In 1994, I could never have imagined that one day we would be discussing such topics.

Dara is a confident speaker, and has spoken to many individuals and groups about hearing loss. I have sat in the audience on more than one occasion, just listening to her speak and thinking, "WOW." I think of the many reasons Dara has become *a listening child who is deaf*: technology (hearing aids and the cochlear implant); professionals (ENT doctors, Auditory-Verbal therapists, speech-language pathologists, itinerant teachers); Dara's friends, her family—and, of course, Dara herself.

We are lucky that we live at a time and in a place where technology and professionals work together with parents to make a child's deafness manageable. Although we have come a long way, I still hear the same stories that were heard 40 years ago: missed diagnoses by physicians, audiologists' misinterpretation of subjective tests, or family members ignoring parents' concerns. Technology is wonderful, but we still require competent professionals to analyze the data.

In the summer of 1994, Dara was planning to take a trip with a few friends. Of course, I was worried and asked her a million questions. She complained that I am overprotective and that I treat her differently from her brothers (I am and I do). She is my youngest, she is a girl, and she does have a profound hearing loss. What does she expect?

She loves her sleep and enjoys reading Shakespeare, the classics, Greek mythology, and books written by Anne Rice and J.R. Tolkien. She enjoys playing baseball and has been a camp counselor.

Dara's favorite painting, like mine, is Monet's "Vetheuil in the Summer." Whenever we have some free time, we go to the Art Gallery of Ontario and enjoy some quiet moments with each other and the art. She has been accepted into university, and I expect her to receive a Bachelor of Arts degree in a few years. She does not know what she wants to do yet, but she knows what she does *not* want to do—which is everything that I have suggested to date.

I remember that my dream of many years ago was to be able to argue with Dara. This may sound like a strange goal, but I felt that if she could argue, it would mean that she was strong-willed and confident in her ideas, that she would not back down, and that she would not be afraid to get her point across. Well, I have learned to be careful what I wish for. Sometimes, all she and I do is argue, and when we are done, no matter how angry she made me, down deep inside (sometimes very deep), I am smiling. My wish has come true. I am very proud of Dara and all that she has accomplished.

In some ways, I believe that she is better adjusted than I am. Over the years, some people have hurt her emotionally, but she is very resilient and seems to have accepted this as part of growing up. I, on the other hand, attribute many setbacks and difficult times to her hearing loss. I confess that on more than one occasion I felt like pushing a pie into someone's face. I realize that this is not a mature way to act, but the ache I felt in my heart when my child was hurt was very real, and maybe a pie in the face would have alleviated some of that pain.

When Dara applied for a scholarship from the Alexander Graham Bell Association for the Deaf and Hard of Hearing, she had to write a concise autobiography. What she wrote surprised me: *"If I had the choice now to start life anew as a hearing person, I would not do it. Being deaf has taught me much more about life and living than I ever could have learned by being exactly like everybody else."*

Bravo, Dara. I will love you forever.

In 2006, Dara was in her second year at the University of Ottawa, studying honors philosophy and classics. Her favourite subjects are ancient Greek and Latin.

DAVID

Max Blum

David's Story: 1986

There is no easy way to face the brutal and abrupt reality of finding out your child is deaf. Until you face it, it doesn't seem so bad. A couple of hearing aids and you're as good as new—it can't be much different from wearing glasses. Learn to deal with it very quickly.

We suspected that David's hearing had been affected while he was still in the hospital recovering from a bout of meningitis at the age of 3 months. It wasn't obvious, but he wasn't reacting to voices or keys jingled near his head. "Could be the temporary aftereffect of the antibiotic!" said one. "Maybe he didn't really hear before either!" said another. A few weeks later, we *knew*. He had a profound bilat-

David Blum (front) and family, 1994

eral sensorineural loss. "But it's hard to tell in a baby"... "It could get better"... "We can't be sure"... "How do you really *feeeel* about this?" from a 20-year-old. "Might as well put him in a special school... he'll never hear or learn to talk—it's not so bad, you can still see him once a month," from a doctor who should know better. David was fitted with hearing aids shortly thereafter, and then the truth that hearing aids don't help everyone was brought home to us. His aided audiogram was no different. Again, people told us that it takes time to adjust, and so on.

We talked to many people and decided that an auditory/oral program was the best we could do to give David a fighting chance at a nearly normal life. There were no guarantees that he would succeed, but it was more appealing than sign language, which we felt limited communication between those who could only sign. That wasn't good enough for our budding genius.

The Learning to Listen Foundation was recommended to us. The clinical staff interviewed us as much as we interviewed them, except that they knew what was needed from the parents, and told us what was expected in no uncertain terms. We didn't know what we wanted or needed.

David started going to therapy at the age of 9 months, once a week, for 1 hour, and we started looking for progress within that first hour. We had another shock. The therapist was the first one to tell the truth—it didn't happen overnight and took a lot of hard work. Slowly, along with learning to put in the aids so that they didn't beep, we felt that David was starting to recognize simple sounds and maybe babble approximations.

We kept looking for magic bullets! Technology should provide us with a better hearing aid for our son! There were reports in the media about implants that allowed the deaf to hear something, but not understand speech. They were used only in postlingually deafened adults and were good if an airplane or train were coming at them from behind. They were very experimental, and definitely not for children. We contacted a surgeon well known for performing cochlear implant surgery on adults and children. He told us that cochlear implantation on children was still experimental, but initial results were promising. Many children were able to discriminate many sounds and even understand speech. The procedure could not be done on children aged under two and a half years. David had just turned one. I would call back next year.

Meantime, David was enjoying his weekly lessons at the hospital and his daily routine of identifying toys by sounds, but it was increasingly clear that he was using mostly visual cues to hear. His perception of sound was still to come. Then he said his first word, "mama" or "moo" or "apple." It doesn't matter—it was great! But, at the current rate, it would take an eternity for him to learn a very limited vocabulary.

David began his second year in Auditory-Verbal therapy, but the clinical staff now added and encouraged lipreading. He eventually lipread several hundred words (well, maybe only one hundred) and made some sort of verbal approximation for many of them, but he was clearly not functioning well in an aural environment.

The following Christmas, I spoke with the surgeon again; although David was still too young to undergo the surgical procedure, we would begin the preliminary testing necessary for the implant. He asked us to have a CT scan done and to bring the original negatives with us when we came to see him. David would also have to undergo a battery of audiological, developmental, and psychological tests to determine whether he was a suitable candidate for the implant.

To make a long story short, David was suitable. He had some apparent calcification of the cochlea, which would make the surgery more difficult and the outcome less promising, but all in all, he could benefit from the implant. He would have to undergo a training program recommended by the New York League for the Hard of Hearing in conjunction with Auditory-Verbal therapy. We used an FM system the whole time to see if that alone would help him. There was no significant improvement.

We scheduled surgery when David was 2 years and 8 months. He passed the required tests at the New York League (or flunked them, depending on your point of view), and surgery followed. We feared that the surgical trauma would make him forget everything that he had struggled so hard to learn. But our fears were unfounded. David's first word in the recovery room at New York University Medical Center brought tears to his mother's eyes. The surgery was uncomplicated and uneventful, the recovery rapid, and we headed home after 3 days.

Although the implant was in place, the external portions of the unit (the speech processor, microphone, and transmitter) could not be turned on for at least 6 weeks, in order to allow the swelling to subside and the wound to heal. We went back to New York 2 months later to be "turned on." The implant was adjusted to sounds that David could tolerate easily. We were warned not to expect miracles, and justifiably so. Although many older patients immediately respond to sound, children usually do not, and it takes many months of therapy until they can "hear." We'd waited 2 years, so a few more months didn't matter! We came home and thought David was responding to some sounds, but couldn't be sure.

We went back to New York every 2 weeks for fine-tuning of the speech processor, slowly adjusting the threshold and comfort levels of each of the 22 electrodes. David still was not responding to sound. His speech was not progressing. If anything, we felt it was getting worse.

One day (nobody really remembers exactly when or where), somebody said, "David's hearing!" It had crept up on him and on us very slowly, but we were all suddenly aware that David was responding to environmental sounds, to his name, and to the voices around him. He knew right away who was calling him, and he started behaving like other 3-year-olds—by ignoring us.

David's next checkup in New York was a total change. He informed the audiologists that he could hear, would not tolerate any undue disturbance to his system, and would they please just get on with their jobs. He was here on vacation with his brother and sisters and they had better things to do than to hang out in a stifling soundproof booth. Well, not quite exactly in those words, but that was the gist of it.

David has not looked back since that day. He hasn't stopped babbling, jargoning, or chatting, either. His new world is full of rich sounds that he cannot assimilate fast enough, but he tries to reproduce words as quickly as he can, even when he doesn't know the meaning. There is no doubt in our minds that he hears almost everything he wants to. His receptive language skills have progressed immeasurably, and he can easily differentiate voices, hear the telephone ring, and respond appropriately to instructions. For us, the real clincher came when he started using phrases he had heard, but had not been specifically taught to say.

When someone tried to take one of his toys, he clearly said, "Don't touch," which was something he had been told many times, but had never been expected to say. Prepositions had always been difficult for him. He had always answered questions with single words, and had been quite happy. Now, when asked where the apple juice is, he invariably responds with, "In da fridge." Before, "Mine" was sufficient to establish his ownership of an object, but now he says, "Diz iz mine."

The changes in David have been so numerous and rapid that we can't keep track of them any more, nor do we try. We almost consider it natural that he progress as well as he does. His self-confidence has been boosted dramatically, and is reflected in the casual attention he now pays to his lessons. He enjoys school much more than he did before.

Later On: 1994

It's been a few years since the implant. Sometimes, it feels as if it was yesterday; usually, it seems like another era long, long ago. It's easy and pleasant to forget the heartbreak and fear that once seemed to dominate our lives. I recently ran into someone to whom I hadn't talked in a few years. After a few banal pleasantries, he asked me how David was doing, and if his implant was any good, and if we were happy, etc. "Well, it's OK. He can't hear some consonants, and has trouble discriminating some other sounds..."

"But he can hear?"

"Yes, but it's not really the same as normal sound, and he has trouble with..."

"But he can *hear*!"

"Yeah, you know, and it's not really perfect and his speech isn't always completely intelligible and..."

"BUT HE CAN HEAR! LAST TIME I SAW YOU, YOU DIDN'T THINK HE WOULD EVER HEAR ANYTHING OR SPEAK AT ALL! YOU HAD GIVEN UP HOPE! IT'S INCREDIBLE! IT'S A MIRACLE!"

Yes, it is a miracle. It sometimes takes someone else to see it and make us aware of how fortunate we are that David has progressed to this level. So what if he doesn't meet someone else's expectations—he has far surpassed our wildest dreams and expectations.

When David entered parochial school, he faced a host of new sounds. When he was expected to learn Hebrew, his mother said, "He has so much trouble with English." I responded, "He can do it" with all the bravado I could muster, and prayed really hard when no one was looking.

David is now 8 years old and life is probably as normal as can be! David says, "Dad, get mellow!" I still make him do his homework and get angry when he forgets it. I still make him read, do his chores, and still get angry when he circumvents me. I don't hesitate to pull the plug on the TV. I do need mellowing. Were my other kids this difficult at this age? No. He's got chutzpah—lots of it. He's worked hard to reach this stage and deserves something for it. He gets it, too, from his mother, who spoils him silly.

Besides all the stuff every kid has to go through at this age, David must cope with a full Hebrew curriculum: masculine and feminine, adjectives, adverbs, plurals. English is so much easier. He just speaks it, easily. He also squeezes in skating, skiing, swimming, horseback riding, baseball, and the basketball league. David's come a long way and is a well-adjusted kid in a maladjusted world. Schoolwork is hard, but he manages.

David also knows that he has a lot to be grateful for. When he gets philosophical, he expresses his sadness at being deaf and his joy at being able to hear and communicate with all those around him, and at loving and being loved—and that's what life is really all about.

David has lived up to and surpassed all our expectations. To allow him to slide along at a slow, easy pace would deprive him of the future to which he is entitled. We continue to pursue the auditory-verbal philosophy as fervently as we did when we first learned he was deaf. The battle is not over, but we are confident that David will achieve whatever he attempts. We still have to break ourselves from the habit of protecting him from everything. He still gets stared at, and always will. All beautiful people do.

Update

Wow, more than 10 years later, but later than what? There are really no middle markers, just an ongoing series of daily events, some great, some greater, and occurrences that blend one into another. So many things have taken place that we cannot honestly look back and point to the important ones. But now, days that go by unnoticed are probably a greater testament to success than the ones we remember vividly.

- *When the processor of David's cochlear implant did not work.* So, we changed the battery and the cords and the microphone and all the easy fixes, and it still didn't work. So we would go to the hospital and replace the processor and then we would panic.
- *When David's implant failed in December 1995.* We were devastated. Thank God David was cool and said, "You just replace it." That was easier said than done. The Hospital for Sick Children in Toronto was shutting down the operating rooms for the holiday season and quick calls to New York were not productive. But some magic happened, and an operating room became available. David was reimplanted, and that was that. It was extremely gratifying that David himself made the conscious decision to be reimplanted. There was no parental influence that time at all. It was such a natural move for him that we really knew at that point that we had done something very right.
- *Then came high school and GIRLS.* Education was a necessary evil to allow the never-ending pursuit of the opposite sex...
- *And then DRIVING...* with the same motivation as above, and more sleepless nights for us.
- *And then high school graduation, and the next step had to be... more girls.* David was accepted into two college programs but felt that his Hebrew education was lacking, and that spending a year in school in Israel would be a good way to catch up. He enrolled in a yeshiva (academy for Biblical studies), which has allowed him the opportunity to pursue his religious studies (and girls) as well as learn the language and explore the country.

David Blum

Moving away from home was difficult. Actually, it was scary, both for us and for David. But it was the (second) best thing he ever did. It allowed him to mature into a young man with an understanding for others and to gain a sense of independence and self-reliance he could not have achieved at home. Thanks to the advances of cell-phone technology and satellite communications, the umbilical cord is not yet broken, but at least it's frayed—so much so that he wants to stay in Israel another year to study culinary arts (and meet the girls he has missed so far) before coming back to open his own restaurant... because girls love guys who cook.

The next 10 years? I'm not a prophet, but they'll be even better, and I expect a whole bunch of grandchildren.

By 2006, David had completed a program at the Jerusalem School of Kosher Culinary Arts and was working as a chef and attending the Culinary Management Program at George Brown College in Toronto.

REFERENCES

Barker, E.J., Dettman, S.J., & Dowell, R.C. (1997). "Habilitation: Infants and young children." In G.M. Clark, R.S. Cowan, & R.C. Dowell (Eds.), *Cochlear Implantation for Infants and Children.* San Diego: Singular Publishing Group.

Bergeson, T.R., Pisoni, D.R., & Davis, R.A.O. (2003). "A longitudinal study of audiovisual speech perception by children with hearing loss who have cochlear implants." *The Volta Review, 103*(4), 347–370.

Clark, G.M. (2003). *Cochlear Implants: Fundamentals and Applications.* New York: Springer-Verlag AIP Press.

Clark, G.M., Cohen, N.L., & Shepherd, R.K. (1991). "Surgical and safety considerations of multichannel cochlear implants in children." *Ear and Hearing, 12*(4), 15s–24s.

Clark, G.M., Pyman, B.C., & Webb, R.L. (1997). "Surgery." In G.M. Clark, R.S. Cowan, & R.C. Dowell (Eds.), *Cochlear Implantation for Infants and Children.* San Diego: Singular Publishing Group.

Dowell, R.C., & Cowan, R.S. (1997). "Evaluation of benefits: Infants and children." In G.M. Clark, R.S. Cowan, & R.C. Dowell (Eds.), *Cochlear Implantation for Infants and Children.* San Diego: Singular Publishing Group.

Estabrooks, W. (Ed.). (1994). *Auditory-Verbal Therapy for Parents and Professionals.* Washington, DC: Alexander Graham Bell Association for the Deaf.

Galvin, K.L., Sarant, J.Z., & Cowan, R.S. (1997). "Habilitation: School-aged children." In G.M. Clark, R.S. Cowan, & R.C. Dowell (Eds.), *Cochlear Implantation for Infants and Children.* San Diego: Singular Publishing Group.

Geers, A.E., & Brenner, C. (2004). "Educational intervention and outcomes of early cochlear implantation." In R.T. Miyamoto (Ed.), *Cochlear Implants: Proceedings of the VIII International Cochlear Implant Conference.* Amsterdam: Elsevier B.V.

Geers, A.E., Brenner, C., & Davidson, L. (2003). "Factors associated with the development of speech perception skills in children implanted by age five." *Ear and Hearing, 24*(1), 24s–35s.

Geers, A.E., Nicholas, J.G., & Sedey, A.L. (2003). "Language skills of children with early cochlear implantation." *Ear and Hearing, 24*(1), 46s–58s.

Holt, R.F., Svirsky, M.A., Neuburger, H., & Miyamoto, R.T. (2004). "Age at implantation and communicative outcome in pediatric cochlear implant users: Is younger always better?" In R.T. Miyamoto (Ed.), *Cochlear Implants: Proceedings of the VIII International Cochlear Implant Conference.* Amsterdam: Elsevier B.V.

House, W.F., & Berliner, K.I. (1991). "Cochlear implants: From idea to practice." In H. Cooper (Ed.), *Cochlear Implants: A Practical Guide.* London, UK: Whurr.

Kuhn-Inacker, H., Shehata-Dieler, Muller, J., & Helms, J. (2004). "Bilateral cochlear implants: A way to optimize auditory perception abilities in deaf children?" International *Journal of Pediatric Otorhinolaryngolgy, 68,* 1257–1266.

Ling, D. (1990). *Foundations of Spoken Language in Hearing-Impaired Children.* Washington, DC: Alexander Graham Bell Association for the Deaf.

Luxford, W.M., & Brackmann, D.E. (1985). "The history of cochlear implants." In R.F. Gray (Ed.), . San Diego: College Hill Press.

Manolson, A. (1985). *It Takes Two to Talk.* Toronto: Hanen Resource Centre.

Mecklenburg, D.J., & Lehnhardt, E. (1991). "The development of cochlear implants in Europe, Asia, and Australia." In H. Cooper (Ed.), *Cochlear Implants: A Practical Guide.* London, UK: Whurr.

Nicholas, J.G., & Geers, A.E. (2004). "Effect of age of cochlear implantation on receptive and expressive spoken language in 3-year-old deaf children." In R.T. Miyamoto (Ed.), *Cochlear Implants: Proceedings of the VIII International Cochlear Implant Conference.* Amsterdam: Elsevier B.V.

Staller, S., Parkinson, A., Arcaroli, J., & Arndt, P. (2002). "Pediatric outcomes with the Nucleus® 24 contour: North American clinical trial." *Annals of Otology, Rhinology and Laryngology,* 111(5) (suppl. 189), 56-61.

Tobey, E.A., Geers, A.E., Brenner, C., Altuna, D., & Gabbert, G. (2003). "Factors associated with the development of speech production skills in children implanted by age five." *Ear and Hearing,* 24(1), 36s-45s.

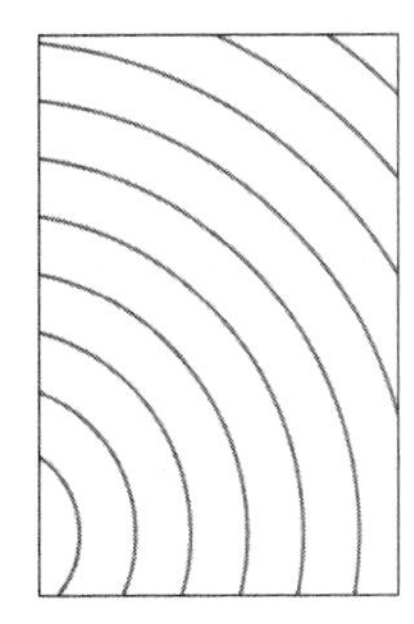

CHAPTER 4

Learning through Listening: A Hierarchy

Carolyne Edwards, M.Cl.Sc., M.B.A.
Warren Estabrooks, M.Ed., Dip. Ed. Deaf, Cert. AVT®

As human beings, we use our hearing for several purposes: to comprehend the speech of others, to monitor our own speech, and to monitor the surrounding environment. Similarly, auditory assessment and auditory skills programs may consider listening activities in any of these areas, depending on the needs of the child (Edwards, 1991). This chapter focuses primarily on the most significant area of listening—the comprehension of others' speech.

FACTORS AFFECTING LEARNING THROUGH LISTENING

The factors that enhance the auditory speech signal must be maximized in the child's therapy sessions and everyday environments. There are four areas in which parents and professionals can collaborate to build the foundations of learning through listening:

- *Use of amplification that is in the best working order throughout all waking hours* ensures that the child has the opportunity to receive auditory input.
- *Troubleshooting the child's hearing aid(s) or cochlear implant on a daily basis,* using acoustic and behavioral listening checks, ensures that any problems with the amplified speech signal are noted immediately and that loaner amplification is obtained while repairs are made. Studies have indicated that 30–50% of children's hearing aids do not function properly on a given day, the percentage varying with the stringency of criteria for proper functioning (Bess, 1977; Gaeth & Lounsbury, 1966; Schell, 1976; Zink, 1972). Thus, the importance of troubleshooting by the parents, therapist, and classroom teacher cannot be overemphasized.
- *Use of clear, well-articulated speech by parents and professionals when working or playing with the child* ensures that an optimal auditory signal is delivered to the child's hearing aid(s) or cochlear implant.
- *Reduction of noise in the child's listening environments* increases ease of listening.

RATIONALE FOR LEARNING THROUGH LISTENING

Even though a single hierarchy of listening skills does not fit every child, it is critical to set goals and overall directions for learning through listening. A child who is deaf or hard of hearing receives partial and degraded auditory input from the onset of language learning. Even with amplification, the child with a sensorineural hearing loss usually receives auditory information at less than optimal listening levels. Often the child with a profound hearing loss may have to listen to speech that is a mere 10–15 dB above the level at which he or she is barely able to detect sound, and there is likely to be distortion within the amplified speech signal, particularly in noisy situations. The degree of auditory distortion varies with the degree and shape of the hearing loss, the etiology, and the individual child.

Within each of the areas of listening, there are four levels of auditory skill, which are sequential and overlapping:

- *Detection* is the ability to respond to the presence or absence of sound. Thus, the child learns to respond to sound, to pay attention to sound, and not to respond when there is no sound.
- *Discrimination* is the ability to perceive similarities and differences among two or more speech stimuli. The child learns to attend to differences among sounds, or to respond differently to different sounds.
- *Identification/Recognition* is the ability to reproduce a speech stimulus by naming or identifying through pointing at a picture, by writing, or by repeating the speech heard.
- *Comprehension* is the ability to understand the meaning of speech by answering questions, following an instruction, paraphrasing, or participating in a conversation. The child's response must be qualitatively different from the stimulus presented (Erber, 1977).

A HIERARCHY OF LISTENING SKILLS

The organization of listening activities described in this chapter is based on increasing levels of auditory difficulty from detection through comprehension. Not all children who are deaf or hard of hearing require such a systematic introduction to auditory activities. School-aged children with mild and moderate degrees of hearing loss may acquire excellent listening through natural language interaction with their peers, and may benefit more from a focus on strategy teaching (Edwards, 1991). Children who are newly identified with mild to moderate hearing loss and those with severe and profound sensorineural hearing loss, however, benefit from focusing on specific listening activities. All auditory skills need to be integrated as quickly as possible into play and other meaningful childhood activities.

Naturally, the expected mode of linguistic input in the everyday environment will be auditory and visual. In therapy, however, therapists want to create systematic and successful experiences using listening only, so that under less redundant auditory conditions in the everyday environment (speech in noise, speech at a distance, muffled or mumbled speech), the child will be able to make optimal use of auditory cues in combination with visual cues.

The majority of listening activities described in the following section have been outlined in the *Auditory Skills Curriculum* (Office of the Los Angeles County Superintendent of Schools, 1976). We have created additional adaptations and activities.

Detection

Detection of sound is the obvious and essential first step in learning to listen. When the child is first fitted with hearing aids, the initial indicators of hearing aid benefits are usually a change in conditioned or spontaneous alerting responses, and increased vocalization. It is critical that members of the auditory management team are cognizant of unaided and aided thresholds obtained by the child in the audiological assessment. This information, a prerequisite for comprehensive Auditory-Verbal therapy and practice, is a valuable predictor of the child's ability to detect, identify, and comprehend auditory stimuli. Although it is important to experiment with detection of a variety of sounds, children need not be frustrated by listening activities that continue to focus on sounds they are unable to detect.

Conditioned Play Response

The conditioned play response used in pediatric audiological assessment protocols requires the child to perform an action upon hearing a sound. The action may be placing a block in a bucket, stacking rings on a pole, putting a plastic animal in a bucket of water, putting a peg in a pegboard, or any other similarly repetitive play response. The activity is first demonstrated for the child. A sound is presented; the therapist leads the child's hand through the action and praises the child at the finish. After six to 10 randomly timed presentations of the sound in which the therapist helps the child to respond, the child is encouraged to perform the action him- or herself.

Teaching a conditioned play response serves two purposes: to consolidate the child's conditioned response to sound and to observe changes in the child's responsiveness to detection tasks. Once a stable response to sound is established, the clinician will have a tool for detection of possible middle ear dysfunction and associated temporary decrease in hearing levels, hearing aid malfunctions, or changes in the acoustical properties of the earmold. Occasionally, changes in responsiveness may signal permanent changes in hearing levels due to progressive hearing loss.

The clinician can use the sounds from the Ling Six-Sound Test—m, oo, ah, ee, sh, and s (/m/, /u/, /a/, /i/, /ʃ/, and /s/)—for teaching and monitoring detection skills. Sounds must be presented at random intervals to ensure that the child does not develop a timed response to the task. Most children are cognitively ready to perform a conditioned play response only around the age of 2 years and above, although a few master the task at 18 to 24 months.

To increase the child's motivation during conditioned play response/detection tasks, the creative parent or therapist may present playdough, water games,

Figure 4.1 Hierarchy of Listening Skills

1. Detection
   - Conditioned play response
   - Spontaneous alerting response
2. Discrimination
3. Identification
   - Suprasegmentals
     - Prosodic features of speech
     - Loudness and pitch
     - Angry and sad voices
     - Male, female, and children's voices
   - Segmentals
     - Initial "sound" vocabulary
     - Words varying in number of syllables
     - One-syllable words varying in vowel and consonant content
   - Words in which the vowel is constant and the consonants contrast in manner, place, and voicing
   - Two critical elements in a phrase
   - Auditory monitoring of segmentals
4. Comprehension
   - Familiar expressions/common phrases
   - Single directions/two directions
   - Classroom instructions
   - Sequencing three directions
   - Multi-element directions
   - Sequencing three events in a story
   - Answering questions about a story: closed set and open set
   - Comprehension activities/exercises in noisy environments

cars running down a ramp, or a bottle of colored water into which the child can drop the reinforcer (see Chapter 5).

Spontaneous Alerting Response

A variety of spontaneous behaviors may be observed in response to sound, including searching for the sound, turning eyes or head towards the sound, cessation of activity, quieting, startling, or vocalizing. Although initial efforts focus on the child's conditioned response to sound, the ultimate goal is the child's spontaneous use of audition throughout the day.

In therapy, the parent or therapist will present various sounds (such as a musical clock) spontaneously during the therapy session. If spontaneous alerting does not occur, the adult will encourage the child to search for the sound. The parents and caregivers are encouraged to create similar experiences at home using sounds relevant to the child's environment. It is essential that the child demonstrate some spontaneous responses to sound before moving on to other levels of the hierarchy.

Discrimination

Discrimination activities involving same–different tasks are used primarily for clarification of identification or comprehension errors. Thus, the therapist tends to return to discrimination activities for remediation, rather than as a developmental step between detection and identification skills. For example, when a child confuses the singular and plural "dog" and "dogs," the therapist may present the pairs *dog–dog, dog–dogs, dogs–dogs* and ask the child to tell whether the words are the same or different. If the child is unable to determine whether the word pairs are the same or different and the "s" is audible to the child, then some word discrimination activities may be useful.

Identification

Suprasegmentals

The auditory channel provides the most complete information on duration, loudness, and pitch. Suprasegmental information obtained through visual or tactile input is often ambiguous or entirely absent. The cues for identification of high versus low pitch, for example, occur primarily through hearing. Visual cues cannot help to differentiate varying pitch levels, although tension in the vocal cords may provide some limited tactile/kinesthetic cues. All children with minimal to severe sensorineural hearing loss, and most with profound sensorineural hearing loss, have the auditory potential to detect and identify suprasegmental features (Ling, 1989). The importance of suprasegmental features for identification and comprehension of speech and for enhancement of speech intelligibility is paramount.

Prosodic features of speech

The auditory identification of prosodic features of speech is most easily learned through the imitation of prosody. The therapist presents a speech pattern (for example, a loud voice or rising pitch pattern) through listening only, and then asks the child to produce the same pattern. Reinforcement (such as dropping colored marbles into a tall glass container filled with water) is provided for correct imitation of the prosodic pattern. The reader is referred to Ling (1976, 1989) for comprehensive information about speech teaching strategies.

Loudness and pitch

The auditory concepts of loudness and pitch are often confused by children with severe and profound sensorineural hearing loss. (For example, "high" may suggest "loud"; "low" is confused with "soft.") Yet it is important for children to acquire a number of words to describe sound, in order to better classify and discuss the sounds heard. Teaching the classification of loudness and pitch separately (high–low or loud–soft) is followed by differentiation of paired loudness–pitch characteristics, such as loud–high versus loud–low voice. The therapist needs to ensure that the child has the linguistic ability to describe loudness and pitch parameters. A preschool child may find simple labeling of voice patterns uninteresting after a short time. Thus, activities may be created using puppets in which one puppet has a high-pitched voice and the other has a low-pitched voice. The therapist may then alter the loudness of each of the puppets' voices to create paired voice characteristics, and the child selects the correct puppet and identifies the voice as loud or soft.

Angry and sad voices

Now the child is asked to attach meaning to changes in loudness, duration, and pitch characteristics in voices. Instead of labeling a voice as high–loud or low–soft, the child learns to label the *emotional content* of a person's voice as angry (high–loud or low–loud) or sad (low–soft). The child can imitate the speaker's voice and body language to integrate the reception and production of appropriate prosodic features. Use of puppets, role playing, and tape recordings are very useful.

Male, female, and children's voices

Pitch differences determine the identification of male and female voices. Differentiation among the fundamental frequency of a male voice (125 Hz), a female voice (250 Hz), and a child's voice (325 Hz) is possible for most children with profound sensorineural hearing loss who have aided hearing within the speech spectrum at 250–1000 Hz. Most children with moderate to severe hearing loss will learn to identify male and female voices without formal intervention, but children with profound hearing loss using conventional amplification may need specific teaching in this area. However, children who have begun using cochlear implants at a very young age appear to acquire this auditory distinction naturally.

To ensure a transition from the easiest to most difficult auditory comparison, the therapist begins by contrasting male and children's voices (125 Hz versus 325 Hz), then male and female voices (125 Hz versus 250 Hz), followed by female and children's voices (250 Hz versus 325 Hz), and finally by comparing male, female, and children's voices. In this activity, children begin by listening to familiar male and female voices. Use of tapes of family members' voices can generalize this auditory skill to the everyday environment. Since this activity involves selection from a maximum of two or three choices, the guessing factor must be considered. It is important, therefore, to randomize the items well, not to use the same pattern of randomization twice, and to choose a pass criterion of 80% or more before moving on to another activity.

Segmentals

Identification of segmentals (vowels and consonants) requires more functional hearing than the identification of suprasegmental information. Children with profound hearing loss who are highly successful in auditory identification of suprasegmentals may rely more heavily on visual cues for identification of segmentals in everyday situations.

Initial sound vocabulary

Most Auditory-Verbal therapy programs use a number of sounds or words called the Learning to Listen Sounds (Figure 1.3, page 13). Some of these are onomatopoeic sounds directly associated with a specific animal or object. Pollack (1985, 1997) utilized such sounds in the development of symbolic language. Most Learning to Listen Sounds can be differentiated on the basis of suprasegmental and vowel characteristics, thus enabling children with functional hearing only at the low and mid frequencies to identify many of them. Therapists may use such sounds as "meow" for the kitten, "ah" for the airplane, "bu-bu-bu" for the bus, and "oo-oo" for the train. Each of these sounds is presented with the associated toy during therapy and in play activities in the home. Parents are encouraged to expose children to these sounds in as many natural language situations as possible. (A comprehensive discussion of the Learning to Listen Sounds is found in Chapter 5.)

Words varying in number of syllables

Once a child is labeling objects with real words or approximations of words, tasks are introduced in which he or she identifies words from a small set of objects. To increase the ease of the task, words differing in the number of syllables are used. The therapist first uses objects and, later, pictures in identification tasks from a closed-set response task (a controlled number of objects in each set).

Because a natural language approach to the acquisition of speech, language, cognition, and auditory development is part of the auditory-verbal philosophy, vocabulary lists may be used only in the early stages of therapy. Initial vocabulary may include such words as "ball," "banana," "cup," "shoe," "candy," "teddy bear," "fish," "night-night," "potty," "yummy," "no! no! no!," "more," and "up" because these are often frequently used in the child's everyday environment. Later, the therapist may ask the parents and caregivers to prepare lists of words for their children to learn, based on the culture and life of the family. The therapist needs to be privy to the interests and activities of the child and family in order to incorporate appropriate vocabulary into the therapy and develop the most meaningful auditory-verbal treatment plan.

One-syllable words varying in vowel and consonant content

The next step is the ability to identify words for which the suprasegmental characteristics are the same and only the segmental characteristics change. The therapist presents a closed set of objects or pictures representing one-syllable words in which the vowels and consonants differ. The child is asked to select a given word from a set that might include "cup," "boat," "fish," "tree," "house," and "dog." An older child may work on word identification within open-set tasks, which involves repetition of the word spoken by the therapist. This is considerably more difficult than the previous task, in which the child can use contextual clues to identify the phrase or expression.

Words in which the vowel is constant and consonants contrast in manner, place, and voicing

The level of auditory difficulty increases as the child must identify words based on consonant differences alone from a closed set of words or objects, and then later from an open set. Consonants vary in manner, place, and voicing, or any combination of these. The appendices of several curricula include word lists contrasting in manner, place, and/or voicing features. The following are operational definitions:

- *Manner* refers to way the sound is produced in the vocal tract. Examples of different manner features are plosives (p, b, t, d, k, g), nasals (m, n, ng), fricatives (sh, s, f, th), affricates (ch, j), liquids (l, r), and semivowels (y, w).
- *Place* refers to the point of greatest constriction in the vocal tract during articulation. Examples include bilabial (b, p), labiodental (f, v), linguadental (th), alveolar (t, d), palatal (sh), velar (k, g), and glottal (h).
- *Voicing* refers to the presence or absence of vocal fold vibration during articulation. Voiced/unvoiced pairs include b–p, d–t, g–k, v–f, j–ch, and z–s.

This identification task is highly specific and geared to the school-aged child. At the preschool level, where the focus of therapy is more on semantics and pragmatics, this type of analytical task has less value (Ross & Giolas, 1978).

Two critical elements in a phrase

This activity can be illustrated with prepositional phrases such as "show me the book on the table," "show me the toy under the bed," and "show me the cow behind the barn," moving from a closed-set to an open-set repetition task over time. The child must be familiar with the vocabulary embedded within the two critical elements of the phrase.

Auditory monitoring of segmentals

Speech perception and speech production are integrally linked. The auditory channel is the most natural route through which to learn to speak, and thus listening skills are vital to the development of accurate speech production of vowels and consonants (Boothroyd, 1982; Estabrooks, 1993; Ling, 1989; Pollock, 1997). Inclusion of auditory detection and identification exercises for segmental contrasts in learning speech production is highly beneficial.

Comprehension

The consideration of comprehension activities last is sometimes misleading, and calls into question the concept of a hierarchy of auditory skills. A hierarchy of listening skills is a theoretical concept that permits an ordering of skill levels. In practice, comprehension activities for very young children are a natural part of communication. Parents are encouraged to develop simple comprehension activities *concurrently* with identification activities.

Familiar Expressions and Common Phrases

Modeling of familiar phrases and expressions begins even before amplification is acquired, and the introduction of expressions follows the language development models for children with normal hearing. Familiar phrases can be found in a variety of language curricula (Ling & Ling, 1978; Manolson, 1985; Northcott, 1978; Rush, 1983) and include expressions such as "Be careful," "I love you," "All gone," "Wait a minute," "All better," "Mmm, that's yummy," "Shhhh... baby's sleeping," "Night-night," "Don't touch it," "Peek-a-boo," "Cover the baby," "Too big," "Too cold," and "It's stuck." As a structured activity, this can be conducted at the comprehension or the identification level. The child is asked to perform the action (comprehension response) or asked to select a card demonstrating the action (identification response). Parents will often give the therapist an array of common expressions used in their home, so that carryover from clinic to home can be maximized.

Single Directions and Two Directions

The child follows the directions of the parent or therapist. For very young children, those directions may concern manipulation of objects ("Give me some bread," "Give the baby a kiss," "Make the bird hop") in a closed-set task, or some action for the child to perform ("Close the door," "Put your coat on," "Brush your teeth") in an open-set task within a structured setting. Once the child has mastered this skill in a structured task, the therapist or parent can introduce the activity as a spontaneous part of each session. Activities involving two directions follow mastery at the level of single directions.

Classroom Instructions

The school-aged child is expected to follow many different types of single or embedded instructions in the classroom. The child who enters 1st grade requires a solid understanding of basic concepts (Boehm, 1967; Bracken, 1982). Without such mastery, the language of directions becomes just one more mystery that the child who is deaf or hard of hearing must unravel (Rush, 1983). Specific teaching in the understanding of basic concepts and the comprehension of typical instructions is therefore important to the child's academic success. Using classroom materials, the therapist asks the child to follow such instructions as "Draw a line under the last word," "Circle the word in the middle," and "Put an X on something you eat." Another level of processing has been embedded in the last instruction—i.e., the phrase "something you eat" is more difficult than "food." When listening alone is insufficient for comprehension of instructions, reading may help bridge the gap.

Sequencing Three Directions

This level of listening involves identification, comprehension, and extension of auditory memory. It is important for the child to practice storing strings of auditory information. In the academic environment, the child is often required to store four to five messages prior to responding. For example, the teacher may say, "Before you get your reader out, I want you to remember that tomorrow is pizza day and you will need to bring money and a signed letter from your parents saying it is OK for you to participate! OK, get your readers out now."

At the preschool level, the child may be asked to manipulate objects placed in front of him or her. Examples of sequencing three directions might include "Give the baby a drink, put her over your shoulder, and burp her"; "Make the fly go up and down, drop it on the table, and swat it"; or "Put the baby in bed, cover her up, and kiss her night-night." As the child gets older, strings of classroom instructions would be appropriate. At this level of complexity, the child may need additional time to process before following the instructions.

Comprehension of Multielement Directions

There are many levels of difficulty within multielement directions in addition to the auditory capability to detect phonemes, identify the language, and retain the auditory information. Successful mastery requires a high level of linguistic competence at the semantic, syntactic, and pragmatic levels. Children have a great deal of fun manipulating objects to follow the therapist's instructions, and planting absurdities ("sabotage") in the directions can be even more fun! Examples of increasingly difficult directions: "Make the cow jump over the fence"; "Make the animal that gives us milk jump over the fence"; "Put something made of glass over a reptile you might see at the zoo."

The child also needs to demonstrate the ability to understand riddles or clues that describe an object, from which he or she must extract the salient cues to identify it. The game of "I Spy" is a variant on embedded directions: "I spy with my little eye something that is gray, swims in the water, has fins, and scares people. What is it?"

Sequencing Three Events in a Story

This activity is similar to sequencing three directions, except that the auditory task arises in the context of a story. The story is presented to the child through listening alone. Pictures of the three events are then shown, and the child places the pictures in the correct order. At a later stage, the pictures are not used; the child is simply asked to say what happened first, second, and third. Three-picture sequence stories are excellent reinforcers once the child has completed the task through listening. Often the child takes the pictures home to share with others, or completes a variety of homework activities connected with the task.

Answering Questions About a Story: Closed Sets and Open Sets

Especially in mainstream classrooms, the child who is deaf or hard of hearing rarely encounters situations in which the teacher or classmates say a single sentence and then give the child time to comprehend and respond. More typically, the child must listen to strings of sentences, extract meaning from them, and then respond. Listening to a story longer than three sentences and answering questions about it, therefore, is more typical of listening expectations within the classroom. It is our experience that humorous stories on topics of interest to the child and family written by the therapist are far more effective than commercially prepared stories (see Chapter 6). Initially, the child sees the story pictures and extracts cues about content from them. The therapist poses selected questions about the story and gives the child a limited set of answers from which to choose (picture set or written responses).

A similar task in the classroom, however, is typically of an open-set nature, so it is important to move to an open-set response as soon as the child is ready. At the early levels, the pictures from the storybook may still be shown, but the child is expected to deduce answers to the questions about the story without any other clues. At later levels, stories presented verbally without visual stimuli are more typical. Listening activities follow a similar transition, from listening to a story with contextual clues to listening to a story through hearing only (see Chapter 6).

Paraphrasing, another type of comprehension task, is essential for clarification of a speaker's message. Paraphrasing blends cognitive, linguistic, and auditory skills, and is critical for children who are deaf or hard of hearing.

Listening in Noise

The presence of background noise interferes with comprehension of speech for all children who are deaf or hard of hearing. The extent to which it affects a child depends on the type and degree of the hearing loss and the individual child. Comprehension activities in the presence of background noise provide the child with a range of noise conditions in which to practice listening. Therapy begins with the least interfering background noise and progresses slowly to the most interfering noise condition. In this manner, the therapist and parent provide successful listening experiences that can change the child's attitude towards noise. He or she may become more willing to persevere listening under difficult conditions for a longer time as a result of positive listening experiences.

The least interfering noise conditions are *steady-state environmental noises* such as fan-type noise, the noise of an overhead projector motor, or the steam from a boiling kettle. Moderately interfering noises include *random environmental noises* with less predictability, such as cafeteria noise or traffic. The most interfering noise is speech from other talkers on topics of relevance or interest to the preschool listener. For example, a speaker reading a familiar fairy tale would be more interfering than the news report on the radio. Finally, background noise from the speech of one to four speakers is more interfering than that of 12 or more speakers. The latter condition more closely resembles less interfering random environmental noise.

Any of the comprehension activities presented in quiet can then be reintroduced in noise, beginning with the easiest noise conditions and moving to more difficult noise conditions *if and when* the child is ready. This is the most challenging and the most tiring listening activity. The child will be the guide and will indicate, either verbally or nonverbally, when it is time to start and stop.

Description of Environmental Sounds: Onomatopoeic Words

This activity is not part of any auditory curriculum of which we are aware, and yet comprehension of onomatopoeic words is important to the child's understanding in reading (J. Saunders, personal communication, 1985). The child who is deaf or hard of hearing often has not experienced words such as *jingling, tinkling, clanging, rustling,* and *cracking*; these words are not often taught through meaningful experience. Yet comprehension of these words gives the child a rich vocabulary with which to classify and categorize sounds in the everyday environment and in literature. The therapist presents a variety of environmental stimuli when the child first learns the specific vocabulary and then later is asked to describe or contrast various sounds. The child may then write sentences, poems, or stories using the sound vocabulary.

CONCLUSION

At its optimum, learning through listening reflects a team approach that honors the unique personalities of each child and every family. The team of support personnel needs to listen to the child and family just as the child learns to listen to others.

When professionals guide parents in a family-centered approach based on their needs and culture, a systematic, step-by-step hierarchy is rarely followed; Auditory-Verbal therapists will guide parents through a hierarchy of listening skills in the most natural way. This chapter provides a variety of listening skills that can guide parents and professionals through the process of teaching children to learn through listening.

REFERENCES

Bess, F. (1977). "Condition of hearing aids worn by children in a public school setting." In F.B. Withrow (Ed.), *The Condition of Hearing Aids Worn by Children in a Public School Program.* Washington, DC: US Department of Health, Education, and Welfare.

Boehm, A. (1967). *Boehm Test of Basic Concepts.* New York: Psychological Corporation.

Boothroyd, A. (1982). *Hearing Impairment in Young Children.* Washington, DC: Alexander Graham Bell Association for the Deaf.

Bracken, A. (1982). *Bracken Basic Concepts Scale.* New York: Psychological Corporation.

Edwards, C. (1991). "Assessment and management of listening skills in school-aged children." In C. Flexer (Ed.), *Seminars in Hearing, 12*(4), 389–401.

Erber, N. (1977). "Evaluating speech perception ability in hearing impaired children." In F. Bess (Ed.), *Childhood Deafness: Causation, Assessment, and Management.* New York: Grune and Stratton.

Estabrooks, W. (1993). "Still listening: Auditory-Verbal therapy for 'older' children. *The Volta Review, 95*(3), 231–252.

Gaeth, J., & Lounsbury, E. (1966). "Hearing aids and children in elementary schools." *Journal of Speech and Hearing Disorders, 31,* 283–289.

Ling, D. (1976). *Speech and the Hearing Impaired Child.* Washington, DC: Alexander Graham Bell Association for the Deaf.

Ling, D. (1989). *Foundations of Spoken Language for Hearing Impaired Children.* Washington, DC: Alexander Graham Bell Association for the Deaf.

Ling, D., & Ling, A. (1978). *Aural Habilitation: The Foundations of Verbal Learning in Hearing-Impaired Children.* Washington, DC: Alexander Graham Bell Association for the Deaf.

Manolson, A. (1985). *It Takes Two to Talk.* Toronto: Hanen Resource Centre.

Northcott, W. (1978). *I Heard That! A Developmental Sequence of Listening Activities for the Young Child.* Washington, DC: Alexander Graham Bell Association for the Deaf.

Office of the Los Angeles County Superintendent of Schools. (1976). *Auditory Skills Curriculum.* North Hollywood, CA: Foreworks.

Pollack, D. (1985). *Educational Audiology for the Limited-Hearing Infant and Preschooler.* Springfield, IL: Charles C. Thomas.

Ross, M., & Giolas, T. (1978). *Auditory Management of Hearing Impaired Children.* Baltimore: University Park Press.

Rush, M. (1983). *The Language of Directions.* Washington, DC: Alexander Graham Bell Association for the Deaf.

Schell, Y. (1976). "Electroacoustic evaluation of hearing aids by public school children." *Audiology and Hearing Education, 2,* 7.

Zink, G. (1972). "Hearing aids children wear: A longitudinal study of performance. *The Volta Review, 74(1)*, 41–51.

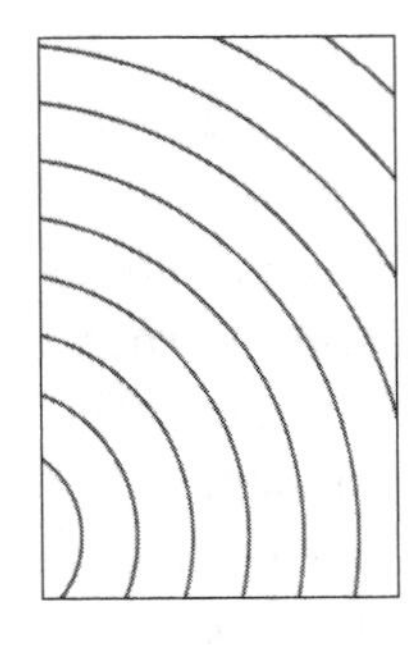

CHAPTER 5

Auditory-Verbal Therapy in Action: Babies Through Age 3

Warren Estabrooks, M.Ed., Dip. Ed. Deaf, Cert. AVT®
Maria Emilia (Mila) De Melo, M.Fga., S-LP, Aud. (C), Reg. CASPLO, Cert. AVT®
Lisa Katz, M.H.Sc., S-LP (C), Reg. CASPLO, Cert. AVT®
Karen MacIver-Lux, M.A., Aud. (C), Reg. CASPLO, Cert. AVT®
Sally Tannenbaum, M.Ed., C.E.D., Cert. AVT®
Beth Walker, M.Ed., C.E.D., Cert. AVT®

Chapters 5 and 6 illustrate the specific roles of parents and professionals in Auditory-Verbal therapy. Each session plan contains goals and rationales, activities, strategies, techniques, parent guidance, and analyses. Most activities and songs in the first two sessions are based on the Learning to Listen Sounds and the songs from *Hear & Listen! Talk & Sing!* (Estabrooks & Birkenshaw-Fleming, 1994) and *Songs for Listening! Songs for Life* (Estabrooks & Birkenshaw-Fleming, 2003). Figure 1.3 on page 13 contains a full listing of the Learning to Listen Sounds, together with the associated toys, activities, and songs.

BEGINNING WITH BABIES

The diagnosis of deafness changes parents' lives in seconds. In their initial shock, most don't know where to turn or what to do. Their fear and confusion may be compounded by conflicting advice from well-meaning professionals, family, and friends. This early period of upheaval is the time when the professional needs to listen attentively and begin to coach, guide, offer support, and chart a course to help parents help their child to maximize his or her auditory potential. Professionals must provide reasonable information and counseling so that parents can affirm their sense of control as their child's primary case managers.

In auditory-verbal practice today, the child-centered approach of previous years has given way to more family-focused work, with the parent as the primary client. As more infant hearing screening programs emerge, more families arrive at intervention programs very early. Auditory-Verbal therapists, therefore, are required to work with young babies and their parents to plan intervention based on the family's culture and priorities. When parents initially arrive at the therapist's place of practice, the therapist may spend many sessions just listening and talking with them so that they experience hope and receive encouragement. The therapist will also spend a lot of time entertaining the baby and getting to know the family so that a bond of trust emerges.

Auditory-Verbal therapy is based on the development of children with typical hearing. In the first year of therapy, the parent and the professional concentrate on developing a rich language learning environment. Babies are active learners: parent–infant routines are powerful, and social routines provide context. The Auditory-Verbal therapist guides the parents in creating environments that make all sounds of speech as acoustically salient as possible. These environments encourage optimal use of communicative strategies to enhance the perception and understanding of spoken language through listening by

- recognizing the baby's interests and drawing attention to them;
- interpreting the baby's communicative intents and responding in a fashion that encourages the repetition of positive responses;
- encouraging interactions that are initiated by the child; and
- encouraging natural turn-taking.

Most parents talk to their babies and expect that they will respond. Some parents of children who are deaf or hard of hearing stop doing so because they get little response back. In Auditory-Verbal therapy, the therapist demonstrates the importance of continuing to talk to the baby in a natural voice using "parentese." In playful situations and during the daily routines of child care, parents are encouraged to respond to their baby's natural behaviors following the child's lead, including following the baby's eye gaze and making the same sounds the baby makes. In these ways, they reinforce communicative behaviors, providing a map by which their child develops the auditory-feedback loop—the self-monitoring process by which vocal and verbal productions are matched to the adult model.

Most parents typically need very little guidance in this area beyond doing what comes naturally. The therapist encourages them to continue talking and singing to their baby and not give up when the child appears not to be attending. Children with typical hearing often exhibit the same behaviors.

The course charted by the therapist and parents as a team will determine whether the baby's hearing aids effectively provide enough spoken language information for the child to learn conversational skills through listening. Through diagnostic therapy, the therapist and the parents can determine how effective the hearing aids are in the acquisition of spoken communcation. If the hearing aids are insufficient, then the family receives a timely referral to the cochlear implant program.

Every AV session needs to be flexible and easily adaptable for parents and be driven by specific goals in audition, speech,language, cognition, communication and behavior. Even though the therapist and parents follow the child's lead by "seizing the moment", the will focus the processes of the session on the predetermined planned goals.

SESSION PLAN #1: ARTHUR (BABY)*

Maria Emilia (Mila) De Melo, M.Fga., S-LP, Aud. (C), Reg. CASPLO, Cert. AVT®
Lisa Katz, M.H.Sc., S-LP (C), Reg. CASPLO, Cert. AVT®
Karen MacIver-Lux, M.A., Aud. (C), Reg. CASPLO, Cert. AVT®

Arthur is an alert, healthy, and curious 6-month-old boy who has a bilateral, severe to profound, sensorineural hearing loss. At birth, he failed his hearing screening. Arthur's parents received confirmation of his hearing loss when he was 3 months of age. Immediately afterwards, he was given behind-the-ear digital hearing aids, and his family began attending weekly Auditory-Verbal therapy sessions at the Learning to Listen Foundation. Arthur's parents were familiar with the auditory-verbal approach, as his older sister had been attending weekly Auditory-Verbal therapy sessions for the past two years.

Arthur wears his hearing aids during all waking hours. His mother reports that he is more vocal when he is wearing the aids. There are some challenges with feedback when Arthur is sitting in his infant carrier seat or in his high chair. As well, Arthur is currently wearing his third set of earmolds, and these have proven to result in less acoustic feedback. Over the past three months of Auditory-Verbal therapy, Arthur has responded only to low-frequency sounds. He demonstrates age-appropriate cognitive and motor skills.

Arthur alerts to low-frequency noisemakers and some Learning to Listen Sounds by widening his eyes and smiling. He will search for noisemaking toys, which are presented on both his right and left sides at ear level. Arthur vocalizes randomly. His vocalizations consist of vowel sounds and the nasal sound /m/.

Goals

Audition:

- To detect environmental and speech sounds, as indicated when Arthur stops the activity, smiles, and widens his eyes.
- To localize sounds presented on both sides, as indicated when Arthur turns his head towards the source.
- To recognize friendly and angry voices by responding appropriately.
- To attend to music.

Speech:

- To increase repertoire of vowel sounds.
- To experiment and explore his own vocalizations by encouraging cooing and vocal play.
- To produce varied suprasegmentals.

Language:

- To listen to the narration of life provided by the caregivers.
- To begin association of some Learning to Listen Sounds with their toys, objects, or activities.
- To encourage vocalization for wants and needs.

Cognition:
- To imitate facial expressions.
- To understand cause and effect.
- To move an obstacle to find a hidden object.
- To anticipate events in familiar routines.

Communication:
- To develop joint attention.
- To maintain appropriate eye contact.
- To maintain focus on a toy or other object.
- To develop early turn-taking skills.

Preparing for the Session

Sometimes we can play with babies for a whole hour while they are seated in a high chair, held in a parent's arms, or seated in a portable car seat—or anywhere else. It is important to ensure that the baby is comfortable and that the microphone of his or her hearing technology is clear of blankets, hats, clothing, etc. Although clinical auditory-verbal sessions last about 60 minutes, activities with the baby may not last all that time, and most of the session may be spent on parent guidance.

Typically, parents of babies prefer to schedule their sessions early in the morning when the children are well rested. During the session, if the baby is hungry or tired, we will use these opportunities to guide parents in how to incorporate the session goals into these daily routines.

Introduction to the Session

As I meet Arthur and his mother in the waiting room, I sing the "Hello!" song (Estabrooks & Birkenshaw-Fleming, 2002). Arthur smiles when he sees me, and his mother joins in singing the song. We pass a mirror on the way upstairs and we stop and sing the "Hi!" song (Estabrooks & Birkenshaw-Fleming, 2002) as he looks at himself in the mirror. As we climb further we say "up, up, up" melodically. Upon entering the therapy room, we notice a colorful jack-in-the-box on the table. As Arthur is intrigued by this toy, it is easy to get him into the high chair. He reaches for the jack-in-the-box and attempts to explore it as his mother and I discuss what happened at home during the week.

Jack-in-the-Box

Arthur's mother and I become quiet. I sing, "round and round" and wait for Arthur to turn towards me. As Arthur looks at me, his mother repeats "round and round." I *wait* and then show Arthur the crank that goes around. We listen to the music, lean towards the toy, sway back and forth to the music, and point to our ears. A clown pops out of the box and we say, "Oh, look! It's a clown that says *ha ha ha.*" Arthur grabs and explores it. I say, "Push the clown dowwwn" as his mommy pushes it back into the box. She gasps and asks, "Where's the clown?" We repeat the game by turning the crank and listening to the music. When we finish, I ask his mom to put it away and she asks, "Okay! Where does it go?" I respond, "'Way up there on the shelf," and she puts it in its place.

Parent Guidance

- Point out wheels, tops, fans, or mobiles that turn or spin around.
- Think about all the natural ways in which you might incorporate the sound and its concept throughout the day: stirring Arthur's food, circles on his pajamas, the hands or face of a toy clock, windmills, wheels on vehicles, etc.
- Say the action rhyme, "*Round and round the garden/ Like a teddy bear* (trace finger in a circle around child's palm)/ *One step, two step* (walk fingers up Arthur's arm)/ *Tickle you under there!* (tickle under chin, underarm, or tummy).
- Sing "Teddy Bear, Teddy Bear, Turn Around" (Estabrooks & Birkenshaw-Fleming, 2003).
- Sing what you say, as singing makes the message easier to hear and more attractive to respond to.
- When you're going down the stairs, or when putting Arthur down onto a blanket, use the word "dowwwn." It's important to contrast "dowwwn" with "up, up, up."

The Airplane

As Arthur looks at his mother, I sing the Learning to Listen Song for the airplane and wait for him to turn towards me. When he does, I reward him with a smile and a toy airplane. I fly the plane into Arthur's tummy and gently tickle him while we make the airplane sound ("ah"). Next time we make the sound, we wait to see if Arthur will anticipate being tickled. When a plane passes overhead outside, we say, "Listen! I hear an airplane outside. Remember, it goes 'ah.'" Arthur's mother picks him up, goes to the window, and looks for the airplane in the sky. Arthur explores the toy, and we point out the propeller and the wheels that go round and round.

Parent Guidance

- Pretend to fly Arthur in the air and make the airplane sound.
- When feeding him, "fly" the food into Arthur's mouth, pretending it's an airplane.
- Ride on a coin-operated airplane at the mall or fair.
- Hang an airplane mobile over Arthur's crib.
- Point out pictures of airplanes in books, on blankets, etc.
- Listen and look for airplanes above your house.
- Think of other activities that you can associate with the "ah" sound. When you see a baby cry, you might say: "*Ah*... the baby is crying; listen!" When

Arthur gets a bump or when you are pleasantly surprised, you may also make this sound. Many of these Learning to Listen Sounds are transferable to other toys and situations.
- Make sure the context has real meaning.
- Play games and sing songs that encourage anticipation (e.g., peek-a-boo).

The Duck

Arthur's mother holds a squeaky toy duck on Arthur's left side and squeezes it. Everyone stops to listen. Arthur finds the duck. We provide him with positive reinforcement by saying, "You found the duck. It goes quack, quack!" Then we sing the song "Six Little Ducks" (Estabrooks & Birkenshaw-Fleming, 2003).

Parent Guidance
- Go to a duck pond, a farm, or a zoo to see the real thing.
- Sing "Six Little Ducks" at home.
- Play with toy ducks in a tub of water. You can create a whole spoken scenario around this activity, complete with role playing.

The Ball

I grab a ball from the basket of toys and bounce it on the floor. I look expectantly at Arthur's mom and point to my ear to cue her to say something about hearing the ball bounce. Mom smiles and says, "Oh, I hear a bouncing ball!" I bounce the ball again. Arthur turns his head in my direction as he hears the ball bounce on the floor. I immediately reward him by holding up the ball for him to see. Arthur reaches for the ball and gurgles. I respond, "You want this ball! Okay... here's the ball," and I place it on the table. Arthur grabs the ball and then releases it. Using the melody from "Row, Row Your Boat" (Birkenshaw-Fleming & Estabrooks, 2003), Arthur's mother sings, "Roll, roll, roll the ball. Roll the ball to Mommy!" I help Arthur roll the ball to his mother as I say, "Let's... roll the ball." After Arthur's mother catches the ball, she sings, "Roll, roll, roll the ball. Roll the ball to Arthur!" and rolls the ball back to Arthur. After several turns of rolling the ball back and forth, Arthur fusses and reaches for his mother. We say "goodbye" to the ball and put it back in the basket.

Parent Guidance
- Play with balls that vary in size and texture. Roll them back and forth and bounce them up and down. Roll them to Arthur's family members as they call out for the ball.
- Point out other things in the environment that roll around like a ball. Roll Arthur's milk bottle back and forth and watch it go around and around.
- Point out balls in the playground. Have a play date with other babies Arthur's age and encourage them to play with balls together.

Fish

When it's quiet and there are no toys or distractions in front of Arthur, I lean to within 6 inches of his hearing aid and say, "Wsh, wsh, wsh." Arthur's mother points to her ear immediately. He looks at her after perceiving the movement of her arm. She says, "Listen! I hear a fish," and I repeat the sound for the fish. Arthur does not respond. We repeat this routine twice. Arthur's mother looks expectantly in my direction and then points to the toy fish I am holding. As soon as he looks at me, I give him a big smile and make the toy fish "swim" in the air. Arthur visually follows the toy fish and raises his arms, and then I make the fish sound again. He looks thrilled. I bring out a transparent container filled with water and a basket full of colorful fish. We enjoy putting them into the water. "Splasshh!" his mother says as the fish go in the water.

Parent Guidance

- Arthur clearly loves playing with water. Take advantage of this! While he cannot wear hearing aids while taking his bath, you can put water in a container and play with rubber toys such as a baby, fish, boat, and duck. Call his attention to the sound of the water as it fills the container. Use simple vocabulary, short sentences, and songs that go with this activity. For example, say "wash, wash the baby" and "we are aaall wet"; sing "tidy up" songs when putting toys away.
- Contact the audiologist to investigate options to improve auditory access to the high frequencies.
- When playing with the toy fish, remember to create a favorable acoustic environment to facilitate responses to high-pitch speech sounds ("wsh, wsh, wsh"). The real world is not as quiet as the therapy room but Arthur is learning to listen, and we know that high-pitch sounds are more challenging for him to hear.
- When playing with the toy fish, remember not to add a vowel to the Learning to Listen Sound. This is so we can obtain more specific information about his responses to high-pitch sounds.
- Call Arthur's attention to other high-frequency sounds in the environment by pointing to your ear and bringing his attention to the source of the sound, such as water coming out the faucet, or when the water begins to boil in a teapot. Observe Arthur's responses and write them down in your parent book (see Figure 5.1).

Musical Clock

A musical clock sits on a shelf close to Arthur's mother. I whisper to her to make the Learning to Listen Sound for the clock and she says, "T-t, t-t, t-t." I point to my ear and say to Arthur, "Listen! I hear the clock that goes (pause)..." and Arthur's mother finishes my sentence by saying "T-t, t-t, t-t." Arthur's mother waits, and then says the sound again. As he shows no response to the sound, I guide Arthur's attention to his mother and the clock toy. His mother reinforces

Figure 5.1 Parent Book Observations

Sound	Distance	Techniques Used	Arthur's Response
barking	3 feet	Pointed to ear and leaned towards the direction of the sound	Did not react to the sound, but smiled when saw the dog

object–sound association by making the clock sound again when he sees the toy. Then, Arthur's mother winds the clock up and it starts playing music. We wait for a few seconds to see his reaction. He smiles. Arthur's mother and I begin swaying to the melody. When the song stops, we stop swaying. Arthur looks puzzled and looks up at us. We say, "All gone." Mom activates the toy again and we start swaying. This time, Arthur screams and moves his legs and arms in excitement. Mom can see that he is imitating us. I say, "Good for him! Our model is powerful!"

Arthur is very engaged by this activity. Before his mother winds the toy up again she looks at me and asks, "Do you want more?" After another few seconds' of pause, I answer with a simple, clear, and excited "Yes!" She winds the clock up again. We repeat the routine. Then she asks Arthur, "Do you want more?" He moves his arms and legs excitedly and laughs. This activity is so much fun for all of us!

Parent Guidance

- Play with different sounds for the clock. During the session we used "T-t, t-t, t-t" because we are investigating Arthur's responses to high-frequency sounds. Play with the clock toy using other key words; for example, "round and round" or "stop!"
- The K.I.S. rule (keep it simple) is key for babies. Simple narrated routines are easy for babies and toddlers to understand. Long and elaborate responses to "Do you want more?" questions ("Yes, I want to listen to more music, please") are harder for children to understand and imitate, and they are not natural.

Bubbles

I start singing "Bubbles in the Air" (Estabrooks & Birkenshaw-Fleming, 1994). Arthur gazes at me. I nod to Mom, and she begins to sing the rest of song. Arthur turns to look at his mother. She picks up the container and raises it in the air as she sings "up so high." She brings the container down to Arthur as she finishes the song. She looks at Arthur and asks, "Do you want bubbles?" and waits. Arthur smiles. She interprets his smile as an affirmative response and says, "Okay... let's blow some bubbles!" As she dips the wand into the bubbles she says, "dip, dip, dip." As she pulls it out, she says, "up, up, up." She holds the wand to her mouth and waits. Arthur watches intently. I say, "Blo-o-o-w," elongating the word. As we pop the bubbles we say, "pop, pop, pop." When the bubbles have disappeared,

Arthur's mother comments that they are "all gone" and gestures naturally. I sing her statement, "All gone." I then point out that the table is "all wet." We sing a "tidy up" song as we dry it. We say, "round and round" as we use the paper to wipe up the table. Then we say "Bye-bye!" as we put the bubbles away.

Parent Guidance

- Blow bubbles at home. Arthur is still too young for us to expect him to use his voice to get what he wants, so model the words and phrases you expect him to produce. Talk about everything that you are doing during daily routines.
- Accept smiles as a response to simple yes/no questions ("Do you want more?"). These are forms of preverbal communication appropriate for Arthur's chronological age.

Baby Rattle

Arthur's mother shakes a colorful rattle beside him. Arthur is looking at me, so I point to my ear to indicate that there is a sound to attend to. Arthur does not respond. After two more presentations, I direct Arthur's attention to his mother and the rattle. "Yes, you found it!" his mother exclaims. "Shake, shake, shake," she says as she shakes the rattle close to her ear. When she holds the rattle still, I lean close to Arthur's hearing aid and whisper, "Shake, shake, shake." Arthur does not turn his head. Then I say, "shake, shake, shake," and Arthur turns to me. Arthur's mother places the rattle on the table and says, "You shake it." Arthur tries to grasp it. He picks up the rattle and puts it into his mouth. Then he bangs the rattle on the table. "Bang, bang, bang," I say. "That's loud!" says Mom, as she covers her ears. Arthur smiles. "My turn," I say as I take a turn shaking the rattle. "I hear that!" says Arthur's mother.

Parent Guidance

- Play with rattles and noisemaking toys, shaking them out of Arthur's view. These toys are age appropriate, so let him explore them by shaking and banging. If he bangs the toys, narrate what Arthur is doing ("bang, bang") and react with the appropriate facial expression. Focus on encouraging localization of the sound. Encourage a response to the "sh" sound by saying "shhhake."
- Ensure that there is a reason or reward waiting for Arthur when you call for his attention. It will encourage him to continue responding meaningfully.
- Expose Arthur to loud and soft sounds. Contrast those that are loud with those that are soft by saying, "It's too loud!" and covering your ears, or whispering, "It's quiet."
- Play games that encourage turn-taking.
- Tickling and "bouncy" games are a delight for Arthur and will encourage him to develop vocalization.
- Involve siblings in the games and routines as much as possible.

The Train

Mom takes Arthur out of his high chair and sits him on the table in front of her. Arthur sees the train that I placed at one end of the table, reaches for it, and vocalizes. Mom says, "You want to see the train! Let's get the train," and slowly slides Arthur closer to the train. As she does this, I say, "ch, ch, ch." Mom points to her ear and waits. I say the sound again, but Arthur does not respond. I lean closer and make the sound again. Arthur reaches forward and fusses. I nod to Arthur's mother and she says, "Choo, choo!" Arthur turns to his mother and smiles. She continues to slide Arthur closer to the toy train as she begins to sing "The Train" (Estabrooks & Birkenshaw-Fleming, 1994).

I bring another train *down* from the shelf and place it *on* the table. Arthur happily explores the toy as Mom narrates his actions and the parts of the train he touches. After several minutes of playing, Arthur fusses and reaches for his mother. We know he is becoming tired. I begin to wrap the session up by providing some more suggestions and responding to any further questions or concerns from Mom.

Parent Guidance

- Point out all kinds of trains as you see them in life, in books, at the playground, and on television.
- Sing songs that you make up about trains.
- Use "ooo" in other contexts. For example, every time you see something pretty, say, "Ooooh, that's pretty."

Analysis: Diagnostic Information

The diagnostic information obtained through observation by the therapist and the parent throughout the course of Arthur's session, was recorded in his chart. This diagnostic information is used to construct the next sessions of the auditory-verbal treatment plan.

Audition:

- Alerts to low- and mid-frequency Learning to Listen Sounds by widening eyes and smiling, and searching for the toys.
- Alerts to low- and mid-frequency noisemakers by smiling and turning head.
- Does not detect high-frequency Learning to Listen Sounds (e.g., fish, clock, and train).
- Does not detect whispered speech.
- Enjoys musical toys and will listen for a few minutes.
- Occasionally quiets, stills, or smiles when Mom sings or speaks.

Speech:

- Uses a variety of vocalizations ("uh," "n").
- Quality of vocalizations sounds natural.

Language:
- Engages in and enjoys vocal play with his family members and therapist.
- Vocalizes more frequently with intent to make things happen.

Cognition:
- Shows awareness of strangers and unfamiliar situations.
- Briefly looks at objects.
- Reaches for objects and attempts to grab them.
- Attempts to match facial expressions made by those who interact with him.
- Did not demonstrate anticipation in games or routines.
- Demonstrated understanding of "cause and effect" with musical clock.

Communication:
- Laughs, smiles and coos while socializing.
- Cries when hungry, tired, or uncomfortable, or when attention is desired.
- Maintains appropriate eye contact with those who interact with him.
- Requires adult assistance to take turns during play with ball and motivating toys.

SESSION PLAN #2: RACHEL (16 MONTHS)

Maria Emilia (Mila) De Melo, M.Fga., S-LP, Aud. (C), Reg. CASPLO, Cert. AVT®
Lisa Katz, M.H.Sc., S-LP (C), Reg. CASPLO, Cert. AVT®
Karen MacIver-Lux, M.A., Aud. (C), Reg. CASPLO, Cert. AVT®

Rachel is a delightful 16-month-old toddler who was diagnosed with a moderate to severe sensorineural hearing loss at 10 months of age. Immediately following diagnosis, she was fitted with behind-the-ear digital hearing aids. One week later, Rachel and her family began weekly Auditory-Verbal therapy sessions at the Learning to Listen Foundation.

During the first few weeks of hearing aid use, Rachel pulled her hearing aids out and put them in her mouth, much to her parents' exasperation. Eventually, she stopped, and discovered the joy of listening throughout the day. She has made good progress in the development of audition, speech, language, cognition, and communication during the first four months of therapy.

Currently, Rachel searches for and locates sounds presented at ear level from most directions. She smiles when she hears her mother's voice and responds appropriately when her name is called. She does not respond to high-pitched sounds, which concerns her parents and the professional team as we make every effort to help her receive optimal auditory access to all speech sounds.

During auditory-verbal sessions, Rachel makes vocal approximations of key words, such as "uh, uh" for "up, up" and "ahh" for roll (the ball). She is beginning to imitate a few Learning to Listen Sounds. If she sees her favorite toy, she will reach for it and vocalize loudly. She enjoys songs, finger plays, and stacking rings.

Goals

Audition:
- To respond to sounds presented at increased distances (e.g., 6 feet).
- To localize environmental and speech sounds at varying angles and distances.
- To respond appropriately to meaningful sounds without attention being brought to them (e.g., name, LTL Sounds, songs, nursery rhymes).

Speech:
- To continue imitating suprasegmental features of speech.
- To increase repertoire of early developing consonants and vowel sounds.
- To experiment and explore vocalizations through vocal play and babble.

Language:
- To respond appropriately to key words and common phrases (e.g., "No!," "bye-bye").
- To vocalize for objects, wants, and needs.
- To respond appropriately to yes/no questions regarding her wants (e.g., "Do you want more?") and simple "Wh" questions ("Where's daddy?," "What's that?").

Cognition:
- To perform increasingly complex one-to-one correspondence tasks (e.g., place rings with smaller hole onto pegs).
- To link schemes in simple combinations during play (e.g., put person in car and push it).
- To associate objects with pictures.

Communication:
- To look from speaker to speaker.
- To develop turn-taking skills.

Introduction to the Therapy Session: Saying Hello

An auditory-verbal session typically begins with greetings in the waiting room, where there are dolls, cars, puzzles, books, and a toy kitchen. We encourage parents to arrive at least 10 minutes before their session to allow the child time to settle in before starting therapy. If it is relatively quiet, we sing a "hello" song (Estabrooks & Birkenshaw-Fleming, 2003). If it is noisy, we reserve the song for just outside the door of the therapy room. On the way upstairs, we discuss the past week at home. The therapist listens carefully, as this information is pertinent to the auditory-verbal session for that day.

Parent Guidance

- Call Rachel's name with no visual or tactile cues. If you call simply to test, or constantly prompt her visually, this will not reinforce listening.
- Be aware of the acoustic conditions of the environment—background noise, position of the speaker relative to Rachel, distance between them, etc. Create the most favorable listening environment by turning off the TV, radio, and other sources of noise, and by talking close to Rachel on the side of her "better" ear.
- Encourage Rachel to answer greetings by providing good models, waiting expectantly, and leaning towards her in anticipation of a response.
- Encourage Rachel to pick up her own toys, or do it with her.

Just Pictures

The walls outside the therapy rooms have photos of all the children who attend Auditory-Verbal therapy at the Learning to Listen Foundation, as well as pictures of the Learning to Listen Sounds. We look at the pictures and either say or sing some of the accompanying Learning to Listen Sounds. Rachel's mother and I comment, ask questions, and reinforce the responses given either by Rachel or by the other adult.

Rachel is encouraged to come "up, up, up" and sit "down, down, down" in the high chair. Rachel's mother sits on her left side and the therapist sits on the right. The primary speaker (either the therapist or the parent) sits on the side of the "better" ear.

Because Rachel's mother has already checked her hearing aids just before the session, the therapist will not double-check unless the parent cites difficulty.

Parent Guidance

- Put pictures of the Learning to Listen Sounds around the house in places where Rachel can visit them readily—on the refrigerator, the staircase, and the front door. This will provide abundant opportunities to engage in listening activities throughout the day.
- Photographs placed near the inside of the front door can be used to indicate where the family is going when everyone puts on coats and boots (to the library, Grandma's house, day care, the park, etc). Some parents put these pictures in a small photo album that they carry with them at all times.
- Although pictures are helpful, there is nothing like the real thing—a real situation, animal, or activity. These are always preferable to pictures.

Conditioned Play

Often the therapist incorporates a conditioning task into the session in which the parent models the targeted responses. For example, I may ask the parent to hold a stacking ring or plastic block to his ear, attend as though anticipating a sound, and, upon hearing it, put the ring on the stacking toy or the block in a pail of water. For children Rachel's age, we begin with the sounds that are most audible and progress to those most difficult to hear as the child's conditioned responses improve. This prepares the child for pure-tone testing, helps us to detect changes in hearing levels due to middle ear dysfunction, detect changes in the functioning of hearing aids/cochlear implants, and determine the effects of distance on the audibility of speech. We typically introduce and model this activity as early as possible—around Rachel's age, if the child is developmentally ready. Children typically master conditioned play audiometry between 2 and 2.5 years of age. Parents will devise the most creative ways of doing conditioned play tasks.

Before I take out a colorful plastic stacking toy, I lean towards Rachel's mom and say, "Guess what I have?" Mom says, "What?" I respond by saying, "A stacking toy. Wanna see it?" Rachel's mother nods and enthusiastically replies "Yeah." I turn to Rachel and ask the same question. She smiles and vocalizes. I bring out the toy and place it on the table. We encourage Rachel to approximate the word "up" as each ring is taken off the peg. After all the rings are on the table, I give one to Rachel's mother and say, "Listen!" as she places it by her ear and waits. I say "Ah," and Rachel's mother enthusiastically places the ring on the peg. I offer the next ring to Rachel, who just puts it on the peg. Because she does not hold it to her ear, we help her do this. As she does not yet grasp the conditioned play task, Rachel's mom and I continue to model it and, from time to time, offer Rachel a turn. Once all the rings have been placed on the peg, we wave "bye-bye" and put the toy away.

Noisemakers

In Auditory-Verbal Therapy, the focus is on establishing good "ear contact." We present a sound stimulus, such as a rattle, squeaky toy, or similar noisemaker before showing it to the child. Typically, the therapist strategically places noisemakers in the therapy room before the session.

Rachel's mother makes the sound under the table and we wait for Rachel to respond. Rachel finds the noisemaker. We point to our ears and say, "Oh, good, you heard that!"

Parent Guidance

- Wait for Rachel to attend to all kinds of sounds around home (birds singing, doorbell/telephone ringing, toilet flushing). Affirm her response by pointing to your ear and saying, "You heard that and I heard that too! It's a..." Allow her time to attempt to localize the source of the sound. If she has difficulty with this, help her to find it.
- Take Rachel on a *Listening Walk* in the neighborhood and point out all the sounds: soft, high-pitch sounds (e.g., birds), loud ones (a fire engine), near sounds (a fountain), and those farther away (an airplane).
- Keep a record in your book of the sounds that you think Rachel can and cannot hear. You might take pictures of things that make sounds and keep them in your book as reinforcement.

The Snake

I say "*Ssssss,*" and Rachel's mother says, "Hey, I hear a snake." I repeat the sound. From a basket on the table, I take out a rubber snake while Rachel's mother sings a song about a snake. While moving the snake, I make the snake sound again. When the toy stops, the sound stops. I put the snake close to Rachel's mother's finger and pretend to bite it. "Ouch! No, no, no, don't bite me, you silly snake!" says Rachel's mother. I give the toy to her mother, who repeats the game. We wait for Rachel's vocal attempts and then put the toy on the table in front of her. She plays with it. We narrate other things about the snake. I then say, "Let's put the snake in the basket. Can you wave bye-bye?" We wait and look expectantly for Rachel's response. When Rachel does not respond, I lean towards her mother, who waves and says, "Bye-bye." I then present the basket, and we move on to the next activity.

Parent Guidance

- Go to the zoo or pet store and visit the snakes.
- You can use another toy or situation for the /s/ sound, as there are many applications of the same activity. Which ones might be better for Rachel?
- Make a snake with recycled materials, such as toilet paper rolls, small cereal boxes, empty plastic water bottles, or plastic bottle tops put together with yarn.

The Clown

The clown says "Ha, ha, ha!" A toy clown sits on the window sill of the therapy room. The clown lights up when its nose is pushed and plays a cheerful song. I ask Rachel, "Where is the clown that says, ha, ha, ha?" She turns in the direction of the toys and finds it. Rachel's mother provides positive reinforcement by smiling and saying, "You found the clown!" We bring the toy to the table and talk about the face parts. Rachel's mother asks me where the nose is. I point to it and she counts, "1, 2, 3...", waits, and looks expectantly for Rachel to vocalize. When she does not do that, her mother offers me the turn. I say, "Go," and she pushes the clown's nose. We sway to the music.

Parent Guidance

Toys are very motivating reinforcers for vocalization. A duck, a yo-yo, pop-up toys, and teddy bears are all good for this, but you do not need a lot of "special" or expensive toys.

- Visit a circus or carnival to see clowns.
- Purchase a clown puppet or jack-in-the box that may double as a music box.
- Wait for Rachel to respond when music is played and then begin to sway or dance.
- Dress up like a clown and "clown around" at home.
- Experiment with face painting and extend the experience—always having fun.
- Expect Rachel to vocalize with intent in daily routines. For example, expect Rachel to use her voice to indicate that she wants more to eat or drink.

The Baby Doll

Rachel's mother whispers "*Ssshhh,* the baby is sleeping. *Ssshhh!*" and points to a picture of a baby on the wall. I repeat the sound and present a baby doll. I rock the doll and give it to Rachel's mother, who whispers "*Ssshhh,* the baby is sleeping." We give the doll to Rachel and wait for her to take a turn. Then, we say, "Wake up!" and make the doll stand up. "Hi, baby," we say. Again, the baby goes back to sleep and we repeat the wake-up game. Then, we feed the baby, saying, "*Mmm,* do you want *more?*" We wipe the doll's face, saying "*Wipe, wipe, wipe.*" We label and reinforce the face and body parts. I ask Rachel to give it a hug. "*Ah,* baby," we say. I then ask Rachel to give the doll a kiss. We change the doll's diaper, saying, "*Pee-oo!*" We hand the *dirty* diaper to Rachel and wait for her verbal reaction. Then we put the doll to bed, whispering, "*Ssshhh,* the baby is sleeping. *Ssshhh.*" We sing "Rock-a-Bye Baby" and sway.

Parent Guidance

- Help Rachel to follow single-step directions in her daily routines. For example, wave bye-bye, blow a kiss, and open the door.
- Explore different smells in the environment—those that smell good (*Mmm*), those that do not (*Pee-oo*)—and talk about them.
- Comment when a pet is sleeping: "*Ssshhh...*"
- Read *The Six-Sound Song* (Estabrooks, 2003).
- Play the sleep/wake-up game with family members.
- Engage in pretend play with dolls, animals and puppets.

The Bus

I say "*bu, bu, bu.*" I pause, and then say it again. Rachel's mother says, "Listen! I hear a bus. *Bu, bu, bu.* Where is the bus?" Rachel looks at me and finds the bus. She plays with it, making it go back and forth on the table. We sing "I Hear the Bus" (Estabrooks & Birkenshaw-Fleming, 1994).

After Rachel plays with the bus, we put people in it and take them out, and then push it and pull it on a string. We also talk about the wheels that go "round and round" and sing "The Wheels on the Bus" with the accompanying actions. I say, "Let's put the bus away. Wave bye-bye" and we wait. I then present a colorful pail, signaling the end of the activity. When the bus is in the bucket, we say, "It's all gone," and make a natural gesture for "All gone, no more."

Parent Guidance

- Go for a ride on a bus.
- Play with a toy bus or make one out of cardboard boxes.
- Sing "The Wheels on the Bus" or "I Hear the Bus" (Estabrooks & Birkenshaw-Fleming, 1994).
- If Rachel vocalizes, imitate her production and then provide the correct model. This is a good way to reinforce development of the auditory-feedback loop.

Depending on how attentive and cooperative Rachel is, we might do a dozen or so more activities in the session following a similar formula. Anything that will totally captivate a child's interest is good enough to "make a lesson."

At the end of each session, we spend about 10 minutes wrapping it up by guiding and coaching the parents through the goals for the next week.

Analysis

A child who has good auditory access to all sounds of the speech spectrum and who matches Rachel's chronological, hearing, and auditory-verbal age may demonstrate the following skills in areas of audition, speech, language, cognition, and communication:

Audition:

- Turn to name when called from a distance of 12–18 feet.
- Localize speakers and noisemakers from side to side, upper and lower right/left angles, and from behind.
- Alert to and localize speakers and noisemakers from most angles at distances up to 3 feet.
- Point to ear when he/she hears a sound.
- Responds appropriately to music and finger plays by swaying, making few hand/finger motions that accompany song, and attempting to sing the lyrics or rhymes.
- Imitate some Learning to Listen Sounds, and respond appropriately by pointing to pictures of associated LTL Sounds.

Speech:

- Use appropriate intonation to scold, tease, state, respond, exclaim, and greet.
- Imitate inflectional patterns of speech and some vowel sounds.
- Imitate a variety of LTL sounds.
- Say a variety of highly motivating words and begin to approximate commonly heard (stereotypic) phrases.
- Use a variety of speech sounds in babble, word and phrase approximations (/m/, /d/, /b/, /p/, /h/).

Language:

- Respond to early negation, such as "no," "stop," "don't touch" by withdrawing hands or stopping activity. Say "no" when protesting.
- Look at common objects and toys when named.
- Understand and follow simple directions (e.g., "Wave bye-bye!;" "Blow a kiss").
- Use clear approximations of words and short phrases to express observations, wants, and needs.

Cognition:

- Demonstrate functional and symbolic use of objects.

- Request or get adults to activate toys (means–end).
- Know a few body parts, foods, and clothing items.
- Complete simple puzzles.

Communication:
- Take turns in simple verbal exchanges or play.
- Respond verbally to adult conversational attempts.
- Use words to request, intiate pretend play, comment/tell information, and acknowledge/answer.

The best lessons are learned and reinforced in regular play and meaningful daily experiences. If the parent and the Auditory-Verbal therapist understand the foundations of how language is learned *through listening* and subsequently use skills to develop them, the opportunities for spontaneous carryover will be abundant (Ling & Ling, 1978; Pollack, 1985; Northcott, 1978).

The Parent Book

Throughout the session, the therapist provides parents with responses and suggestions. We term this "online guidance." At the conclusion of the session, 5–10 minutes are spent to ensure that the parent is certain about what needs to be developed at home in the areas of audition, speech, language, cognition, and communication. We review the notes the parent has made during the session and discuss any other concerns.

Occasionally, the parent may wait until the last moment to tell the therapist about significant concerns. We accommodate these by scheduling ample time between the sessions.

The next two session plans document lessons conducted by certified Auditory-Verbal therapists with young children and their families. Although these sessions were used with children who have cochlear implants, the goals and activities are equally appropriate for children who use hearing aids.

SESSION PLAN #3: JORDON (AGE 2)*

At the time of this session, Jordon was 2 years, 2 months old, an only child living at home with young working parents. His profound, bilateral sensorineural hearing loss was diagnosed at age 13 months by a combination of auditory brainstem response (ABR) and behavioral testing. At the age of 15 months, Jordon received two powerful hearing aids, and his parents chose the auditory-verbal approach. After 2 months of intensive Auditory-Verbal therapy and more

* By Beth Walker, M.Ed., C.E.D., Cert. AVT®. Adapted from W. Estabrooks (Ed.), *Cochlear Implants for Kids.* Washington, DC: Alexander Graham Bell Association for the Deaf and Hard of Hearing, 1998. Used with permission.

audiological testing, Jordon demonstrated aided responses to sound only at 250 Hz and 500 Hz, outside the speech range.

Although Jordon's parents worked with him consistently and enthusiastically, continued testing revealed that he had minimal hearing, and he made little progress. When he was 20 months old, his parents began an auditory/oral approach, and a recommendation was made to investigate cochlear implantation.

Jordon had cochlear implant surgery shortly after his second birthday, and the implant was hooked up when he was 25 months of age. On the second day after its initial stimulation, all electrodes were activated. He immediately wore the speech processor all day long, and the family resumed Auditory-Verbal therapy.

The following session took place 1 month poststimulation.

Introduction to the Therapy Session

Jordon and his mother began coming for weekly therapy sessions. His father was able to attend sessions about once a month. During the first sessions, Jordon and his mom would knock on the door and wait until I called, "Come in!" After a brief greeting, we moved towards a table where Jordon could immediately see an exciting toy in front of a highchair. This encouraged him into the chair, where he played with the toy while his mom and I discussed his progress since the last session. During this time I listened for any particular concerns and rejoiced in Jordon's progress. I also planned any adjustments I wanted to make in our time together that day, in case his mom had questions that could be addressed during the session.

On a typical visit, after the initial chat, we briefly discuss the goals of the first activity. I begin each activity with Jordon, modeling strategies used to reach the goals. Often I explain the purpose for each strategy as I play. After the parents have watched for a few minutes, I turn the activity over to them, and they practice the strategies with my coaching until they are comfortable using them at home. Jordon usually stays in the highchair for the first few activities and then moves to the floor. Mom and Dad may take notes during the activity, or they may wait until the end of the session, when we summarize.

Since Jordon's parents know how to check the cochlear implant themselves, I take a moment to encourage Mom to check the speech processor to ensure that it is functioning.

Conditioned-Response Activity: I Hear That!

Goals

Audition:

- To prepare for audiologic testing to update the speech processor MAP.
- To detect the Ling Six Sounds.

Cognition:

- To attend to a task for 1–2 minutes.

Rationale

I begin the session with an important conditioning activity. As Jordon will learn language primarily through audition (listening), the audiologist must be able to reMAP Jordon as often as needed to obtain the clearest auditory signal from the speech processor. Jordon must be able to do the conditioned-response task consistently during the time of the audiological appointment. We do a conditioned-response activity at the beginning of every therapy session to determine which sounds he is hearing as he typically does.

Activity: The Ling Six-Sound Test

Even though Jordon must *play this game* when his parents or I ask him, we try to make it fun. He must hold small rubber balls at his cheek and put them into a cup when he hears a speech sound (one of the Ling Six Sounds). After he has collected five or six balls, he can throw them into a plastic tub of water.

Analysis

Jordon makes fairly consistent responses to five (/a/, /u/, /i/, /ʃ/, /m/) of the Ling Six Sounds. He is not showing a consistent response to /s/. We need to know if this is because he isn't receiving enough stimulation in the frequencies where /s/ has its energy, or whether he has not yet learned to pay attention to that sound. In order to make the /s/ more acoustically salient, we move closer to his microphone, present a slightly louder /s/ than we would at normal speaking level, pair it with a whispered /u/, which slightly lowers the acoustic energy of the /s/, and pulse the /s/ (*ssoo—ssoo—ssoo* rather than *ssss*). He does respond to this, so we begin to take away one modification at a time until he is responding consistently to /s/ spoken at the level of natural conversation.

Parent Guidance

- Modify the /s/ in order to help Jordon respond. Use strategies modeled in the session. Write these down to share with his father.
- Practice a conditioning task for a few minutes each day until Jordon learns it and responds appropriately. A few suggestions for conditioning-task reinforcers are: breaking up branches and sticking them in dirt; rolling cars down a ramp; tossing tub toys into the sink; and throwing dirty clothes, one at a time, into the washer.
- Check responses to the Ling Six-Sound Test daily.

One Frog Too Many

Goals

Audition:

- To identify common phrases given through audition.
- To attend to the Learning to Listen Sounds (Figure 1.3, page 13).

Speech:
- To imitate duration of common phrases.

Language:
- To comprehend a core of common phrases.
- To develop basic turn-taking skills.
- To initiate communication about Jordon's own ideas.

Cognition
- To develop response to the Hand Cue.
- To attend to a short story.
- To learn how to interact with books (right side up, page turning from left to right).
- To recall what happens on the next page of a familiar story.

Rationale

I use the same book we had in last week's session. This activity encourages Jordon's parents to *share* a book *with* him instead of reading *to* him. Jordon's parents have been frustrated because he hasn't seemed to enjoy stories. In our last session, we discussed sharing books. In this session I want to demonstrate a variety of ways to share books, to extend Jordon's interest in books, and to integrate language and auditory targets in the process. I use the wordless picture book *One Frog Too Many* (Mayer, 1975). As there are no words, there is no "right" way to tell the story. These books are especially good for parents who tend to read at, rather than with, their children.

Activity

I say, "Listen, Jordon!" Then I make a quiet rustling noise with a plastic grocery bag. I say, "I have something that goes 'hop, hop, hop.' Want to see?" I encourage him to take the frog prop out of the bag. We proceed in a similar way with the other props, which include a second, smaller frog, a dog, a boy, a turtle, and a boat. I get his attention through listening by making a soft sound with the bag, and then call his attention to the Learning to Listen Sound for each prop. Then Jordon plays with the toys. We act out the story together, using all the props.

I share the first few pages with him, acoustically highlighting the common phrases associated with each picture. He plays with the props, acting out the pictures and making up some of his own actions.

I then hold the book facing me so that Jordon can see neither my mouth nor the pictures, and I tell his mom about the next picture. I again use a common phrase associated with the picture: "The frog said, *'Ow! That hurts!'* " I acoustically highlight the common phrase. I let Mom see the picture and say, "Let's tell Jordon the frog said, 'Ow! That hurts!' " I use the Hand Cue when I say, "Ow! That hurts!" to prompt Mom to imitate the phrase.

While Jordon is looking at that picture, I encourage his mom to read the next page to him and to encourage him to tell me about it by imitating the common phrase. We continue reading pages to each other and acting out the story.

When we reach the next-to-last page, I hold the book back, look questioningly at his mom, and ask her to recall what happened on that page by telling me and using the props. On the final page, I make the same request of Jordon. Mom helps him act out the final page with the props.

Analysis

Jordon alerts to the soft sound of the rustling bag after three presentations. He needs continued exposure to soft environmental sounds in order to respond consistently.

His excitement when manipulating the story props indicates that he *does* enjoy books when we *follow his lead* and encourage him to take a turn. Other ways of using props will increase his interest in stories and extend his dramatic play skills.

As Jordon plays with the props, he spontaneously imitates the Learning to Listen Sounds twice, when the sound is paired with movement, such as accompanying each hopping movement with the word *hop.* He approximates both the duration and the vowel. His initial imitation of the dog's sound, *woofwoof,* is one long *uuhhh,* indicating perception of the length of the two syllables together, not of two distinct syllables. When prompted slightly, however, to make the break between the two syllables more obvious (*woof—woof*), Jordon spontaneously imitates a closer approximation of duration.

His developing perceptual skills are indicated by Jordon's vocal approximation of the duration patterns in the phrases *No! no!* and *That hurts!*, including approximations of "ah" and "uh." Approximations of early developing consonants (/p/, /b/, /m/, /h/, /w/) are expected as he continues to learn language through listening.

Parent Guidance

- The main purpose of reading with Jordon is to create a love of books.
- Share stories he enjoys over and over with him. Use props to maintain interest and generate the foundations of conversation. Encourage Jordon to initiate play and act out story elements with the props.
- Encourage use of the Learning to Listen Sounds and imitation of common phrases.
- When encouraging imitation, remember that later Jordon will be paying closer attention to vowel and consonant features. He is just beginning to focus on differences in duration, intensity, and pitch.
- Act out and tell the story of *One Frog Too Many.*
- Begin collecting props for other books.
- Bring a book and props to our next session and *read to me.*

Ride a Horsie!

Goals

Audition:

- To attend to the abundant prosodic features in nursery rhymes.

Speech:

- To encourage spontaneous vocalizing.
- To encourage spontaneous use of varied suprasegmentals.
- To develop approximations of varied suprasegmentals through imitation in vocal play.

Language:

- To demonstrate understanding that spoken language has meaning through production of a higher rate of speech-like vocalizations.

Cognition:

- To create an interest in the rhythmic patterns of spoken language.
- To respond to the Hand Cue when encouraged to imitate on demand.

Communication:

- To develop basic turn-taking skills.

Rationale

Jordon has been sitting in the highchair for awhile, and this rhyme provides an opportunity for active interaction. The activity is short and highly motivational. Jordon will want to play it again and again, providing many opportunities to encourage him to initiate the game repeatedly through vocalizing. This activity is so much fun that it usually causes the child to raise vocal pitch and change intensity spontaneously. This provides an opportunity for the stimulation of varied suprasegmentals through vocal play.

Activity

I explain the main goals of the activity and then ask Jordon, "Want to *get down*?" I wait for him to respond and when he does not, I repeat the question, holding my hands out to him, and wait again. When he begins to move back and forth in the seat, I ask his mom, "Yes?" and use the Hand Cue to prompt a *yes* response.

I quickly get Jordon out of the seat and begin to bounce him on my knees while saying the *ride-a-horsie* rhyme. I bounce him in rhythm first, with the faster first part of the rhyme, and then slow the bouncing towards the end as my voice slows ("youuu'll faalll..."). When I get to the last word, "dowwwn!," I lean him way back to protect him from falling. I imitate his squeal of delight and look at him expectantly, hoping he will imitate my squeal. When he does not, I squeal to his mom, and she squeals back. I tell her I'll play one more time before her turn. I pull Jordon back up to a sitting position on my knees and wait, looking at him expectantly, as if to say, *Do you want something?* He just smiles back at me so I ask his mom, "Do you want Jordon to play *some more?*"

She says, "Yes, some more!" and I begin the rhyme again. I want Jordon to associate his mom's talking with the fun's beginning. He squeals a bit, so I repeat his squeal and he squeals again. Mom holds Jordon and waits for him to vocalize to initiate the rhyme. When he does not, I model the *more-play* scenario, and his mom starts over again. The next time she begins the rhyme she waits, looks expectantly, asks him if he wants more, and uses the Hand Cue. Jordon vocalizes a little bit.

Analysis

Waiting and looking expectantly prompted fewer spontaneous vocalizations than I had anticipated and consequently, I used other strategies to encourage vocalization. First, I established an expectation for repeated activity in the game and then waited for Jordon to initiate another round. Second, I paused and looked expectantly, as if to say, "Is there something you want?" Then, I asked his mom to model the response vocally, and finally, I prompted with the Hand Cue.

Jordon's voice quality was quite weak owing to infrequent vocalizing. He will do more listening than talking during his first weeks of cochlear implant use. Consistent use of strategies to prompt listening and talking, in conjunction with excellent technological management, is critical for spoken communication development.

The repeated actions and rhyme did provide several opportunities for vocal play, and Jordon's repeated squealing indicates development of his auditory-feedback loop.

Parent Guidance

- Jordon's use of his new hearing potential should increase vocalization, thereby improving his voice quality.
- Help Jordon pay attention to the frequency of and variation in the new signal from the cochlear implant.
- Initiate activities where motion is associated with Jordon's talking. Repeat the activity a couple of times, and wait for Jordon to initiate it again by vocalizing.
- Play active games to encourage spontaneous use of variation in duration, intensity, and pitch (suprasegmentals). Imitate playfully when he makes sounds. This develops auditory *self-monitoring* (listening to his own voice).
- Tickle games, roughhousing, water play, and stacking up and knocking over blocks are good activities to enrich suprasegmental behaviors.
- To encourage communication, use strategies such as *looking expectantly, pausing, waiting, using another person to model talking,* and *using the Hand Cue.*

Swinging Sounds!

Goals

Audition:

- To attend to a soft environmental sound.
- To provide exposure to a variety of Learning to Listen Sounds.

Speech:

- To encourage imitation of suprasegmental features.

Language:

- To help Jordon attach meaning to the Learning to Listen Sounds.
- To encourage comprehension of a few functional words.

Cognition:

- To encourage memory for where things belong.
- To match a picture to an object.

Communication:

- To help Jordon to initiate a conversation by verbal or nonverbal means.
- To develop turn-taking.

Rationale

Although Jordon had a good deal of exposure to the Learning to Listen Sounds prior to receiving his cochlear implant, we have begun this process all over again to help him pay attention to and begin to derive meaning from the new information it provides. The Learning to Listen Sounds provide opportunities for a variety of suprasegmental features. His parents had grown weary of playing with these sounds during the months Jordon wore hearing aids because they observed no responses. In this session, I created an interesting play scenario with the Learning to Listen Sound toys. As it requires little preparation, it can easily be replicated at home.

Activity

Before the session I tie one end of a long, thin rope to the handle of a plastic bucket, put the bucket on a nearby filing cabinet (up high and out of sight), and tie the other end to a hook in the ceiling. When I pull back on the bucket and then let it go, it swings back and forth. Mom picks up Jordon and walks near the spot where I have put the bucket. I ask her to distract him for a second while I pick up the bucket containing a toy and put it behind me.

I say, "Listen!" and when I have his attention, make a soft sound by tapping a toy cow on the side of the plastic bucket.

I say, "You heard that! It was a toy cow that says 'mooo!' " I wait and say, "Want to see the cow that says *moooo*?" When he nods, I help him pull the cow out of the bucket. After he pulls it out he is not interested in playing with it further until I say, "Let's swing the cow over to Mommy." I show him what we will do by pulling back on the bucket and then looking at his mom. She steps back, and Jordon and I pull the cow "up-up-up" and then I say, "gooooo!" and the bucket swings over to his mom. She dumps out the *cow that says moo* and chats a bit more about it. When she swings the bucket back to Jordon and me, I repeat the entire sequence, beginning with the soft tapping of a different Learning to Listen Sound toy. Jordon delights in swinging the bucket back and forth, so we are able to play with several Learning to Listen Sounds. After the swinging is over, I take two toys out of the bucket and ask Jordon to put them back, matching them to pictures in a segmented box. I continue to take toys out, two at a time, choosing sounds that are very different acoustically (*moo* and *bububu*, rather than *moo* and *ahhhh*). Finally, I bring out a new Learning to Listen toy, the top, and I sing its accompanying song from *Hear & Listen! Talk & Sing!* (Estabrooks & Birkenshaw-Fleming, 1994). Mom practices singing with me so that she can sing it at home.

Analysis

As with his responses to soft environmental sounds during the *One Frog Too Many* activity, Jordon required several presentations before he detected the tapping on the bucket. We will continue to expose him to a variety of soft sounds and expect him to respond.

The technique of *waiting* yielded verbal and nonverbal responses to questions and also prompted Jordon to direct the course of the activity. After the second sequence, Jordon understood the routine and indicated that he wanted to do the swinging himself by imitating the swinging motion of the bucket. After the fourth sequence, he indicated that he wanted to switch roles with his mom by vocalizing and pointing at her.

One month after Jordan's cochlear implant was activated, I had reintroduced eight of the Learning to Listen Sounds (cow, bus, airplane, car, dog, pig, baby, and boat). Jordon benefits greatly from exposure to Learning to Listen Sounds, which contain a broad range of acoustic information across the speech frequencies.

Jordon's developing perceptual skills are confirmed by his repeatedly choosing the correct Learning to Listen Sound from a set of two when putting away toys.

A big challenge in this game is distance, because one adult involved in the conversation is sometimes across the room and we need to be within Jordon's critical listening distance (*earshot*).

Parent Guidance

- There are many ways of making the Learning to Listen Sounds fun again both for you and Jordon:
  - Repeat mini field trips to see real Learning to Listen Sounds in action at a nearby farm, the airport, or a pond.

  - Pull the Learning to Listen Sound toys out of unlikely objects such as socks and pillowcases.
  - Make a sneaky game of putting the Learning to Listen Sound pictures in unlikely places, such as on the ceiling, under chairs, or in shoes.
  - Tape paper flaps over the Learning to Listen Sound pictures in Jordon's room.
  - Repeat the Swinging Sounds game at home.
- Get Jordon's attention before providing verbal language for the Learning to Listen Sounds.
- Introduce the new sound and song for *round and round* with anything that goes around such as tops, wheels, and circles drawn on paper with crayons.
- Jordon successfully identified the Learning to Listen Sounds from a set of two different durational patterns, so increase the set to three.
- Jordon is receiving a clear signal with the implant. There is no need to test his perception skills constantly. He is learning language through listening, and this is encouraging.
- Sing Learning to Listen songs from *Hear & Listen! Talk & Sing!* (Estabrooks & Birkenshaw-Fleming, 1994) and *Songs for Listening! Songs for Life!* (Estabrooks & Birkenshaw-Fleming, 2002). Use the accompanying CDs to help memorize the songs.
- Call Jordon's attention to a variety of quiet sounds throughout the day.

Wash the Baby

Goals

Audition:

- To identify common words and phrases through audition.
- To expand auditory attention.

Speech:

- To practice prespeech behaviors.

Language:

- To comprehend a core of common phrases.
- To comprehend functional words.
- To initiate actions.

Cognition:

- To problem-solve.

Rationale

This activity replicates a typical play scenario for young children and utilizes household objects. Jordon's parents have the idea that fancy toys are more interesting and will promote language development faster than ordinary objects in his environment. I emphasize that fancy toys are not necessary to develop language. Like other activities, this one combines several goals and provides opportunity for interaction, development of prespeech skills, and exposure to common words and phrases.

Activity

With Jordon's mom's knowledge, I have hidden a *dirty* baby doll in the corner of the room before Jordon comes to the therapy session. We will find the baby, pretend to be upset that it is dirty, and wait for Jordon to initiate some action.

"Waa! Waa! Listen, Jordon! I hear a baby!" I say, and then repeat softly. Jordon *attends* to the auditory stimulus for about 15 seconds and then looks around for the source of the sound. Together, his mom and Jordon find the baby. Mom and I playfully feign being upset, and she says, "Ooooo—she's dirty!" Jordon begins to wipe the dirt off the baby's face.

I say, "Good idea, Jordon; let's wash the baby!" I acoustically highlight the phrase *wash the baby.*

All the items needed for washing the baby (wash cloth, pitcher of water, and liquid soap) are in a cupboard in my therapy room. The items are in small plastic bags in a cardboard box so that we have to take them out one at a time and then open each one, providing many opportunities to hear these functional words. We then wash the baby.

The conversation during each part of this activity provides much opportunity for repetition of common phrases and functional words. We pour a little water into the tub (*pour it*) a little at a time (*more water*) until Jordon indicates by gesture or vocalization that we have enough (*stop!*). The water is *all gone* from the pitcher. We put the baby in the tub (*put her in*) and pretend that she is cold (*Brrrr! It's cold!*). We frequently comment, "Oooo, she's dirty!" When Jordon tires of washing, we are *all done.* I use thick liquid soap, which bubbles easily. We scoop the bubbles in our hands and playfully blow them towards each other (*blow it!*). There is a big wet spot on the floor (*uh-oh!*), so we wipe up the floor (*wipe, wipe, wipe it up*) and put all the materials back in their containers (*put it away*).

Analysis

Jordon attended to the auditory input of the baby's cry for more than a few seconds *only* when I accompanied it with a lot of facial expression and drama. Extended attention to auditory stimuli is a target.

After Jordon's mother commented, "Oooooh, she's dirty!" Jordon stopped, looked to his mother, and waited 15–20 seconds before he wiped the baby's face. Jordon's mother initially appeared uncomfortable when I asked her to *wait.* Solving problems for Jordon is normal reaction, but he is capable of indicating his own desires and generating solutions to small problems when encouraged.

Jordon waited several seconds after listening to simple directions before he could follow through. This is typical of children soon after initial stimulation of a cochlear implant. He will require context to process directions over the next few weeks, but I expect his follow-through time to reduce. As his parents wait for Jordon's response, he will process phrases more quickly. Jordon's parents have heard the erroneous analogy that a child who is deaf is like a vessel and if adults pour language in, it will eventually come spilling out the top. Consequently, adults often monopolize potential interactions and neglect critical *wait time.*

Jordon's blowing was initially more like spitting, but after a few turns he began to approximate blowing. He had demonstrated neither imitated nor spontaneous blowing at home.

Parent Guidance

- Wait for Jordon to initiate actions and problem-solve on his own whenever possible. He will be motivated to use spoken language if he is given opportunities to initiate actions and events. In your notebook, list times when this would be appropriate—for example, when milk is spilled, shoes need tying, toys get broken, doors need opening.
- Talk with Jordon about what he is thinking, feeling, and doing. Talk in phrases rather than single words. There is much more acoustic information in a phrase.
- Jordon will demonstrate understanding of language by the rate, rhythm, and stress patterns of phrases before he understands actual words.
- Create opportunities for Jordon to hear the repetition of common phrases such as *Uh oh—fall down!, Pick it up, All gone, Take it out, Open it.* He will begin to make sense out of the strings of words he hears.
- List daily home activities during which common phrases occur naturally. Detailed notes help you to *follow through.* This is especially important when both parents cannot come to each session.

Session Summary

Prior to receiving the cochlear implant, Jordon did not respond consistently to loud sounds, vocalized infrequently, and understood very little language without accompanying gestures. Since receiving the implant, he consistently stops activity upon hearing loud and moderately loud sounds in a quiet environment. He often puts his hand to his ear to indicate he has heard something. He responds by looking up when his name is called on the first or second call when the environment is quiet, and when he is not highly involved in an activity. He detects five (/a/, /u/, /i/, /ʃ/, and /m/) of the Ling Six Sounds most of the time, and sometimes /s/. I expect him to detect all these sounds, both at close range and at varying distances, within the next few weeks. We will encourage consistent alerting responses to soft sounds such as quiet knocking, whispering, quiet whistling, and talking from another room when the environment is quiet. We will look for him to respond consistently to his name in a variety of situations.

Jordon currently identifies several Learning to Listen Sounds from a set of two that differ in duration, and he can identify a few common words and phrases with abundant contextual support. We will develop identification of all the Learning to Listen Sounds and more common phrases with minimal contextual support.

Since receiving the implant, Jordon vocalizes more frequently, though not abundantly. Most vocalizations approximate the vowels "ah" and "uh," and his voice quality is still breathy. He sometimes uses his voice to attract attention and he imitates some duration patterns, but does not yet imitate or spontaneously vary intensity or pitch. Although he does not imitate consistently in response to the Hand Cue, his spontaneous imitations are increasing. We will encourage imitations varying in duration, intensity, and pitch, and stimulate production of back and front vowels. We will help him develop blowing.

Prior to receiving the cochlear implant, Jordon communicated by gesture, pointing, crying, and pulling adults towards desired items. Though his parents attempted to gain his attention via sound, they had to resort to touch. Jordon understood his parents only when they used gestures, such as pointing to a chair to indicate that he was to sit down or holding up his plate when it was time to eat. He now communicates his needs and wants by gesture sometimes accompanied by vocalization. He is beginning to understand that sound is used for communication. His parents are able to gain his attention through sound, and he can move farther from their view without constant need for supervision. We anticipate that Jordon will learn to use his voice consistently for communication.

Before the cochlear implant, Jordon demonstrated comprehension of one Learning to Listen Sound, the cow, when he was able to speechread, and showed no interest in nursery rhymes or singing. He now attaches meaning to several Learning to Listen Sounds. He comprehends a few simple words and common phrases and is attentive when his parents sing to him. We will encourage comprehension of common phrases and functional words through listening, and imitation of familiar nursery rhymes and songs.

Previously, Jordan demonstrated cognitive skills typical for his age except in areas related to language. Current goals include enjoyment when sharing books with parents, attention to spoken language for longer periods, acting out stories with props, response to the Hand Cue, and matching pictures to objects.

Jordon's parents are delighted that he responds to sound and is beginning to make sense out of spoken language. They believe he has the potential to develop spoken language and to participate academically, socially, and emotionally with his friends and family. They plan for their son to have a happy childhood and fulfilling future, just like other kids.

SESSION PLAN #4: EVAN (AGE 3)*

At the time of this session, Evan was nearly 3 years old. At 3 months of age his hearing loss, of unknown etiology, was first suspected, and at 8 months he received hearing aids. His parents were told that he had a left-corner audiogram with no responses past 2000 Hz in either ear. His mother reports an unremarkable pregnancy and delivery, and there is no history of hearing loss in the family. It took several months for Evan to wear hearing aids consistently.

When Evan was 11 months old he and his family enrolled in their school district's parent–infant program, which they attended twice a week until Evan was 2 years old. They began to use sign language, and Evan wore both his hearing aids throughout this period. According to his parents, however, he received little benefit from his amplification and did not turn to his name nor to any environmental sounds. They reported that Evan responded about the same whether or not he was wearing his hearing aids.

Evan began to use sign language at 12 months old, when he also became very quiet and made few vocalizations. His signing increased, and by 2 years of age he was putting two signed words together. At that time Evan's parents started to gather information about cochlear implants by reading the literature and meeting with families whose children had an implant. After comprehensive evaluations, the implant center recommended Evan as a candidate.

In November 1995, at 2 years, 4 months of age, Evan received a cochlear implant. His parents report that he loved the implant from the beginning and asked for it to be put on. He does not wear a hearing aid in the contralateral ear. Evan and his family enrolled in an auditory-verbal program when he was aged 2 years, 8 months, and therapy began immediately.

Parent Orientation Session

Prior to beginning therapy, the parents and I reviewed the audiological information and discussed the principles and goals of an auditory-verbal program. I tried to address any questions and concerns. Evan's parents wanted to know how to move from a Total Communication program to an auditory-verbal approach, and how I would react when Evan used sign language in therapy. This is a very valid concern, since Evan's primary mode of communication was sign language. A young child with a cochlear implant receives a great deal of auditory information, and as listening and language goals are achieved the amount of sign language is usually reduced.

In order to create an optimal listening environment at home throughout Evan's waking hours, I recommended that Evan's parents

- stay close to Evan while talking and singing to him;
- reduce ambient background noise;

---

* By Sally Tannenbaum, M.Ed., C.E.D., Cert. AVT®. Adapted from W. Estabrooks (Ed.), *Cochlear Implants for Kids.* Washington, DC: Alexander Graham Bell Association for the Deaf and Hard of Hearing, 1998. Used with permission.

- get Evan's attention through listening;
- point to their own ear and say *Listen*;
- ensure that Evan wears his cochlear implant during all waking hours;
- speak in a natural voice and sing songs throughout the day;
- use meaningful situations to encourage Evan to pay attention to the environment;
- when coming home from work, knock on the front door and wait while the other parent calls Evan's attention to the sound: "Listen, I hear Mommy knocking on the door; let's go open the door." Mommy can then give Evan a special greeting such as, "Hi, Evan; you heard me knocking on the door";
- use the Learning to Listen Sounds on placemats, clothing, dishes, books, puzzles—even diapers! Using these sounds throughout Evan's day will provide repetition and help him process what he is hearing;
- practice skills such as blowing, lip-smacking, tongue-clicking, licking, and "blowing raspberries," all of which are prerequisites for developing speech. Blowing helps a child to whisper and develop voiceless consonants such as /p/ and /t/. Chewing and swallowing help develop the muscles necessary for speech production. Many of the Learning to Listen Sounds incorporate these prespeech skills.

I demonstrated a variety of ways to use the Learning to Listen Sounds, explaining that the big vehicles and animals make a loud sound while the smaller ones make a quieter sound.

Evan's parents learned to listen carefully to his vocalizations. I discussed early developing sounds of young children and reviewed the vowels and diphthongs that are informally learned through everyday applications of the Learning to Listen Sounds. I encouraged them to keep a diary of Evan's development and to bring this book to all sessions. They were to record what Evan was hearing, any sounds to which he was not responding, his vocalizations, and the language Evan understood without visual cues. I needed to know if Evan was turning when called, or if he was pointing or looking at his mother when asked, "Where's Mommy?"

We discussed everything about Evan so that I knew his daily schedule and routines, favorite toys, television shows, pets, friends, and family. This would help me incorporate familiar topics and situations into Evan's therapy sessions.

Introduction to the Therapy Session

I am in private practice, and my therapy room is located downstairs in my house. It is a relaxed place for children and parents where we have fun *learning to listen.*

My session starts the moment Evan and his family arrive in the neighborhood. I want to hear them coming down the street. Therapy is not an isolated session that takes place at a table. I encourage parents to *march, run fast, walk slowly, jump, skip, walk backwards,* or *sing* all the way to Sally's Gate. After they knock on my door and call my name, we exchange greetings. Then we talk about what we are wearing and what the weather is like. I take the time to talk about what is happening. The focus of the session is structured around highlighting speech and language through listening, with communication being closely related to Evan's interests.

The Freeze Dance

Goals

- To create a relaxed and enjoyable listening environment.
- To give Evan a few minutes to adjust to the therapy room.
- To demonstrate the absence or presence of sound.
- To develop auditory attention.
- To encourage localizing the source of a sound.

Activity

Evan's mom holds him in her arms. I turn on my tape recorder and play the "Freeze Dance," a children's song containing pauses throughout it. When the music begins I start to dance and point to my ear and say, "I hear that, I hear the music." Evan's mom is a little shy about dancing and I tell her, "Come on, Mom, dance to the music." She begins to dance and Evan smiles. When the music pauses, we stop dancing; I point to my ear, shake my head, and say, "Sh, it stopped! I don't hear it! It is all gone!" When it begins again, I point to the tape recorder and back to my ear and say, "I hear it, I hear the music." After a few times of stopping and starting I tell his mom, "Wait a few seconds to see what Evan does by himself when the music starts up again." Evan starts to move his body as if to say, "Come on, Mom." When the song is over I clap my hands and say, It's over, it's all gone, I don't hear it."

Analysis

The Freeze Dance is a great activity to start a first session with a small child. It is one we will do again in later sessions. Sometimes everyone has a bracelet of bells to shake while we are dancing or puppets to move to the music. In this session both his mom and Evan enjoyed the dance, and Evan adjusted to the new environment.

Parent Guidance

- Play the Freeze Dance at home and encourage dancing to various songs.
- Sing to Evan; it will help him develop natural-sounding speech.
- Form a small marching band; each time you stop banging the drum, everyone must freeze.
- Be sure to point out the presence or absence of sound by saying, "I hear it" or "I don't hear it."

The Calling Game

Goals

- To detect the presence of sound.
- To learn to listen to his name.
- To encourage vocalizing for attention.
- To develop greetings.
- To encourage turn-taking.

Activity

Evan's mom holds him with his back on her chest so they are both facing the same direction. I stand a couple feet behind them and, using a sing-song voice, call "Evan!" Mom turns around holding him, points to his ear and says, "I heard that."

I then put a Cookie Monster puppet on my hand and say, "Hi, Evan." Cookie tickles Evan to reward him for turning to his name.

"It's my turn to turn around," I say. "I am going to listen for my name."

I ask Evan's mom to count to 10 before she calls my name. This helps Evan become aware of the absence of sound. During this absence I point to my ear, shake my head, and say, "I don't hear anything."

His mom then calls my name and I immediately turn around and say, "Hi, I heard that."

We play the game a few more times. When I call his name again, Evan's mom waits a few seconds before turning him around, but we see no indication that he heard his name. He does not blink or start to turn his body. Lack of response is typical at this early stage. Evan does vocalize, but not to get my attention. He wants to get down and starts to complain.

I immediately turn around when he vocalizes his complaint and say, "I heard that."

Analysis

There has to be a good reason for Evan to turn to his name. Once he is turning to his name in this structured setting, I expect him to do the same in situations throughout the day. A typical 2-year-old, however, does not always listen to his name being called. Any vocalization that Evan makes can be used to demonstrate that *sound can make things happen.* We need to *respond* to his vocalizations in order to develop the auditory-feedback loop.

Parent Guidance

- Play the Calling Game at home with Evan's brother or dad.
- Help Evan watch others play the Calling Game. Once he is able to respond he will play variations of the game, such as standing on his own and listening to two different people call him (not at the same time) from various parts of the room. Evan will have to identify the location of the sound.

- Mom and Dad can take turns calling Evan; encourage him to identify the speaker.
- Be creative with the Calling Game: you can use a colorful box with a surprise inside to encourage Evan to turn to his name.
- When you call Evan, be certain to have a good reason for him to turn to you.

The Cat

Goals

- To identify that sound has a specific meaning.
- To learn that vocalizing can make something happen.
- To encourage listening to suprasegmental and vowel information of this particular Learning to Listen Sound.
- To encourage development of auditory feedback through imitation.

Activity

My first sessions with Evan always included the Learning to Listen Sounds. These sounds can be presented in a variety of ways through puzzles, books, stuffed animals, small toys, and beanbag toys.

I have a wooden feely box that I use to introduce the sound *meow*. I place a soft stuffed kitty inside the box and hold it under the table. I point to my ear and say, "Listen, I hear a kitty, meow, meow, I hear the kitty." I secure Evan's auditory attention when I say "meow." He becomes very still and looks at me as if to say, "I hear that."

I put the box on the table and continue to say the kitty sound. I give Evan's mom a turn calling the kitty. After she says *meow*, I bring the kitty out of the box. Next, it is Evan's turn to call the kitty. I put the kitty back in the box and hold it in front of Evan, waiting for him to vocalize.

Evan does vocalize an "ee" sound, which I immediately reinforce by having the kitty come out of the box. I say, "I heard that, you called the kitty, meow."

The kitty has eyes that open and close, so I put it on the table and say in a very soft voice, "Sh, kitty is sleeping." Evan immediately responds to the "sh" sound by turning to the sound. I then tell the kitty to WAKE UP! in a very loud voice. We all take turns saying *Night-night* and *Wake up!*

Analysis

I picked the sound *meow* first because it has good suprasegmental information and I know that Evan has a cat at home.

It is important to wait for Evan to vocalize. I still need to remind myself to wait!

I reinforce any vocalization Evan makes to show him that language can make things happen. Had Evan not vocalized, which is not unusual in the first session, his mom would have had another turn to call the kitty.

My primary goal here is to evaluate how Evan responds to the Learning to Listen Sounds, but I also target comprehension while playing with the cat. Evan turned each time I said the "sh" sound, which indicates that he is hearing up to 2000 Hz.

Parent Guidance

- Point out all the cats you hear and see in your neighborhood. Say *meow* each time you see a cat.
- Evan needs a lot of repetition.
- Visit a pet shop with Evan.
- Use a variety of materials to reinforce the Learning to Listen Sounds, such as puzzles, books, stuffed animals, clothing, stickers, labels, and of course the real things!
- Present the Learning to Listen Sounds through listening first. Say the sound, point to your ear to get Evan's attention, and say the sound again. Help him find the sound if he can't find it himself.
- Put toys aside in a Learning to Listen basket. Use these toys for a week or two and then switch them with some other toys to keep his interest.
- Evan is very young, so give him a lot of time to play with the toys.

Sound Conditioning

Goal

- To encourage auditory detection of a variety of sounds.

Activity

Since this is Evan's first session, I ask his mom to model this activity. I stand beside her where Evan can watch both of us. Mom holds a beanbag up to her ear. When she hears the clicker she drops the beanbag in the bucket. She smiles and says, "I hear that."

Analysis

Evan indicates he is hearing the clicker by turning to it and then turning back to his mom as if to say, *You can drop the beanbag now.* Putting blocks in a container, pegs in a pegboard, and objects into playdough are good reinforcers for this important structured activity. Within a few sessions Evan is expected to pick up the beanbag on his own and drop it in the bucket by himself. If Evan shows no auditory response to the clicker, I try a drum or another noisemaker.

Then, I move on to the Ling Six-Sound Test (/a/, /u/, /i/, /ʃ/, /s/, and /m/). Once Evan is conditioned to these sounds, I add distance to the task and encourage him to repeat the sounds he hears and learn to identify them. When Evan can do this task for the MAPping procedure of his cochlear implant, his audiologist can obtain important information.

I carefully document what Evan is hearing and at what distance. Each change in his MAP may result in different auditory responses. As a team, the parents and I will inform the audiologist about Evan's listening performance.

Parent Guidance

- At this level Evan is watching the activity closely, so it is important to have more than one person present. If you are alone and drop the object and present the sound at the same time, Evan will imitate what he has observed. Thus, he will hold up a beanbag, perhaps make a sound, and drop the beanbag. This is not the goal. Evan is required to listen for the sound and, upon hearing it, drop the beanbag into the bucket.
- Model *sound conditioning* with Evan's dad or his brother while Evan is watching.
- You might try some other reinforcers. These, however, should not be *too* interesting, so that Evan gets right to the task instead of playing with the reinforcers.

The Airplane

Goals

- To listen to the sound /a/ ("ah") for the airplane.
- To identify that a sound has a specific meaning.
- To develop vocalization with adequate breath flow (vocalize /a/ with a sustained breathstream).
- To encourage the use of vocal play (the use of voice patterns varying in intensity, duration, and pitch).

Activity

I point to my ear, calling Evan's attention to the sound and say, "Listen, /a/. I hear an airplane." The airplane is hidden inside a plastic egg. I bring out the egg and say /a/. I hold the container near Evan's mom's mouth and she says the sound.

Next, I hold the container near Evan's mouth and wait for him to say the sound. Evan is quiet and doesn't repeat the sound. I hold it near my mouth and say the sound again. Next, I shake the egg, point to my ear, and say, "I hear that, it is an airplane. /A/." I shake the egg near his mom's ear; she points to her ear and says: "I hear that; /a/, it is an airplane." I shake the container next to Evan's ear and he reaches for the container. We open the container and Evan finds the airplane. While he is playing with it I say the airplane sound again, varying my pitch. While the airplane is flying high I make the sound high, and as the plane comes down I lower my voice. When the airplane stops flying I say, "Sh, I don't hear it, it stopped."

I bring out two more airplanes, repeating the same pattern. Evan does say /a/ for the last airplane.

I immediately reinforce this by repeating the sound and opening the egg, letting him find the airplane. I give one of the airplanes to his mom and the other one to Evan. We all fly the airplane while vocalizing /a/. When it is time to put them away I ask his mom for her airplane and we say, "Bye-bye." I repeat this with Evan's airplane and with my airplane. Evan waves *bye-bye* to the airplanes but he does not vocalize. I point to my ear and say, "I don't hear you saying bye-bye." I use the Hand Cue and say, "Bye-bye." I repeat this with his mom, who says, "Bye-bye," and then use the Hand Cue with Evan, who says, "Ba" and waves.

I say, "I heard you say bye-bye."

Analysis

Evan vocalized /a/ for the last airplane and was able to sustain the sound for a few seconds. In the next session I will use airplanes first to reinforce this sound and then quickly move on to talk about the airplane: *"The airplane goes up, up, up and around and around and down."*

If Evan had not waved bye-bye I would have taken his hand and waved it for him. This is a childlike way to develop pattern perception of an often-heard phrase.

Parent Guidance

- Listen for airplanes throughout the day. When you hear one, point to your ear and say the airplane sound: "Listen, I hear an airplane. *Ah.* It's up in the sky. There it is. *Ah.* Bye-bye, airplane."
- Look at books about airplanes while reinforcing the sound /a/.
- Make paper airplanes and fly them while saying the sound "ah."
- Place a toy airplane or a picture of one in a couple of rooms at home. When entering the room, say the sound "ah" and ask Evan where the airplane is. If Evan looks in the direction of the airplane, he is beginning to identify what he is hearing.
- Work on duration by flying the airplane around while sustaining the sound "ah." Contrast the sound "ah" with short airplane trips: *ah, ah, ah.*

About Face

Goal

- To develop the identification of a sound that is *too loud* or *too quiet* by listening to voices that are *loud, quiet,* and *just right.*

Activity

I bring out three pictures of faces. The first face is *huge* and is *shouting* Evan's name! I make a face, cover my ears, and say, "It is too loud, I do not like it!" The next face is tiny and is calling Evan's name in the softest voice possible. "It is too quiet, I do not like it." The last picture is a face with a smile that, of course, is calling Evan's name in a pleasant voice. "It is just right, I like it." Next, I bring out a container of tokens. I hold up the picture and repeat each phrase, using the appropriate intensity, and place a token on a picture.

I ask Evan's mom to listen and, when I say the phrase, to pick up the token off the correct picture and drop it into the container. Evan watches and listens throughout this activity. When I put the pictures away I ask Evan for each picture one at a time. Evan's mom helps him select the correct picture, waves *bye-bye*, and puts it away.

Throughout the session, we use loud and quiet voices and point out when something is too loud, too soft, or just right. A truck goes by during the session and Evan puts his hands over his ears. His mom immediately reinforces this gesture by saying, "I hear the truck, it's too loud!… Listen, I don't hear it. It went away. It's okay now."

Analysis

Acoustic cues to vocal intensity occur throughout the range of speech frequencies. During this activity, Evan only observed. After a few more sessions I anticipate that he will identify loud and quiet voices. Identifying a sound as *too loud* or *too quiet* will help the audiologist MAP Evan's cochlear implant.

I will engage Evan in vocal play in which loud and quiet voices and high and low voices are contrasted.

Parent Guidance

- The story "Goldilocks and the Three Bears" reinforces the goals of intensity, pitch, and duration, so this is a good time to enjoy it with Evan.
- Using the strategies of the About Face activity, point out *loud*, *quiet*, and *just right* voices.
- Pretend to go to sleep. It will take a *very loud* voice to wake you up!

The Car

Goals

- To develop identification of the Learning to Listen Sound for the car.
- To enhance prespeech skills and vocal play through "blowing raspberries" and the *beep-beep* sound as we play with the cars.
- To develop some early functional language.

Activity

I have a toy car hidden inside a small box. I say the car sound, *brrr, beep-beep,* while pointing to my ear. Evan's mom points to her ear and says, "I hear a car." I hold the box near my mouth and say the sound again. Using the box as a

Hand Cue, I hold it near Mom's mouth and she says the car sound. When I hold the box near Evan's mouth he blows raspberries but does not say "beep-beep."

I repeat the sound correctly and tell Evan, "I hear the car."

He opens the box to discover a car with a dent in one door.

"Uh-oh, the car is broken! It was in an accident," I say.

I bring out more cars and continue to say the car sound.

Analysis

Speech skills are made meaningful through their use in spoken language. Evan imitated the "raspberries" while playing with the cars. In the next few sessions I anticipate that he will imitate the *beep-beep* sound following the raspberries. I document his imitations and spontaneous utterances and note his voice quality and vowel and syllable production. He imitated one syllable, produced the vowels /a/ and /i/, and blew raspberries.

Parent Guidance

- Evan loves vehicles, so spend a lot of time on the vehicle sounds and present these in various ways. A feely box, a shoe box, and egg containers can provide interesting motivators.
- *Blowing raspberries* will stimulate Evan's strength and coordination for talking.
- Every time you get into a car you have a wonderful opportunity to say the car sound. So, go for car rides often, especially to a farm, where many sounds "live."
- Create cars at home out of a laundry basket or a box.
- Make a book of sounds using stickers and pictures of the car and other Learning to Listen Sounds.

Blowing Bubbles

Goals

- To develop blowing, a prerequisite for speech production.
- To develop vocalizing, vocal pitch, and duration.
- To promote language development by listening to meaningful phrases containing functional words.
- To develop self-esteem through positive reinforcement.

Activity

This activity requires a plastic bottle containing commercial bubble solution or home-made soap solution, plus a wand for stirring.

I talk about the bubbles before I present them. I say, "I have something to blow."

We practice blowing. I pretend the bubbles are floating in the air, and I start to pop them.

I say, "There is a bubble. Pop, pop, pop! Whee, the bubbles are coming down."

Then I present the bottle of bubbles to Evan. I show him the picture of the bubbles on the bottle. I hand the bottle to his mom and ask her to open it. I take the wand and stir the bubbles. Then, I take the wand out. His mom tells me to "blow the bubbles." We all take turns blowing and popping the bubbles.

Before I put the bottle away I talk about how wet the table is: "Uh-oh, the table is all wet. We need to wipe it up. Here is a towel, wipe, wipe, wipe."

I give the towel to Evan's mom, and she wipes the table in front of her. Then she shows Evan how his section of the table is wet, and gives him the towel to wipe it up. As Evan is wiping the table, his mom tells him what he is doing.

Analysis

Evan was not able to blow the bubbles through the wand, which is not unusual for a child his age. Blowing is a prerequisite for developing speech. Evan needs a variety of things to blow, including ping-pong balls, feathers, cotton balls, and windmills. We will also blow on hot food and tea.

Parent Guidance

- Bubbles are fun! Have a good time and enjoy the experience together.
- Play with the suprasegmental aspects of speech through vocalizing *Whee* and changing the pitch as the bubbles float down.
- When the bubbles spill, which is highly likely with a 2-year-old, remember to make it a language experience!
- Listen for vowel production in the words *blow, down, pop, wipe.*
- Watch how Evan visually tracks the bubbles. Does he follow them with his eyes?
- Pay attention to how Evan is communicating, both nonverbally and verbally. How does he communicate that he wants another turn to blow?
- Encourage Evan to blow a variety of things, such as ping-pong balls, feathers, cotton balls, windmills, paper, hot food, and water.
- Always finish your session at home with a smiling child. Playing with bubbles or playdough, doing a Freeze Dance, or reading a story can usually accomplish this.

Session Summary

At the end of the first session, I review the goals and activities with Evan's mom. I stress the need to provide him with numerous opportunities to engage in listening activities throughout his waking hours. Evan's mom records the following suggestions in her notebook:

- Dance with Evan and point out the presence and absence of sound.
- Sing with Evan throughout the day.
- Play the Calling Game. Remember, when you call him there must be a good reason for doing so!
- Play with the Learning to Listen Sounds, especially the sounds of cats, airplanes, and cars.

- Put together a basket of Learning to Listen Sound toys.
- Call Evan's attention to sounds that are too loud, too soft, and just right.
- Point out environmental sounds.
- Encourage Evan to watch and listen as we demonstrate the sound conditioning task.
- Encourage Evan to blow bubbles, and to blow on cotton balls, hot food, and slips of paper.
- Use functional phrases, such as *all gone, open the door, sit down in your chair, it's hot, don't touch.*

Evan responded well in his first session. He vocalized spontaneously and upon request. He watched intently and made good eye contact. He played appropriately with the toys and appeared interested in all the activities.

My goals for Evan with his cochlear implant are not very different than if he were wearing hearing aids. I find that children with the implant move through the early Learning to Listen stages quickly.

Each therapy session incorporates listening targets that are important for the cochlear implant MAPping process. Evan's listening goals include sound conditioning, comprehending intensity, identifying spondee words (two-syllable words with equal accent on each syllable, such as *ice cream, airplane,* and *highchair*), and pattern perception.

Open communication with the implant team is critical, especially since Evan cannot tell the audiologist what he is hearing yet. This involves real teamwork. Evan's parents, the audiologists, and I work together to ensure that the cochlear implant is doing what it is supposed to do: helping Evan learn to listen!

Although he has a hearing loss, Evan has the same needs as any 2-year-old: he wants to play and have a good time. While we are reviewing the session, Evan starts to act mischievously. His mom gives him a loving hug and says, "You're so cool, I love you."

That's exactly what it's all about!

CONCLUSION

Sometimes, the best-laid auditory-verbal session plans take an entirely different direction than was intended by the therapist. Following the child's lead in a playful way, while incorporating the goals of the session, will result in the best outcomes. At other times, no matter what the therapist or the parent attempts through listening, the child may not wish to cooperate. At these times, there are at least 50 ways to save the session. (Appendix F).

REFERENCES

Eastman, P.D. (1960). *Are You My Mother?* New York: Random House.

Estabrooks, W. (2003). *The Six-Sound Song.* Washington, DC: Alexander Graham Bell Association for the Deaf and Hard of Hearing.

Estabrooks, W., & Birkenshaw-Fleming, L. (1994). *Hear & Listen! Talk & Sing!* Washington, DC: Alexander Graham Bell Association for the Deaf.

Estabrooks, W., & Birkenshaw-Fleming, L. (Eds.) (2003). *Songs for Listening! Songs for Life!* Washington, DC: Alexander Graham Bell Association for the Deaf and Hard of Hearing.
Kunhardt, D. (2001 [special edition]). *Pat the Bunny.* New York: Random House/Golden Books.
Ling, D., & Ling, A.D. (1978). *Aural Habilitation.* Washington, DC: Alexander Graham Bell Association for the Deaf.
Mayer, M. (1975). *One Frog Too Many.* New York: Dial Books.
Northcott, W.H. (1978). *I Heard That! A Developmental Sequence of Listening Activities.* Washington, DC: Alexander Graham Bell Association for the Deaf.
Pollack, D. (1985). *Educational Audiology for the Limited-Hearing Infant.* Springfield, IL: Charles C. Thomas.
Schwartz, S., & Heller Miller, J.E. (1996). *The New Language of Toys: Teaching Communication Skills to Children with Special Needs.* Bethesda, MD: Woodbine House.
Tannenbaum, S. (1998). "Lesson Plan for Evan." In W. Estabrooks (Ed.), *Cochlear Implants for Kids* (pp. 113–127). Washington, DC: Alexander Graham Bell Association for the Deaf.
Walker, B. (1998). "Lesson Plan for Jordon." In W. Estabrooks (Ed.), *Cochlear Implants for Kids* (pp. 128–143). Washington, DC: Alexander Graham Bell Association for the Deaf.

CHAPTER 6

Auditory-Verbal Therapy in Action: Ages 4 Through 6

Warren Estabrooks, M.Ed., Dip. Ed. Deaf, Cert. AVT®
Teresa Caruso-Peters, M.Sc. (A), Aud. (C), Cert. AVT®
K. Todd Houston, Ph.D., CCC-SLP, Cert. AVT®
Lisa Katz, M.H.Sc., S-LP (C), Reg. CASPLO, Cert. AVT®
Karen MacIver-Lux, M.A., Aud. (C), Reg. CASPLO, Cert. AVT®
Judith I. Simser, O.Ont., B.Ed., Dip. Ed. Deaf, Cert. AVT®
Pamela Steacie, M.Sc., Cert. AVT®

After a few years of auditory-verbal experience, the professional and the parent will know that the child is going to learn spoken language very effectively through listening. This is not an assumption; it is known through the ongoing diagnostic nature of Auditory-Verbal therapy. By the time a child reaches age 4 or 5, especially if diagnosed early, he or she may have reached age-appropriate development in the acquisition of spoken language.

Sometimes Auditory-Verbal therapy is initiated much later than in early infancy. The earlier therapy begins, the better the outcomes will be. From time to time, however, therapy has been started much later and has still provided some exceptional outcomes.

Following are six session plans showing Auditory-Verbal therapy in action for the 4 to 6 age group. Even though five of these children have cochlear implants, the same hierarchies are followed with children who wear hearing aids.

SESSION PLAN #1: CHASE (AGE 4)*

At the time of this session plan, Chase was 4 years, 6 months old and approaching his second anniversary with a cochlear implant. He was taking two Auditory-Verbal therapy sessions per week and attending a self-contained auditory/oral preschool program 2 days per week plus a church-based preschool the remaining 3 days.

Chase's parents first suspected he was not hearing when he was 6 months old. After visits to his pediatrician and finally to an audiologist, Chase was diagnosed with a profound hearing loss in the right ear and a severe to profound

* By K. Todd Houston, MSP, CCC-SLP, Cert. AVT®. Adapted from W. Estabrooks (Ed.), *Cochlear Implants for Kids.* Washington, DC: Alexander Graham Bell Association for the Deaf and Hard of Hearing, 1998. Used with permission.

hearing loss in the left. The detailed case history revealed that Chase's hearing loss was attributed to cytomegalovirus (CMV).

He was immediately given bilateral behind-the-ear (BTE) hearing aids, but his aided responses were not within the speech range on the audiogram. At 11 months, after a second opinion from another audiologist, Chase was given more powerful aids. His aided responses were just within the speech range at 500, 1000, and 2000 Hz but outside the speech range above 2000 Hz.

After a year of therapy, formal evaluations revealed that Chase had made limited progress in communication development. The therapist discussed the limited amount of auditory information available through Chase's current amplification and suggested that cochlear implantation be considered.

Chase was evaluated by the implant team and, 2 months later, received his cochlear implant. His aided responses with the implant were between 30–35 dB HL across all frequencies of the audiogram.

Assessments revealed that Chase had auditory pattern perception and some word recognition. That is, he could discriminate between one-, two-, and three-syllable words containing a variety of stress patterns and recognize familiar words in a known context through audition alone. Spontaneous speech was limited to a few early developing consonants (/b/, /m/) and vowels such as "ah" (/a/) and "oo" (/u/). He repeated and alternated syllables to approximate one- and two-word utterances, and occasionally, he approximated some three-word combinations.

After nearly 2 years with the implant, Chase had made remarkable progress in communication, at least partly due to excellent family support and consistent intervention. In fact, 9 months after receiving his implant, Chase was evaluated using a variety of assessments normed on children with typical hearing. Results indicated consistent word recognition, auditory processing of four critical elements (e.g., *Put the yellow car in the box*), ability to follow two-step directions, age-appropriate receptive language, and only a 6-month delay in expressive language. In conversational speech, however, Chase did exhibit numerous substitutions, omissions, and distortions.

In this session, I focus primarily on fine-tuning Chase's listening skills, expanding expressive language, and improving speech intelligibility.

Introduction to the Therapy Session

The auditory clinic consists of a main building and an annex, where my office and therapy rooms were located. Therapy sessions began in the parking lot, where I usually met the family getting out of their car.

Today, as Chase walks ahead, his mom and I discuss what has occurred since the last session. Interesting events such as a birthday party, trips to the zoo, or a football game can be used as topics of conversation.

The therapy room is small, containing a child-sized, rectangular table and toddler chairs. I was sharing the therapy rooms with six speech-language pathologists and, at this time, did not have one room designated just for Auditory-

Verbal therapy. I kept all therapy materials in my office and transported required items to the therapy room prior to each session.

After nearly 2 years in therapy, the interesting-toy-on-the-table strategy is no longer necessary with Chase, and he comfortably follows the *rules of therapy*:

- We listen to each other.
- When we talk, we use our *quiet* voice.
- We cooperate and help each other.
- We have fun!

Chase readily enters the therapy room and goes straight to his seat. I sit beside him on his right in order to speak close to the microphone of his cochlear implant. His mom sits across the table from Chase, ready to record the important points of the session, and a graduate clinician sits across the table from me.

The session begins with a conversation that engages everyone in the room, especially Chase. This seems very informal, but conversation is the most natural way to target developmentally appropriate vocabulary.

The Initial Conversation

Goals

Audition:

- To follow a conversation about a known context through listening only.

Speech:

- To generalize emerging speech sounds to connected speech.

Language:

- To increase utterance length using correct grammar and syntax.

Cognition:

- To learn developmentally appropriate vocabulary, concepts, and figurative language during natural discourse.

Communication:

- To develop the conversation skills of initiating, maintaining, topic transition, and closure.

Discussion

Chase's conversational language is above average compared to other children with similar case histories. He is able to initiate a discussion and respond to the comments of others, but he experiences difficulty maintaining a conversation. I ask his mother and the graduate student to help him: If I ask a question and pause expectantly for Chase to answer and he doesn't, one or the other will model the correct response. Chase will usually repeat it, and we continue the conversation. I introduce new vocabulary such as *grandparent, grandmother, grandfather, aunt, uncle,* and *cousin* throughout the conversation.

Activity

Todd: "So Chase, Mom said you are going on a trip this weekend."
Chase: "Yes! I'm going on a trip."
T: "Where are you going?"
C: "I'm going to see G-Pop in Georgia."
T: "Oh, yes, G-Pop. He's your *grandfather,* right?"
C: "What?"
T: "G-Pop is your *grandfather* and Grandy is your *grandmother.*"
C: "Yes, grandfather and grandmother."
T: "G-Pop and Grandy are your *grandparents.* You will visit your grandparents in Georgia."
C: "My grandparents wive in Georgia."
T: "That's right, Chase. They do *live* in Georgia. How *long* a drive is it?"
C: "We drive for a *wong, wong,* time. Two hours!"
T: "That is a *long, long* drive! What do you do while Mommy and Daddy drive?"
C: "I watch movies in the van."
T: "You watch movies in the van?"
C: "Yes! The Wion King. I watch the Wion King."
T: "Wion King… what's that? I've never heard of the Wion King."
C: "No, it's not WION King… it's Wion King."
T: "Oh, you mean the *Lion* King… Simba!
C: "Yes… Simba in the Wion King."
T: "Chase, *you're pulling my leg.* You can't watch *The Lion King* in the van."
C: "What?" (Chase looks under the table at my legs.)
T: "You're pulling my leg. I think you're *teasing* me."
C: "No, I'm not!"
T: "You really have TV and VCR in your van?"
C: "Yes!"

Analysis

In addition to conversational skills, I carefully monitor speech production. Chase substitutes /w/ for /l/ and /d/ for /g/, which are current targets. I model correct production of these phonemes and use acoustic highlighting when necessary. This conversation provided an opportunity to introduce a new idiom—*you're pulling my leg.*

Chase used individual nicknames to refer to his grandparents, so the terms *grandfather, grandmother,* and *grandparents* were new. This new vocabulary was introduced naturally in the conversation.

Although Chase has made tremendous progress in receptive and expressive language, more abstract language, such as idioms (*you're pulling my leg*), words with double meanings, and homonyms, are challenging. Even though he did not initially understand the idiom, I repeated it and provided a definition (*you're teasing me*), and Chase was able to grasp the idea. This is learning from the known to the unknown, the easy to the complex, and the concrete to the abstract.

I carefully monitor his speech production of /l/ and /g/. If Chase misarticulates or omits these phonemes, I provide the correct model using acoustically highlighted sounds. I also repeat exactly what he has said and ask him if the statement or word was correct (e.g., when he mentioned the "Wion" King). Through my puzzled expression, Chase was able to discriminate what was wrong, but when he corrected me, he still made the error. This diagnostic information tells me that he can discriminate between the /w/ and /l/ sounds when he hears them but cannot self-correct this speech error. The /l/ is emerging. He can discriminate the sound through listening and must now learn its production. If Chase is not able to acquire this sound through listening alone, I will provide more acoustic information, using a variety of techniques before presenting visual cues. If visual cues are required, the final therapeutic step is to *put the sound back into listening.* That is, once Chase correctly produces a target sound that requires a visual cue, he is encouraged to listen to it and imitate it through audition only. This helps develop his auditory-feedback loop.

New vocabulary was introduced, and pragmatic skills were reinforced. Chase was able to maintain the conversation by providing relevant information and introducing new topics.

Parent Guidance

When developing conversational competence:

- Capitalize on natural interactions, especially at the dinner table or when Chase wants to share something important, such as what he did at school that day.
- Use vocabulary and language introduced during this session, such as *grandfather, grandmother, grandparents,* and *you're pulling my leg,* in conversation at home.
- Find books and stories containing the same vocabulary and expressions in other contexts. In the library you might find interesting stories about relatives or books of idioms.
- Draw pictures of some simple idioms such as *you're pulling my leg, a green thumb,* and *it's raining cats and dogs.* You can talk about each picture and what the expression really means. You will extend Chase's comprehension from the literal meaning of the phrase to the abstract.

Speech Babble

Goals

Audition:

- To detect and identify misarticulated phonemes and to develop correct production through listening.
- To continue development of auditory self-monitoring of speech.

Speech:

- To improve speech intelligibility by repeating and alternating targeted phonemes at the syllable level.

Discussion

Even though Chase has intelligible speech, he still misarticulates a few current targets, such as /k/ and /l/. Chase enjoys reinforcement for correct productions by writing steeples (+'s) on the data sheet developed for tracking progress.

I usually start speech babble with the Ling Six-Sound Test (Ling, 2005), and I know immediately if his implant is functioning correctly by the quality of Chase's responses. I say each of the six sounds—/ʃ/, /m/, /i/, /u/, /s/, /a/—and vary my pitch with each one. Chase repeats all sounds correctly and quickly writes six steeples on the data sheet. This takes less than 2 minutes.

Activity

I begin speech babble by saying, "gagagaga." Chase responds "dadadada," and writes more steeples on the data sheet.

T: "Chase, I want you to try gagagaga once again."
C: "Dadadada."

(I try to use an anticipatory set of phonemes to elicit correct production of /g/.)

T: "Chase, let's try babababa."
C: "Babababa."
T: "Very good! Now try dadadada."
C: "Dadadada."
T: "Great Chase. Let's do gagagaga."
C: "Dadadada."

(I double-check to see if he can discriminate the sounds through listening.)

T: "Chase, are these sounds the same or different—*dada... gaga*?"
C: "Different!"
T: "Yes. Now, let's listen again—*gagaga.*" I lean over to within 6 inches of the microphone and repeat the stimulus.
C: "Dadada."

T: "Good try. Listen for this sound... *kakaka.* Can you say kakaka?"
C: "Kakaka. Like *cat*, right?"
T: "Yes, like the word *cat.* Can you feel where the *kakaka* sound is made—way back, right?"
C: "Kaka—yep."
T: "That's the same place for gagaga. Try it again, *gagaga.*"
C: "Dada... gagaga!"
T: "Excellent, Chase. Now, let's try *gugugu.*"
C: "Du... gugu... du... gugu."
T: "Good. You are doing fine. Let's try a different sound—*lalala.*"
C: "Wawawa."
T: "Try it again... lalala." (I again move to approximately 6 inches from the microphone.)
C: "Wawawa."
T: "Wawawa... is that the same as *lalala*?"
C: "No!"
T: "You're right. These are different, too. Let's try *a l-l-l.*" (I place the /l/ in the final position of the syllable and lengthen its duration.)
C: "Ah... all!"
T: "Great, Chase. That's right, *all.* Try it again, *a l-l-l.*"
C: "Ah... ah... all." (Chase noticeably pauses between productions before he correctly says *all.*)
T: "Here's a harder one. Try, *a l-l-l a.*" (I purposefully lengthen the /l/ again and release it into the same initial vowel, /a/.)
C: "All... ah."
T: "Good, Chase, but listen for my long sound and say /a/... *a l-l-l a.*"
C: "All-la."
T: "Right, Chase! Now, try *alalala.* Remember where we make that long sound." (When I say the word *long,* I use acoustic highlighting to emphasize the /l/.)
C: "Ahlalala!'
T: "Perfect, Chase. That's it! You got it!"

With the correct productions, speech babble ends as Chase records more steeples.

Analysis

Short sessions of speech babble give Chase specific cues about correct production of these phonemes at the syllabic level. He was able to produce each successfully after specific strategies were used. I began by using an anticipatory set to reinforce the correct manner and voicing of the phoneme /g/, but Chase was still unable to produce /gagaga/ accurately. I moved closer to the implant's microphone to provide a more audible speech signal. Unfortunately, this still did not work. Lastly, building on his responses and knowing that he knew the correct manner and voicing characteristics for the /g/, I gave him a place-of-production cue with the /k/. Since he has mastered the /k/, it was easier to remember the tongue placement and correctly produce the voiced correlate, /g/.

Chase substituted /w/ for /l/. He did not have the correct tongue placement. I moved closer to the microphone of the implant, but Chase still could not produce the /l/. I determined he could hear the difference between the /l/ and /w/, so I continued to target the /l/ by placing it in the final position of the syllable. Using the /a/, I modeled the production, releasing the /a/ into a sustained /l/ which can be an easier context in which to learn it. During his first successful production of the /l/, Chase noticeably paused to check his tongue placement before saying *all.* This indicated that he was self-monitoring his speech. I quickly tried to elicit /l/ in the medial position by saying *alla.* Essentially, /l/ is moved to the medial position, lengthened, and released into the /a/ and then moved to the initial position.

Parent Guidance

- Continue to work on these sounds by selecting books and other materials that contain them.
- Do not correct Chase's misarticulations or approximations of /g/ or /l/.
- Reinforce correct production of the sounds through modeling and acoustic highlighting.
- Reduce visual cues and encourage Chase to listen to the sounds.

Story Time

Goals

Audition:

- To increase auditory memory.
- To sequence events in a story with and without the use of pictures.
- To develop the ability to retell a story by including its critical elements.

Speech:

- To develop appropriate suprasegmental features (pitch, loudness, duration, and intonation).
- To emphasize target speech sounds such as /g/ and /l/ through acoustic highlighting.

Language:

- To increase length of utterance using correct grammar and syntax.
- To introduce new vocabulary, such as *huge* and *gigantic,* and idioms in story context.
- To reinforce the question form, *Which one?*

Cognition:

- To reinforce the concept that a story has a *beginning, middle,* and *end.*

- To reinforce the concepts of *first* through *fifth,* and *last.*
- To reinforce the concept of *left* and *right.*

Discussion

In each activity, I try to incorporate goals in listening, speech, language, and cognition as often as I can. The primary goal of Story Time is to develop Chase's auditory memory so that he can retell the story by correctly sequencing the events. I use a variety of clinician-made and commercial sequence cards that complete a story, instead of the somewhat limiting single-event cards. I can illustrate a complete story and embellish it as much as I wish. I often create silly character names that contain the targeted speech sounds. Chase loves to listen to these!

Activity

I hold the set of cards for a story titled "Gus Goes Fishing." I hold each card and tell the story, using targeted vocabulary, concepts, or both. Chase listens to the story through all five pictures. He listens as I begin:

"One day, Gus decided to go fishing. He went to the pond and fished off of the pier. Suddenly, his fishing pole starts to bend. Gus thinks he has finally caught a huge, gigantic fish. He lifts his pole out of the water and there is something on his fishing line. What do you think it is, Chase?"

C: "It's a huge fish!"
T: "A big, huge fish? Do you think it is a GIGANTIC fish?"
C: "Yeah!"
T: "Sorry, it's not a fish! It's an old, stinky, soggy boot! Let's find out what Gus does next. Maybe he'll catch a fish now."
C: "Yeah... a huge fish."

I present the fourth card.

"Gus's fishing pole was bent over again. He has something very, very heavy on his fishing pole. He pulls it out of the water and guess what?"

C: "What... what?"
T: "It's another boot. He caught another old..."
C: "He got another stinky, soggy boot!"
T: "That's right... another stinky, soggy boot. Now he has two boots to wear. This time a fish was in the boot, and it jumped back in the water."
C: "Why did the fish jump in the water?"
T: "Fish live in water. If he stayed out of the water, he'll die."

"After Gus pulled the second boot out of the water, he dried them both off. Gus decided that catching a pair of boots was better than nothing at all. He decided to keep his boots, and he wore them home to show his Mom."

After finishing the story, I turn the cards face down on the table and mix them up. I tell Chase to turn over one card at a time and tell me what is happening in the picture. He must also decide if the scene occurred at the beginning, middle, or end of the story. He turns over the first card.

T: "What's happening here, Chase?"
C: "He has a boot on the pole."
T: "Who has a boot? What's the boy's name?"
C: "His name is Dus."
T: "Dus or Gus?" (I again move to approximately 6 inches from the implant's microphone and acoustically highlight the /g/ in *Gus.*)
C: "Dus."

(I instruct Chase to remember the cat sound, *meow,* as a cue for correct tongue placement and ask him again, "Was it Dus or Gus?")

C: "Um... Du... Gus!"
T: "Right! So, Gus has one boot. Was that at the beginning, middle, or end of the story?"
C: "Uhhh... beginning."
T: "That's right, Chase. This happened at the beginning."

I place the card face up on the far left side of the table. As Chase turns over each card and describes the scene, he decides where each will go on the table (far left, in the middle of the table, or on the far right, depending on *where* the scene occurred). He carefully sequences the story cards.

T: "Chase, what happened *first?* Look at the cards on the *left.* They happened in the beginning of the story. Which one happened *first?*"
C: "Uhhh... This one. Du... Gus is fishing on the pier."
T: "That's right. Gus is fishing on the pier, and his pole is really bent over! What happened *next?* What was the second thing that Gus did?"

We continue until he has correctly sequenced all the cards. Chase pauses, looking at all the cards, and retells the story:

"This boy... his name is Dus. He does pishing and he caught a boot. Then, he catches another boot. He cweans the boots, because they stink and they are wet and soddy. He puts them on his feet and does home to show his mommy."

I compliment Chase on his story and then ask his mom and the graduate student to take turns randomly describing one card, while expanding the story. Chase listens in order to select the scene that is being described. I encourage at least two or three sentences in each description. Chase pauses, thinks, and selects the appropriate card. We continue until all the cards are put away. Then, without looking at the pictures, I tell Chase another story called "Leo the Pig":

"One day Leo decided to go for a walk in the forest. It was a beautiful spring day. It was warm, the flowers were blooming, and the birds were singing. Leo was very happy. As he walked, he met his friend, Mr. Duck. Mr. Duck told Leo that his foot was hurting and asked if he could ride on Leo's back. Because Leo was such a good friend and was in a very cheerful mood, he allowed Mr. Duck to ride on his back. Leo and Mr. Duck contin-

ued walking through the forest. Then, suddenly, they met another friend, Mr. Kackle, a chicken. Mr. Kackle saw Mr. Duck sitting on Leo's back. Because he, too, had recently injured his foot, he asked if could join Mr. Duck. Leo, a true friend, said 'Sure, the more, the merrier,' and the three friends continued walking through the forest, enjoying the beautiful spring day."

Chase retells the story:

"Weo was this pig and he was walking in the forest and saw a duck. The duck hurt his foot and climbed on Weo's back. Then, Weo saw a chicken. He hurt his foot, too. He wanted to sit on Weo's back... like the duck. The chicken and the duck sat on Weo's back and they walked in the forest."

His mom asks, "Chase, how was the weather when Leo went on his walk?"

C: "It was warm outside."
M: "Which season of the year was it... spring or summer?"
C: "Uhhh... summer."

Mom replies, "No, think again. Remember, the birds were singing and the flowers were blooming. When does that happen?"

C: "Spring!!"

Mom replies, "That's right!" Then, the graduate student asks, "Chase, who did Leo meet *first*?"

C: "He met the duck, then the chicken."
GS: "Good, Chase!"

Analysis

Chase had the benefit of the pictures for the first story, which made it easier to retell. He was successful retelling the story without the pictures. The ultimate goal is to listen to a long, detailed story and to retell it from memory.

Sequencing a story is an important task because it reinforces that stories have a beginning, middle, and end. As Chase develops conversational competence, he will learn that his own stories must have the same components. Within these components, there are critical details that he should remember and retell. This is important diagnostic information about his auditory memory.

Throughout both stories, I expanded vocabulary and concepts such as *huge, gigantic, beginning, middle, end, left, right,* and *first* through *last.*

I often stopped to evaluate his comprehension and used auditory closure to help him ("He caught another old..."). I paused to check his understanding of specific vocabulary (in this sentence, *stinky* and *soggy*). Chase was primed for this vocabulary, and he answered correctly.

Chase substituted /d/ for /g/, especially in the word *Gus.* I moved closer to his microphone and asked him to discriminate between these two sounds. This was ineffective, so I reminded him of the placement cue (the "cat" sound). He remembered the correct tongue position and accurately repeated *Gus.* When he retold the story, however, he was unable to produce the /g/ correctly in *Gus, goes,* or *soggy.* Chase also continued to substitute /w/ for /l/ in the second story. Both phonemes are emerging. He is stimulable for each at the word level, but needs more practice at the phrase, sentence, and conversation levels. Because he has acquired these sounds through listening and verbal cues (the "cat" sound), I will speak closer to the microphone and use acoustic highlighting to encourage correct production. He demonstrated some ability to self-correct both sounds, a vital step in building his auditory-feedback loop.

When Chase's mom asked him about the season of the year, he answered incorrectly. She immediately offered a closed set of two choices, *spring* or *summer.* Chase, who was probably not really listening, answered with the last word he heard, *summer.* She then described exactly what happens in the spring, using another *closed set* of choices. Chase easily responded correctly. Although reducing choices to a closed set is a good strategy to use in some situations, it was not the best here. Instead, when Chase could not remember the season, she could have asked him an *open-set* question such as, "What do you remember about the story?" Or, "What did Leo see on his walk?" As he remembered the things Leo heard and saw on his walk (birds singing and flowers blooming), Chase might have reasoned that the season was spring.

Parent Guidance

- Read and tell stories to Chase that have a clear *beginning, middle,* and *end.*
- Use the vocabulary *first, second, third, fourth, last,* and *next.*
- Encourage Chase to make choices by using the question, *Which one?*
- Use puppets or other props to practice retelling stories.
- Common children's stories such as "The Three Little Pigs" or "Jack and the Beanstalk" are excellent to use because they contain repetitive vocabulary and build shared knowledge with Chase's peers. These are important readiness skills for inclusion in a mainstream school.
- Develop conversations by sharing what you did that day while Chase was at school.
- Encourage him to tell the events of his day in sequence.
- Use *open-set* questions to challenge Chase's auditory memory.

What's Wrong?

Goals

Audition:

- To process various question forms.

Speech:

- To reinforce speech intelligibility by developing emerging phonemes, especially /g/ and /l/ at the word and phrase levels.

Language:
- To appropriately respond to *What's wrong?*, *How?*, and *Why?* questions.
- To increase expressive language using appropriate grammar and syntax.

Cognition:
- To reinforce reasoning, abstract thinking, and problem-solving skills.

Discussion

One of Chase's favorite activities is talking about *What's wrong?* picture cards. This set of cartoon-like cards consists of scenes portraying events that are obviously wrong or illogical (such as a person driving a car on water). Chase refers to them as the *sil-we* (silly) pictures. He looks at one card at a time and must describe what's happening to his mother and the graduate student without letting them see it. They must try to figure out what's happening and then ask Chase questions about it. If there are obvious errors in his speech production, grammar, or syntax, Chase's mom, the graduate student, or I will provide correct models.

Activity

Chase starts with a card involving a woman driving a car on water.

C: "There's this woman. She is driving a car. It's on a wake (lake)."

Chase's mom says, "Oh, that's silly. What's wrong with that? Why can't she drive on a lake?"

C: "She can't drive on water. The car will sink."

His mom continues, "You're right, Chase. The car will sink. It can't..."

C: "Fwoat (float)!"
M: "Right, the car can't float. It will sink and go to the bottom of the lake." (Mom replies as she acoustically highlights the fl-blend in the word *float.*)
C: "She can drive on the road, not on the water. That's a silwy picture." Chase hands me the first card and quickly asks for another.
C: "There's this chair and a girl is sitting on it... but it doesn't have any wegs (legs)."

The graduate student replies, "*Legs,*" as she moves closer to him and slightly emphasizes the /l/.

C: "Yes... la... legs."
GS: "No legs? What do you mean... the girl had no legs?"
C: "No, silwy... the chair. The chair doesn't have wegs."
GS: "Oh, the chair doesn't have legs. Then, how does the girl sit in the chair without falling down?"

C: "I don't know. That's very silwy. She might fall down!"
GS: "It is silly. If the chair doesn't have legs, she should fall down. It can't hold her up."
C: "Yes, very silwy picture.

We continue until we have worked through approximately 10 cards. This game is highly motivating for Chase.

Analysis

The silly pictures are useful in developing a variety of skills. Abstract thinking, reasoning, problem-solving, vocabulary building, expansion of expressive language, speech production, and conversational competence were all targeted and/or reinforced.

Chase is stimulable for the /l/ at the word level, so the graduate student simply repeated the word *legs* with a slightly highlighted /l/, moving the sound from a known context (single word) to an unknown context (connected speech).

The graduate student asked Chase if the girl was missing legs, but Chase had already used the pronoun *it* to refer to the legless chair. It was not the best question and interrupted the natural flow of the conversation.

The silliness, comedy, and light-heartedness of each situation portrayed by these cards is very motivating. Chase loves the idea that only he and I see the cards at first and feels that he is the authority and can share information that the others do not know.

Parent Guidance

- Use home situations to develop abstract thinking, reasoning, and problem solving, such as telling Chase to cut his sandwich with a spoon, cut paper with a ruler, or paint a picture with a hairbrush.
- *Sabotage* of a situation can also be effective for reinforcing problem-solving skills, such as coloring a picture with an empty box of crayons or cutting paper without scissors.
- Predictable books and stories also reinforce abstract thinking. Books such as *Brown Bear, Brown Bear* (Martin, 1992) and *Hattie and the Fox* (Fox, 1992) will encourage Chase to predict what might happen next.

Rhyming Bingo

Goals

Audition:

- To discriminate between rhyming words having sounds that differ in manner, place, and voicing.

Speech:

- To use targeted speech sounds correctly at the word level and in conversation during a game activity.

Language:
- To increase understanding and use of synonyms and homonyms.
- To develop rhyming words.

Cognition:
- To begin to develop sound–letter associations.

Discussion

Discrimination skills at the word level help with understanding and perceiving rhyme. The ability to understand rhyming words demonstrates that Chase can recognize both similarities and differences in speech sounds. He needs to develop this reading readiness skill as he prepares to enter kindergarten.

To play this clinician-made game, each player chooses a game card that has eight monosyllabic (one-syllable) words illustrated on it. The game also contains single-picture cards, which players select and label. The object is to listen to a player name a card and then try to find an object that rhymes with it among the eight pictures on one's game card. For example, a player may select a card that is a picture of a cat. The player says, "Cat." The remaining players look at their cards and try to find something that rhymes with *cat.*

Activity

The activity begins by passing out a game card to each player, and the single cards are stacked in the middle of the table. I turn over the first card and begin by calling out the word *coat.*

T: "Coat. Who has something that rhymes with *coat*?"

M: "I do… I do," Mom replies as she quickly covers a picture on her card with a chip.

T: "Chase, what do you think Mom has on her card?"

C: "I don't know."

T: "What's something that sounds like *coat*?"

C: "I forgot!"

T: "Well, I can think of an animal… the word sounds like *coat…*"

C: "Oh, a doat (goat)!"

T: "Yes, a *goat.* Goat and coat rhyme, don't they? (I acoustically highlight the /g/ in *goat.*) OK, Mom. Let's see what's on your card." (Mom moves the chip to reveal a picture of a goat.)

T: "Chase, our first word was *coat.* What's another word for *coat*?" I pause to wait for Chase to answer.

C: "Uhhh… I don't know.'

T: "If it is cold outside, you could wear your coat or you might wear your…"

C: "Jacket!"

T: "Right, your jacket or parka. Those words *basically* mean the same thing as coat. Let's see… who's next?"

The graduate student says, "OK, the next card is a *shell.* Who has something that rhymes with *shell?*"

"I do," Chase replies, as he quickly covers the item on the game card.

GS: "Well, Chase, what could it be? I guess we'll need to guess."
We each take turns asking Chase what the item is.

T: "Is it a *pail?*"

C: "No."
His mom says, "It must be *mail,* like a letter or envelope."

C: "Nope."

"I know. I think you have a *bell* on your card, " the graduate student says.

"Yeah... I have a *bell,*" Chase replies.

We continue the game in this manner until someone has acquired at least four covered pictures in a row and yells "Bingo."

Analysis

At first, Chase had real difficulty discriminating between these words. Often, as illustrated with the word *coat,* I extend the game by asking if he knows another word that also rhymes. This reinforces the concept of rhyme and encourages him to think. This is an open-set task that fine-tunes his listening skills at the word level.

I extended the activity by asking for a homophone of *coat* to expand vocabulary. Being from the warm South, I doubt if Chase is familiar with term *parka.*

I reinforced correct production of /g/ by moving closer to Chase and emphasizing the target sound while repeating the word. He subsequently misarticulated the sound again during connected speech, illustrating the need for continued work at the word level.

Rhyming Bingo is a *word discrimination through listening* task, but many other speech, language, and cognitive goals can easily be incorporated. Generalizing Chase's discrimination skills to as many contexts as possible helps expand his receptive and expressive language and encourages auditory self-monitoring of speech.

I may use auditory closure activities to help Chase understand rhyme. For example, I could give him an open-ended statement such as, "Jack and Jill went up the..." He will *close* the sentence with the correct rhyming word. Card games such as "Go Fish" with rhyming words are also motivating.

Parent Guidance

- Highlight rhyming words found in children's poems and songs. Dr. Seuss books such as *The Cat in the Hat, Hop on Pop,* and *There's a Wocket in My Pocket* are ideal.
- Make up games to target auditory closure.
- Practice a poem or nursery rhyme; take turns saying each line.
- Cut homonym and synonym picture cards from magazines, catalogs, or sale flyers.

Listening in Noise

Goals

Audition:

- To comprehend sentence-length information and instructions in the presence of noise.

Discussion

Recently, Chase's mom has noticed that he has difficulty playing a board game while the radio is on. He also has difficulty responding to her when his grandparents are engaged in a conversation only a few feet away. It is time to introduce noise into the therapy sessions.

I introduce a portable radio placed slightly behind Chase approximately 3 feet from his chair. It is tuned between two radio stations, which produces *white noise* or static. I begin with white noise, because it is easier to understand spoken information in white noise than in speech. Chase is required to follow relatively simple directions that will become progressively more complex. I use drawing as the reinforcement for this activity.

Activity

T: "Chase, draw a picture of a boy with a red hat."

As the noise plays, Chase listens and successfully completes the picture. I am careful not to increase the volume of my voice and try to maintain a normal, conversational level. After each successful drawing, I add a little more information, using the carrier phrase, *Draw a picture of...*

A boy with a red hat.

A big flower next to the boy.

A girl with long, blond hair next to the flower.

The instructions become more difficult and more complex. Chase begins to have some difficulty.

T: "Draw a picture of a red ball next to the tree."
(Chase pauses and does not start to draw.)

C: "What ya say?"

T: "What did you *hear*?"

C: "Draw a picture of a ball..."

T: "Right. Draw the ball *where*... (pausing)... next to the..." (I pause again.)

C: "Draw the ball next to the tree!"

T: "Very good, Chase. What color is the ball?"

C: "Uhh... blue!"

T: "No. Listen as I repeat the entire sentence again. Draw a picture of a red ball next to the tree."

C: "Oh... red!"

Analysis

Chase demonstrated improved listening skills in white noise. In this session, he had difficulty hearing all the words in the sentence, "Draw a picture of a red ball next to the tree." I used the carrier phrase *Draw a picture of...* for each presentation to reduce the level of difficulty. When he had difficulty, I did not repeat the entire sentence. I encouraged him to recall as much information as he could. He was able to recall only a little, so several adaptive strategies for listening were required.

The ultimate goal is that Chase will understand spoken language when competing conversations are occurring around him (listening to the teacher's voice while classmates are chatting or to conversations while the radio and television are playing). I will eventually move from white noise to single-talker to multi-talker taped stimuli.

Parent Guidance

- Situations such as listening with the radio or television on or with a competing conversation are challenging! We want Chase to be able to communicate effectively in these situations.
- Think about how situations can be altered to help him hear optimally.
- Listening in noise develops in a hierarchy (see Chapter 4). Chase needs experiences listening in white noise as the information increases with complexity. After he refines his listening in white noise, we will introduce cafeteria-type noise that contains a mixture of environmental sounds and speech. Tuning out competing linguistic information is a much more difficult task than simply listening in white noise.
- As his listening skills develop in the presence of various kinds of noise in the sessions, Chase will have more successful listening experiences with competing stimuli in various settings.
- In school, make sure Chase has an appropriate FM system.

Session Summary

This therapy session targeted three major areas: listening, expressive language, and speech intelligibility. Listening skills were addressed in three different ways: by encouraging development of auditory memory and sequencing with story retelling, enhancing discrimination skills through rhyming words, and challenging Chase's listening skills in the presence of noise. Expressive language and speech production were targeted throughout the session.

Chase is making good progress in receptive and expressive language. He demonstrates the ability to discriminate between rhyming words that differ in manner, place, and voicing of the initial consonant, which is an important readiness skill for reading. He comprehends increasingly longer and more difficult *strings of information* in the presence of noise. His speech intelligibility is improving, and I expect him to master /g/ and /l/ soon.

Exactly 2 years and 1 month after receiving his cochlear implant, Chase entered a mainstream kindergarten for 5-year-olds at his local public school. He is a highly motivated child and, with the support of his family, friends, and the professionals on "Chase's team," this kid is on a roll!

SESSION #2: LAUREN (AGE 4)*

Lauren was diagnosed at 18 months of age with a profound bilateral sensorineural hearing loss of unknown etiology. She was immediately fitted with bilateral behind-the-ear hearing aids and began Auditory-Verbal therapy.

During her first 6 months of therapy, Lauren made maximum use of her aided residual hearing. She heard differences in auditory patterns and was able to detect low- and mid-frequency speech sounds. Lauren learned many of the Learning to Listen Sounds as well as some stereotypical phrases, such as "Uh-oh!" and "It's all gone." She was able to perform closed-set selection tasks and was highly motivated to communicate by using words, phrases, and gestures. As her profound hearing loss prevented her from monitoring her speech, her vocalizations were neutralized, pharyngeal, and high-pitched.

Lauren received a cochlear implant at the age of 2 years, 10 months, after which her listening and communication skills developed very well. At the time of the following session, she was aged 4 years, 10 months (2 years postactivation) and was receiving Auditory-Verbal therapy once a week. Lauren attended kindergarten at her local school, where despite some initial shyness she adjusted socially. According to her itinerant teacher, she was coping well.

Introduction to the Therapy Session

This session begins as I greet Lauren and her mother in the waiting room. I inquire if Lauren has recently had her hair cut and comment on the toy barn with which she is playing. On the way to the therapy room, I talk to her mother about events of the past week.

At the table, I initiate a conversation about the weekend. At first, Lauren is not forthcoming, but she eventually becomes chatty. This session helps evaluate development towards the goal of conversational competence.

Goals

Audition:

- Follow directions.
- Identify objects based on a related description.
- Extend auditory memory and sequencing to five items.
- Expose Lauren to rhyming words.

---

* By Lisa Katz, M.H.Sc., S-LP(C), Reg. ACSLPO, Cert. AVT®. Adapted from W. Estabrooks & L. Birkenshaw-Fleming (Eds.), *Songs for Listening! Songs for Life!* Washington, DC: Alexander Graham Bell Association for the Deaf and Hard of Hearing, 2003. Used with permission.

Speech:
- Develop production of /l/ at the word level.
- Elicit production of /s/ in the final position in words.
- Sing songs with appropriate imitation of the suprasegmental features.
- Enhance voice melody.

Language:
- Develop use of regular past-tense forms of verbs.
- Develop use of plurals.
- Develop clarification strategies.
- Enhance the use of articles and conjunctions.

Cognition:
- Reinforce and expand counting.
- Learn letters of the alphabet.
- Continue the development of age-appropriate concepts.

Ling Six-Sound Test

I place 10 small plastic cups on the table. Lauren's mom or I make one of the sounds; upon hearing it, Lauren puts a scoop of ice cream (made of colored balls of playdough) into a cup. Prior to giving her each scoop, I ask Lauren to guess its color by providing her with an association (e.g., "This scoop is the same color as the snow").

Parent Guidance

- Visit an ice cream store. Talk about all the flavors.
- Use the word *favorite.* Lauren can survey friends and family members about their favorite flavors.

Sensational Sundaes

I tell Lauren that we are going to make ice cream *sundaes* (a new word) and show her a finished product. I introduce the materials needed (colored pompoms for the various flavors of ice cream, small brown beads for chocolate sprinkles, brown confetti for nuts, red beads for cherries, and colored bowls). I begin by asking Lauren to prepare a sundae with *three* scoops of *strawberry* ice cream, chocolate *sprinkles,* and *two cherries.* I add that I would like my sundae served in the *blue* bowl. We then switch roles for Lauren to place her order. When specifying her desired toppings, Lauren omits /s/. We acoustically highlight /s/ or /z/, and she produces the words correctly. Her mom and I incorporate such concepts as *some, or, a few,* and *except.*

Parent Guidance

- Make real ice cream sundaes and talk about toppings. Have Lauren take orders from other family members and help prepare the treats.
- Help Lauren develop her auditory memory skills in daily routines (e.g., setting the table and cleaning up after dinner).
- Reinforce the concepts *some, a few,* and *except.*
- Use *or* by providing choices.
- Highlight /s/ or /z/ in the final position of words in games and books.

I Like Ice Cream

I sing the song "I Like Ice Cream" (Estabrooks and Birkenshaw-Fleming, 2003) while snapping my fingers and clapping my hands alternately, and Lauren and her mother join in. Next, we listen to the song on CD. I then take out a set of cards depicting a variety of food items and select a card. I sing the song again, substituting the item depicted on the card for the word *ice cream,* and then place it face down on the table. Lauren and her mother follow suit. We continue singing until five items have been presented. I then ask for Lauren to recall the items, verifying the responses by revealing the corresponding picture. If Lauren has difficulty remembering an item, I provide a brief description (e.g., "It's a fruit that a monkey likes to eat"). Mom encourages her to remember the items in the correct order and to sing the song. We sing the song several times, and Lauren enjoys it.

Musical Suggestions

- In addition to clapping and snapping fingers to the beat, you can clap or play the rhythm pattern of the words on the drum, tambourine, wood block, or an upended plastic ice cream tub.
- Each person in the session can have a different percussion instrument. One plays the rhythm of measure one, another plays the rhythm of the second measure, the third person plays the rhythm of the third measure, and then all play for the "all day long" measure.
- The song can be changed to discuss things that children *don't* like: *thunder, hail, bullies, liars, turnips...*

Parent Guidance

- Singing songs is an excellent way to improve voice quality and refine the suprasegmentals of speech. The song is also useful for the expansion of auditory memory and the development of auditory sequencing. We rely on memory throughout the day, from remembering telephone numbers to recalling directions.
- Memory skills are important for success at school, as children are typically required to store a substantial amount of auditory information prior to

performing a task (e.g., "Before you turn to page five in your books, make sure that you have handed in your field trip money and you have thrown away all the scraps of paper from the art activity").

- Singing this song helps Lauren arrange items into categories. The category *food* can be subdivided into fruits and vegetables, snack foods, breakfast foods, and so forth.
- The song can also be sung alphabetically or by phoneme. This is great way to incorporate speech targets.
- Avoid modeling the correct production while Lauren is singing. This interrupts the song. A better time to model and acoustically highlight the final /s/ or /z/ is when Lauren is recalling the items.
- Clapping and/or snapping fingers reinforces the beat and rhythm of the song.
- Although this song can be used to introduce new vocabulary, Lauren's inability to recall new words may be due to a lack of familiarity with the vocabulary as opposed to a problem remembering the items.

A Decadent Delight

I conclude the session by reading the poem "Eighteen Flavors" (Silverstein, 1974, p. 116). I pause after each line and prompt either Lauren or her mother to repeat. We talk about the meaning of new vocabulary words (*luscious, scrumptious*). We also discuss the colors and ingredients of each flavor (*mocha contains chocolate, rocky road has marshmallows*).

Parent Guidance

- Read this poem and reinforce the new vocabulary.
- Discuss flavors and help Lauren recall the ones mentioned in the poem.
- Learn the ice cream rhyme: "I scream, you scream, we all scream for ice cream."

Session Summary

Lauren's session consisted of targets from which diagnostic predictions can be made for the development of long-term goals. The song activity in the lesson is used to extend auditory memory, evaluate Lauren's ability to arrange objects into categories, and further develop the suprasegmental and prosodic features of speech inherent in song.

SESSION PLAN #3: HEATHER (AGE 5)*

Heather was diagnosed with a significant hearing loss at 4 months of age because of parental concern and a family history of deafness. Heather's 11-year-old brother has a severe to profound hearing loss.

---

* By Teresa Caruso-Peters, M.Sc.(A)., Aud.(C)., Cert. AVT®. Adapted from W. Estabrooks (Ed.), *Cochlear Implants for Kids.* Washington, DC: Alexander Graham Bell Association for the Deaf and Hard of Hearing, 1998. Used with permission.

Initial auditory brainstem response (ABR) testing suggested a moderately severe to severe hearing loss in the left ear and a severe to profound hearing loss in the right ear. Based on this information, binaural Widex ES2HA hearing aids were prescribed, and Heather was enrolled in an auditory-verbal program.

A follow-up aided audiological assessment was carried out, at which time no definite responses could be measured. Impedance audiometry suggested abnormal middle ear function, and a consultation with the ENT doctor was recommended. The physician recommended a myringotomy and the insertion of PE tubes. An ABR was carried out following the myringotomy, which revealed no response at the limits of the equipment.

At further follow-up aided audiological assessments, there were no observable responses to auditory stimuli. More powerful hearing aids were prescribed, and Heather experienced difficulty with feedback. She then received temporary binaural body aids and, later, powerful behind-the-ear hearing aids. Repeated audiological assessments revealed aided responses in the 80–90 dB HL range in the low-frequency spectrum, and her responses in therapy supported these audiological results. Although quite a vocal child, Heather was using primarily a neutral vowel sound such as "uh" (/ʌ/) for "up." Her parents reported that she sometimes appeared to respond to her name at home when called loudly and at close range.

Evaluation for cochlear implantation ensued, and preimplant assessments indicated that Heather was a candidate.

Heather's middle ear status continued to be abnormal, a concern regarding the surgery. Repeated myringotomies and placement of PE tubes did not clear the middle ear disease. The implant surgeon required Heather to be free of middle ear problems after removal of the tubes for 6 months prior to surgery. Once the tubes were removed, Heather suffered another bout of otitis. It was suggested that her parents look into the possibility of allergies and discuss the potential benefit of a tonsillectomy and adenoidectomy (T&A) with their physician. Heather was already a snorer and a mouth breather. The parents discovered that in some cases, children were relieved of middle ear problems after the T&A surgery. As the ENT doctor did not agree with the procedure, the parents sought a physician who would conduct the surgery. After the T&A, Heather's left ear became disease-free for 6 months without PE tubes. A year and a half after initial discussions, Heather underwent cochlear implant surgery. She has since had normal middle ear function in the implanted left ear; her right ear has continued to have abnormal type B tympanograms (stiff eardrum mobility).

At the time of the following session, Heather had been successfully using her Nucleus® 22 Channel Cochlear Implant on the side of her left ear for 2 years. Her aided responses with the implant were in the 25–35 dB HL range. She does not use a hearing aid on the right ear, as her residual hearing is such that she does not benefit from even a powerful hearing aid coupled to that ear.

Introduction to the Therapy Session

As is customary in auditory-verbal sessions, the goals for audition, speech, language, and cognition are interrelated in natural language contexts for overall development of spoken communication.

Toy Story

This activity involves acting out a story using toys. Various toys, including people, vehicles, playground toys (such as a slide and merry-go-round), and food, are placed on the table. Heather, her mother, and I each have a turn playing teacher and student. The teacher will tell Heather a story about what the characters will do; Heather then selects the right people and enacts the story.

Goal

Audition/Cognition:

- To follow a direction recalling five items, including the pronouns *she* versus *they*.

Activity

Heather's mom plays teacher first. She acoustically highlights (stresses) the words italicized below to help Heather focus on salient items, in this case the five items that Heather is encouraged to store in auditory memory.

"OK, Heather, are you ready?" her mom asks. Heather nods. "*She* is going to go for a ride in the *wagon* and *they* are going to go *swimming* in the turtle pool and then have *ice cream.*"

Heather takes the girl to the wagon and the children to the swimming pool and then to the freezer for the ice cream. She hesitates, repeating the stimulus silently, then follows through. To her delight, she carries out the direction and, with a grin, says, "There!"

"It my turn," Heather says. "Mommy, listen. The girl wanted to go on merry-go-round and slide and daddy and the boy have to go on swing."

Heather's mom reinforces the pronouns *she* and *they* and models the phrase: "Oh, *she* wanted to go on the merry-go-round and the slide and *they* are going on the swing*s*." She highlights the pronouns and the plural, which Heather omitted, by acoustically stressing them; then she carries out the direction.

"Good job, Mom," Heather says.

Analysis

She versus *they* were contrasted in teaching pronouns rather than *he* versus *she* because *she* and *they* are more acoustically different. As Heather develops her listening, it is important to follow the hierarchy of listening skills (Chapter 4), from most audible spoken language to least audible.

Heather has good comprehension of the pronouns *she* and *they*, and these pronouns are being integrated into auditory memory tasks. We must ensure that Heather has the vocabulary necessary to do the task, otherwise it is not possible to determine whether the difficulty lies in recalling five items or in weak vocabulary. Heather does not use the pronoun *they* expressively and overgeneralizes the use of *she*. By encouraging her to play teacher, we can help her to integrate her language goals with an auditory activity. We are not simply asking Heather to recall five miscellaneous items; we are integrating her developing pronouns into what may appear to be a strictly listening-only activity. Her mom is counseled that no activity ever targets listening, speech, *or* language; all serve as a vehicle for one another and are interrelated.

Because we rely extensively on memory in everyday situations, it is important that Heather develop auditory memory skills. This is particularly important in the classroom, where teachers often unknowingly expect their students to follow a number of directions in sequence. For example, "Get your *red book* from your desk, turn to *page 18*, pick up your *pencil*, and *wait* for further instructions." Auditory memory is critical in order to recall telephone numbers, addresses, and road directions. Heather needs strategies to help her recall information.

Parent Guidance

- Try having Heather visually scan the objects on the table, associated with the direction, to help develop her visual memory. You might also have her rehearse the direction silently ("in her head"), as one might do with a new telephone number.
- Provide opportunities during daily routines for Heather to develop her auditory memory skills. When setting the table, Heather might be asked to get the *salt and pepper, napkins, forks,* and *juice*. In folding laundry, Heather might pick up the *white socks, girls' underwear,* and *T-shirts*. (A parent should remove the laundry from the dryer to avoid exposing Heather's cochlear implant to electrostatic electricity.) Heather can also help pack her own lunch and get the *bread, peanut butter, jam, juice box,* and *cookies*.
- Since Heather loves paper-and-pencil activities and crafts, have her trace the letters of her name on construction paper using liquid glue and glitter. To integrate thinking skills into this activity, ask her to create a pattern with five colors and recall the order of these colors: "We'll do *red, yellow, blue, green,* and then *orange*... The letter 'h' will be red, the letter 'e' will be yellow," and so on. Then she can do Mom's name and her brother's name. As all contain more than five letters, Heather will have to repeat the pattern and begin with the first color again.

Playdough Fun

This activity requires pictures or photographs that describe an event and a container of playdough. Heather demonstrates discrimination of particular sentences by placing a ball of playdough on the correct picture. Examples of some of these sentences are: "Oh, shoot, I missed the ball!," "May I have some paper?," "Let's unload the dishwasher!," and "Oh, it's pouring outside!"

Goal

Audition/Communication:

- To help Heather discriminate sentences of similar length and subsequently to encourage the development of expressive language.

Activity

Heather loves playdough. To expand her vocabulary of colors, we choose *lime green* and purple. This gives Heather two strategies from which to learn the new shade of green: coupling it with the known word *green*, and contrasting it with the color purple. In our lessons, we integrate one new color (word) with the colors Heather has acquired, to build vocabulary.

Her mom plays teacher first. She asks Heather to select the color of playdough and says, "May I have some paper?" Heather imitates the phrase and proceeds to place a ball of playdough on the correct picture. Heather is now the teacher.

"OK, you can have *line*... The lady going take dish out."

"Oh, I'll take the *lime* playdough and put it on the picture of the lady who is *unloading the dishwasher*." Mom has rephrased Heather's sentence using correct grammar. As Heather did not say *lime* correctly, her mom says, "But do you mean *lime*?"

"Yup," Heather says.

Her mom helps Heather imitate "amamam, imimim, *lime*" (phonetic speech babble).

Heather produces the sound correctly, and her mom proceeds to place the lime playdough on the correct picture. As the activity proceeds, we incorporate the concept of *a couple of*, where Heather selects "a" playdough ball versus "a couple of" balls.

As I commend her mom for assisting Heather in producing the word correctly, Heather says, "I'm waiting for you!"

"OK, sorry." I say to Heather, "The lady is *peeling the oranges*."

Heather scans the pictures and places her playdough on the correct picture. She doesn't select the picture of the lady peeling the *orange*, which demonstrates her discrimination of plurals.

"Heather, it's your turn to listen," her mom says. "Take *a couple of balls* of playdough and find the man *washing the dresses*."

Heather selects the picture of the man washing the *dress*, and places the couple of playdough balls on the picture.

"Oh, there he is washing the *dress*," I highlight. "Can you see where he is washing the *dresses*?" Heather does not follow through. "He's washing *two dresses*, see?" I highlight. Heather attends to the number *two* and takes the playdough to the correct picture.

Analysis

The purpose of this activity is twofold: first, to improve Heather's discrimination skills and second, to teach the everyday phrases or sentences that are nonliteral. Her mom is guided to provide Heather with phrases that teach her to discriminate minor differences, such as *behind/beside, he/she,* being sure to incorporate rhyming words (*tea/key/pea*) and words that differ in final consonant only (*cap/cat, coat/coke, pen/pet, dog/doll,* etc.); for example, "The *lady doesn't* want to unload the dishwasher" versus "The *baby can't* unload the dishwasher." Heather is expected to make the manner discrimination between /l/ and /b/ in the rhyming pair *lady/baby.* Expressively, we are also encouraging Heather to use appropriate negation. Heather needs to improve her discrimination of words by place cues, such as in the *lime/line* example. Heather's discrimination error was due to the minor acoustic differences between the consonants /m/ and /n/.

Consonants are described according to the way in which they are produced, according to three articulatory dimensions (Ling, 1976): manner, place, and voicing. The acoustic energy related to these distinctions makes some consonants more audible than others. The consonants /m/ and /n/ differ in their *place of production* (place cues). The acoustic energy providing information on place of production lies in the mid-frequency and high-frequency range and occurs at relatively low intensity (loudness) levels. Most children with hearing losses have better hearing in the low- rather than high-pitch range; therefore, discrimination of consonants that differ in place of production are the most difficult. *Manner* cues occur in the lower-frequency range and are more readily audible. *Voicing* is related to vocal cord vibration: if the vocal cords vibrate as the sound is generated, the sound is voiced; if the vocal cords do not vibrate, it is voiceless. Cues for voicing are in the low-frequency range of hearing and are audible to children with even small amounts of residual hearing.

When Heather's mom used phonetic speech babble to elicit the word *lime,* she did so for two reasons: to help Heather discriminate /m/ from /n/, and to help her use /m/ in meaningful communication in the word *lime.* As consonants that differ in place cues are the most difficult to discriminate, phonetic babble of specific consonants with specific vowels can help Heather improve discrimination of place cues.

Phonetic babble was also used to help Heather produce the target *lime* correctly. At a segmental level, phonetic speech babble involves imitation of vowels and consonants or consonant blends in single, repeated, or alternated syllables on demand. In the above lesson, Heather was asked to imitate the consonant /m/ in the vowel contexts of /a/, /u/, and /i/ in repetition. Phonetic babble is used to determine how automatically Heather is able to produce different speech patterns. If she has difficulty producing a speech pattern on this phonetic "babble" level, it is unlikely that she will be able to use it in everyday communication (phonology).

The second purpose of this activity is to help Heather learn everyday sentences and expressions that are not interpreted literally. When Heather imitates the sentence, she is also encouraged to expand the length of her utterances and to use the targeted expressions correctly. In the example above, Heather described the picture correctly but did not understand or use the phrase "unload the dishwasher" expressively. Imitation helps Heather use the "little words" in language. She will often not hear these "little words" because of coarticulation and contractions.

Coarticulation occurs when the sounds of a word (acoustic properties) or the way it is produced (articulation) change depending on the words that precede or follow them. Speech is not produced one sound at a time, like beads on a string; sounds overlap and flow into one continuously changing stream of sound. For example, in the phrase "picked it up," the "ed" at the end of the word "picked" is produced as a "t" sound, whereas in the phrase "picked the apple," the "ed" at the end of "picked" is not produced as a "t" sound at all.

A *contraction* is a shortening of a group of words, often marked with an apostrophe, for example, "I'll" for the words "I will," or "it's" for the words "it is." Contractions are difficult to hear because acoustic information is reduced. Acoustic highlighting can be used to overcome the reduction of acoustic information due to coarticulation and contractions.

Parent Guidance

- To improve Heather's discrimination skills, in worksheet activities ask her to circle the *ball* or the *doll*; with sticker activities, have her place the sticker "on *me*" or "on your *knee*." At dinnertime, various family members pass the *cheese* or the *peas*. At snack time, Heather can have an *orange* or *a couple of oranges*. In setting the table, ask Heather to get a *glass* or the *glasses*.
- In everyday routines, use figurative or nonliteral expressions such as "pick up the mail," "stock the pantry," "put out the trash." Work on one idiom per week, using it appropriately in routines. Other examples include: "Get cracking," "Break a leg," "Let's boogie." Use colloquialisms such as "Oh, shoot," "Man oh man," "I can't believe it!" English is rich in figurative language, and the understanding and use of it is necessary for natural communication.

Building a Highway

This activity involves "driving" a variety of vehicles along a "highway" and placing them in relation to other vehicles. The necessary props are an assortment of different vehicles and masking tape. The masking tape is cut into long and short pieces and stuck to the table to simulate a highway. Heather and her mom are challenged to come up with a way to create a highway given only the masking tape.

Goal

Language:

- To evaluate Heather's understanding and use of the following prepositions: *behind, beside, between, in front of, next to, over.*

Activity

In setting up this activity, a number of linguistic targets are identified:

- Question forms—*"How could we make a highway?" "What does it look like?" "Why do we have tape?" "What's it for?" "Where do we put it?" "How many lanes should we make?" "How wide apart should we place the tape?"*
- Concepts—*long, short, sticky, masking, beige* (to describe the tape), *edges, center* (to describe where to put the tape).
- Verbs—*cut, rip* (to describe what to do with the tape).

The highway is created by placing two long pieces of tape along the edges of the table and several shorter pieces in the center to create the broken line for passing. A basket is pulled from under the table, revealing an array of colorful mini vehicles mixed with some dinosaurs. We discuss the dinosaurs and decide they "don't belong." Heather's mom is selected to be first and models how to play.

"Mommy, you can go first," I say. "Find the yellow fire engine and put it anywhere on the highway." Heather's mom proceeds by placing the fire engine in the center of the right lane.

I say, "My blue car is going to go *behind* the yellow fire engine."

I then instruct Heather to select a vehicle to travel over the highway. "Heather, you find one that could go *over* the highway."

Heather does not select the airplane, nor does she "drive" her vehicle over the highway. I say, "Let's see, could a car go *over* the highway?" I pick up a car and pretend to fly it over the highway.

"No, that silly," Heather says.

"Oh. How about a school bus, could it go *over* the highway?" I demonstrate again as I did with the car.

"No way!" says Heather's mom.

"What do you think, Heather? Could you pick one that would go *over* the highway?" Heather selects the orange airplane. "That's right!" I say. Airplanes can fly *over* highways."

"It's my turn," says Heather's mom. "The purple school bus is going to pass all the other vehicles and pull *in front of* the fire engine." Mom carries out her own directions.

"OK, Heather," I say. "You get the orange car." Heather selects the orange car. "Drive your car *between* the blue car and the yellow fire engine." Heather follows the instructions. "Good for you! Now you be the teacher and tell Mommy what she should do."

"Mom, take blue school bus and put *behind* the blue car." Mom does so and Heather reinforces her, "Good job!"

Analysis

These types of directions are appropriate for Heather as she has developed an auditory memory for four items (color + noun, color + noun). During this activity, I determine that Heather is still having some difficulty discriminating *behind* from *beside.* When directed to place a vehicle *behind* another, she often places it *beside* and vice versa. With acoustic highlighting techniques, Heather hears the difference. In fact, she uses both prepositions correctly. The following prepositions are targeted for development: *over, in front of,* and *next to.*

Prepositional concepts are used to describe spatial relationships. There are many different prepositions and prepositional phrases, and some describe the same spatial relationship, such as *next to* and *beside.* This is the challenge for Heather. She has learned *under,* and must now learn *underneath* and *below.* We first introduce *on* versus *under* (one syllable versus two) and then *under* versus *behind.*

Parent Guidance

Integration of prepositions and prepositional phrases into daily routines is important.

- Hide things under Heather's pillow each night and have her look *under* her pillow to find the surprise. At breakfast, Heather can look *under* her cup or her plate to find a surprise. By hiding something unfamiliar, you encourage new vocabulary.
- In Heather's closet, her party dresses are kept *in the back* and her school clothes are kept *in the front.*
- Ask Heather to slide her slippers *under* her bed and, after her bed is made, her pajamas get tucked away *under* her pillow. She puts her schoolbag *behind* the sliding door in the hallway and her favorite toy *between* her teddy bears on her dresser.
- When loading the dishwasher, Heather might place the cups and glasses *above* the dishes. In the refrigerator, the drinks go *in the side of* the door.
- In getting into the car to go shopping, Heather can sit *behind* Mommy while her sister sits *next to* her in the *back* seat.
- Mom and Heather can discuss where her friends are seated in the classroom. Heather's best friend is seated *next to* her, and Heather sits *in front of* the teacher.
- In placing stickers in her sticker book, Heather might place the seal sticker *below* the giraffe sticker or *to the right of* it.

Speech and Speech Babble

Formal speech teaching is carried out to develop speech sounds automatically, following the Ling Phonetic Level Evaluation (Ling, 1976) as a guide. Speech sounds are presented through audition only, with visual or kinesthetic cues used to supplement *only if necessary*, followed by putting the production "back into listening." That is, once Heather correctly produces a target phoneme that requires a tactile or visual cue, she is asked to listen to the phoneme and imitate it through audition only.

Production of specific consonants should be expected in spontaneous speech consistently when they can be produced readily, without concentration on a phonetic level (speech babble). Sounds are always developed from the known (what Heather is able to produce) to the unknown (what she is developing). If Heather is able to produce a particular phoneme with a particular vowel or in a word, then that vowel or word can be used to facilitate production in other contexts.

Heather was working on the phoneme /g/. She was able to produce this phoneme only with the vowel /o/ as in "go go go!" In order to develop this phoneme with other vowels, speech babble was initiated with "go go go" and modified to "go go gah" "go go goo," and other vowel contexts. In this way, the phoneme /g/ can be transferred to other vowel contexts and developed in repetition ("gogogo gahgahgah geegeegee") and alternation ("gogahgoo gee googah") until Heather produces it effortlessly (to a level of automaticity).

Speech babble is prompted using many specifically selected games that have many pieces or reinforcers. Games such as Operation™ (Hasbro), and Call the Plumber™ (Grand Toys) are excellent. Battery-operated games that vibrate, jiggle, and spin are highly motivating. Speech babble is conducted quickly and for short periods of time.

Space War Ring Toss

This game consists of orange pegs and a yellow one for the center, red rings, blue rings, and a gameboard. The board consists of two portals, which hold the rings for launching. The pegs get placed in a circle in the middle of the board, with the yellow peg in the center of the circle having the most worth. The object of the game is to launch one's ring from the portal and encircle one of the colored pegs. Each peg and ring is earned by producing the targeted phoneme, as illustrated in Figure 6.1.

Goal

Speech:

- To develop the phoneme /t/ for automatic production in initial positions and to use /t/ in everyday speech.

Activity

The /t/ is elicited in the same way with a variety of vowels. In reinforcing Heather's correct productions, players earn the pegs and the rings for playing the game. As Heather and her mom earn their rings, they place them in the portal and we all count backwards from five: "5, 4, 3, 2, 1, blast off!," and the players shoot. Sometimes we trick players by counting "5, 4, 3, 2, 1, 1, 1, 1, blast off!," encouraging Heather to listen for the go-ahead. After the shot, questions are asked, such as, "Who got more/less?," "How many does Mom need to catch up?," and "Who is keeping score?"

Figure 6.1 Target Phonemes for Heather

Therapist	Heather	Comments
"teeteetee"	"keekeekee"	• a discrimination error based on place cues is made, a "good" error
"/t/ /t/ /t/" (whispered)	"/t/ /t/ /t/" (whispered)	• I whisper the /t/ to help Heather hear it better • whispering increases audibility because the air stream is very easy to hear*
"teeteetee"	"keekeekee"	• same discrimination error
"/t/ /t/ /t/" (whispered)	"/t/ /t/ /t/" (whispered)	• I use the known (whispered form) and quickly pair it with the unknown ("teeteetee")
"teeteetee"	"teeteetee"	• after two presentations, Heather discriminates the phoneme correctly
"teeteetah"	"teeteetah"	• I use Heather's correct production of "teeteetee" to elicit its production with other vowels
"tahtahtah"	"tahtahtah"	• /t/ is produced in repetition in the context of the vowel /a/

*Whispering intensifies voicelessness; voiced/voiceless cues are based on durational or timing cues, which are audible to children with even very little measurable residual hearing. Also, whispering intensifies consonants, not vowels, which are louder than consonants and can mask or cover them up.

Parent Guidance

Speech is very challenging to teach. In developing the phoneme /t/, I guided Heather's mom with the following techniques:

- /t/ should initially be produced with /i/, since /t/ and /i/ are both produced at the front of the mouth. Less articulatory control is required to produce this combination than others.
- If Heather has difficulty with this phoneme, try to elicit it with a different vowel, such as "oo," "ah," or another vowel. The particular vowel will depend on which is easiest for Heather to say and which consonant–vowel combination can serve as an easy model for its development with other vowels.
- Consonants should be paired with a vowel and presented in repetition (which provides greater acoustic information and is easier to hear). "*Teeteetee*" is better than "*tee.*"
- Consonant–vowel combinations should also be presented in alternation, for example, "*teetahtoo tahteetoe.*"
- The acquired phoneme should be encouraged in expressive speech.
- In everyday interactions, use phonetic babble if Heather misproduces a word, and encourage it in spontaneous speech (phonology). For example, if Heather says, "My koes are cold," elicit the correct production by presenting "*teeteetee teeteetoe* My *toes* are cold." This usually produces a correct utterance.

- When Heather requests gum saying, "I want *dum*, please," elicit the correct production by modeling "*gogogogogo gum* I want *gum*, please." This takes a known form ("g" with "o") and extends it to a context that is unknown ("g" with "u"), encouraging phonetic to phonologic transfer (Ling, 1976).
- Do not do this for every speech articulation error. This would be frustrating, prevent natural communication, and discourage Heather's drive to use speech to communicate. Heather needs to develop the sound at the phonetic level and then transfer it to meaningful language. Rather than correct speech incidentally, babble Heather's speech targets for a few minutes four or five times per day and integrate the targets into her routines. In Heather's sessions, we may work on a few targets at one time.
- Promote babbling, not necessarily to expect correct productions of a particular sound in communicative speech, until all the subskills (the phonetic level) have been developed.

Session Summary

Heather's mom will reinforce expressive use of the pronouns *she* and they; contrast the prepositions *over* and *in front of* (e.g., *in front of* the house, *in front of* your door); use three new nonliteral phrases (her mom suggests those most important for Heather); use the idiom "Don't pull my leg!" at meaningful times (events can be contrived to provide opportunities to use these); and improve production of "t" and "sh." Family life and school progress are also discussed.

We review the notes that Heather's mom has taken during therapy. She keeps a "vocabulary box" in the bottom right-hand corner of the page, where she jots down any words that come up that Heather doesn't know. She will teach this vocabulary during the week.

Heather has been using her cochlear implant successfully for approximately 2 years and 6 months. Prior to receiving it, she was expressing herself by using limited verbal language, such as "up," "no," "pop up," and some sound–object associations. One year after initial stimulation of Heather's implant (hearing age = 1 year), her average sentence length was 3.5 words. She is now speaking in sentences and is understood by most people. On formal language assessments for children with typical hearing, Heather scores one standard deviation within the norm (fairly close to average). On the *Test of Auditory Comprehension of Language—Revised* (TACL-R) (DLM Teaching Resources), Heather obtained an age-equivalent score of 47–49 months when she was 59 months of age with a hearing age of only 19 months.

Heather is integrated in the kindergarten classroom at the local school and actively participates in her community. She is able to have conversations with many people. She hears music and loves to sing along in Sunday school and church. The cochlear implant, in conjunction with regular auditory-verbal sessions, has changed Heather's life.

SESSION PLAN #4: CHRIS (AGE 5)*

Chris's profound sensorineural hearing loss was diagnosed when he was 13 months old. An auditory brainstem response (ABR) test yielded no response. After 14 months of diagnostic therapy with effective parent participation following the auditory-verbal approach, it was determined that Chris had very little hearing potential. He had some difficulty doing play audiometry, and the only thresholds obtained indicated vibrotactile responses. Both the parents and our professional team felt that Chris and his family would benefit from a total communication (TC) approach. It was suggested that the family consult the local school for the deaf, where they began a home visiting program using TC. When he turned 3, Chris attended a class for children who were deaf at a public school in his city. Chris's parents took sign language classes, and they and their son became fluent in sign as their primary mode of communication.

With the advent of cochlear implants, Chris's parents became interested in the device. He was assessed and judged to be a candidate. When he was 4 years, 6 months of age, Chris had cochlear implant surgery. Six weeks later, the device was switched on, and Chris continued with the same self-contained program he had attended for the past 2 years.

Chris's aided thresholds with his cochlear implant are shown in Figure 6.2.

Chris used sign language to communicate with his parents and others who knew how to sign. Even after 6 months of cochlear implant use, however, his parents saw that Chris continued to use sign language and only neutral vowels to communicate. In their concern to maximize his newly acquired hearing potential, they requested that Chris rejoin the auditory-verbal program.

Chris's parents and I discussed the following options:

- Continue the TC program in the expectation that sign language would probably be Chris's preferred mode of communication, as he would still be learning visually.
- Integrate Chris into a segregated oral class, where he would learn through speechreading, with audition as a supplement.
- Reenter the auditory-verbal program with the goal of transition from sign language to the development of spoken language through listening.

Because this was an important decision, Chris's parents were asked to consider the options and return a week later. They chose option three. We agreed upon a 3-month trial, after which we would reevaluate their choice.

Introduction to the Therapy Session

The session plan that follows was used 1 month after Chris returned to the auditory-verbal program. He was 5 years, 1 month old and 7 months postimplant.

---

* By Judith I. Simser, O. Ont., B.Ed., Cert. AVT®. Adapted from W. Estabrooks (Ed.), *Cochlear Implants for Kids.* Washington, DC: Alexander Graham Bell Association for the Deaf and Hard of Hearing, 1998. Used with permission.

Figure 6.2 Chris's Aided Thresholds (with Cochlear Implant)

Frequency	250 Hz	500 Hz	1000 Hz	2000 Hz	4000 Hz
Threshold	30 dB HL	35 dB HL	35 dB HL	30 dB HL	35 dB HL

Discussion

As Chris was unable to hear for the first 4 years of his life, he naturally learned to rely on a visual mode of communication. Because of his inability to respond to listening targets, he had become unreceptive to auditory teaching. Chris's parents needed to develop confidence in their son's ability to learn through listening. In developing his goals, it was imperative that auditory tasks follow a hierarchy (see Chapter 3), progressing from easy to more difficult to hear. If the initial auditory targets were too advanced and difficult, Chris and his parents would experience a feeling of failure.

Parent Guidance

- Always provide an optimal acoustic environment. Reduce background noise by turning off the radio and the television unless it is being watched. Be aware of the noise of air conditioners and refrigerators; close windows to outside environmental noises. Sit beside Chris on the side of his implanted ear when providing speech stimuli.
- Remember to talk in ways that increase the audibility of speech in order for Chris to have the best opportunity to learn to listen: use clear speech, speak in simple two- to four-word phrases, use increased rhythm and pitch contrasts, increase repetitions, and emphasize key words.
- Use the Hand Cue to alert Chris to listen and to emphasize listening rather than lipreading. In the early stages, the Hand Cue should be used especially when there is a situational cue. Tell him, while you are putting on your coat, "Put on your coat; we're going in the car. Get your coat." Also use the Hand Cue when you are reinforcing weekly targets integrated into your daily routines and play.
- Reduce use of sign language. In situations involving complex language, offer lipreading in combination with listening. We want to reduce reliance on signing and lipreading while simultaneously developing spoken language skills through listening.

Goals

Audition:

- To demonstrate consistent response to his name.
- To learn to identify vowels "au," "ah," "oh," and "ee" (/aʊ/, /a/, /ΣΣəʊ/, and /i/); identify consonants varying in manner cues: /m/, /b/ or /p/, and /h/.

- To develop the ability to process one-item auditory memory tasks:
  - in phrases containing repetition of sound-word associations, such as, "The ball goes *bounce, bounce, bounce*";
  - with single objects representing nouns, verbs, adjectives and adverbs that vary in vowel content, number of syllables, and suprasegmental features (e.g., "Do you want an *apple,* here's an *apple,*" "Where are your *shoes,* go get your *shoes,*" "*Cut, cut, cut* the paper");
  - with a known word presented at the end of the sentence (e.g., "Where are the *bananas?*");
  - with a known word presented in the middle or beginning of the sentence (e.g., "Please put the *spoons* on the table").
- To try *selection by description;* to teach Chris to attend to longer segments of information and to extract familiar words necessary for comprehension:
  - where the familiar word or sound-word is used repeatedly (e.g., "It goes *up, up, up* in the sky; it goes *ah ah ah ah;* you ride in it; what is it?");
  - where known words are in a single repetition in the description (e.g., "It has *four* legs; it *hops;* it swims in the *water;* it's *green;* what is it?").
- To identify expressive phrases that have different rhythms and contain identifiable phonemes and/or words (e.g., "*Mmmm,* that's good!" "*Shhhhh,* Daddy's sleeping," "*Bye, bye,* Chris," and "*Ow,* that hurts").
- To encourage the development of a listening attitude by drawing Chris's attention to sounds and speech throughout the day, and by stressing the development of listening through alerting Chris to sound by saying, "Listen! I hear that!"

Speech:

- To develop differences in duration, pitch, and intensity using sound-word associations (e.g., rising and lowering *oo-oo-oo* for a train, and short phrases, "*oh, oh,* it fell down").
- To reinforce voiced versus voiceless phonemes (e.g., *mmmm* versus */h/ /h/ /h/,* repeated).
- To extend vowel production to higher-frequency vowels (e.g., /ʌɪ/ as in *aye;* /ɪ/ as in *hit;* /i/ as in *feet*).
- To alternate known vowels (e.g., *ah-oo* and *o-o-ah, oo-w-ah* to create *wa-wa-wa*).
- To improve /m/ in syllabic babble with a variety of vowels (e.g., *ummm, ummm, ummu-ummu, mmmu-mmmu, mmmoo, mmmoo*).
- To reinforce /p/ /p/ /p/ and /h/ /h/ /h/ (whisper these and alternate them).
- Once syllables are developed, to alternate those varying in manner cues (e.g., *ma-ma, bo-bo*).
- To expect Chris to use speech to attract attention and to communicate.

Language:

- To develop fundamental vocabulary containing a variety of parts of speech.
- To develop comprehension and expression of frequently used phrases.

- To begin using negatives such as *no* and *not the.*
- To develop verbs as directives (e.g., *Wash your hands*; *Open the door*).
- To identify family names such as *Mummy, Daddy, the baby,* and familiar animals such as *dog* and *cat* to prepare for noun–verb phrases.
- To develop comprehension and use of question forms *What's that?* and *What's he doing?*
- To capitalize on everyday situations to reinforce listening and language development.

Communication:
- Whenever Chris attempts to communicate through gestures and/or sign language, to acknowledge this and provide three- to four-word spoken phrases to encourage and reinforce verbal interaction.
- To develop and expect use of greetings and courtesy language.
- To encourage Chris to listen at all times but especially whenever there is a situational cue (e.g., when the table is set and you've come out from the kitchen: *"It's time for dinner"*).

Cognition:
- To arrange objects in categories.
- To select objects that don't belong (from a set of four).
- To sequence a four-part story.
- To associate objects with pictures.
- To identify three to four letters.
- To reinforce number concepts to five.

Saying Hello

Chris and his Mother arrive at the clinic and I go to the waiting room to call him. He is playing with a toy and does not respond to his name. I gesture to his mom not to touch him. I go behind him close to the microphone of the cochlear implant and call him three times. No response! So I visually cue him to *listen,* go behind him again, and practice the same task twice more.

I remind his mom to expect him to respond when she calls him and to teach him to respond in this way. At this stage, she should try not to call him to test his response, but call only when she has something specific that she wants or needs.

Outside the therapy room, within reach of the children, there are coat hooks with pictures above them. Chris takes off his coat, and I ask him to hang it *on the cat that says meow, meow.* Then, while he is holding his boots in his hand, I ask him to put them *under the fish.* I tell his mom that these auditory tasks are considered a single-item auditory memory because Chris has the objects in his hands. That is, Chris only has to listen to *where* to put the objects. In the future we will expand by creating a two- to six-item memory task, e.g., "Put your *coat* on the *frog*," "Put your *boots* under the *ball* and your *hat* on the *dog*." Instead of saying, "Good boy," I suggest that there is more auditory reinforcement in saying, "Right, you hung your coat on the fish."

As Chris can say a form of *sit down*, his mom knows to wait beside her chair until Chris tells her to do so. She expands the phrase to, "Thank you, I'll sit down on the chair."

Phonetic Identification Game

The object of this game is to practice the auditory perception of early phonemes or speech sounds. Chris's auditory level is below his cognitive level; the use of enjoyable games is highly motivational. The game Probe™ uses a long plastic strip onto which you can insert an equally long strip of paper. It has little covers that snap over the strip of paper where you can put stickers or pictures, or write letters inside each little compartment to conceal them. Chris is an early listener, so I write down a closed set of five letters from the auditory targets. We take turns choosing and writing one letter. While the players try to guess the hidden letter, Chris has practice listening to the phonics of speech sounds and identifying them. We keep score of the number of tries for each person to guess the hidden letter correctly, low score being the winner.

Mom's turn: "Is there a /p/, *puh, puh, puh, puh*?"

I use the Hand Cue to prompt Chris to imitate what he heard. This eliminates guesswork and promotes auditory feedback. I do this only if I know that he can produce a reasonable imitation of the phoneme. This prevents poor or inaccurate auditory feedback. He may need further experience in listening to the phoneme before he is able to produce it.

Chris: (Shakes his head to indicate a negative response.)
Judy: "You say to Mommy, no-no" (I use a Hand Cue to prompt imitation). "It's my turn."

Parent Guidance

- This activity can also be practiced by hiding a letter written on a piece of paper in a container; by writing letters on a whiteboard, identifying them, and then erasing them; by using letter stamps or magnetic letters; or by hiding papers with letters on them around the room and asking Chris to find a specific one. Many hints can be given through listening (e.g., "It's near the door, open the door").

Tactile Game

In this activity, Chris is to select a single object by listening to familiar vocabulary. To add motivation for listening, once Chris has selected a picture of the item requested, he will try to find it hidden among other objects within the box, by his sense of touch.

I have about six objects known to Chris, and I put them into a shoe box with a rectangular hole in one end, one at a time. To prompt answering the question, "What's that?" I ask his mom to turn around so that she cannot see the objects. She asks Chris the identity of each object as I hand them to him.

Mom: "What's that?"
Chris: "Wa ah?" He attempts to imitate, rather than answer, the question.

Mom asks me the same question and I answer briefly, "A shoe."

When children don't know how to answer questions, the answers need to be modeled without repeating any components of the question in order to be a natural part of expressive language. The question should be highlighted or emphasized by repeatedly asking the same question with many different known objects. To make the game meaningful, the answer should not be known to the person asking the question.

Once I have placed all the objects in the box, I ask Chris to put the pictures representing the objects on the table in front of him. He is to select the picture requested to indicate a correct response (e.g., "Where's the ball that goes *bounce, bounce, bounce*?"), then see if he can find it in the box without looking, but by feeling only. While he is feeling the objects, his mother has the opportunity to expand receptive language by saying, "Can you find the *ball*?" "No, no, no, that's *not the ball*," promoting the negative form.

Parent Guidance

- This game can also be used to reinforce other parts of speech using verb and/or adjective pictures and objects associated with them (e.g., soap for *washing*, scissors for *cutting*, a birthday candle stuck in playdough for *hot*, some tape for *sticky*).

More Games

To reinforce the perception and production of speech targets, I give Chris a choice between the games Hungry Hungry Hippos™ or Mr. Mouth™ (both manufactured by Milton Bradley). It is important to give a choice whenever possible so that the child has a feeling of control. Almost any game can be used to develop almost any target. Chris chooses Hungry Hungry Hippos™. To play this game you need to place about 15 colored balls into the center area of the board. As Chris is motivated, he is eager to imitate speech sounds to obtain the balls from me. In the early stages of practice the child must have a reason to imitate sounds; you must have something that he wants.

I whisper, *"hhhh-hhhhh-hhhhh,"* and use a Hand Cue to prompt Chris to imitate.

Chris produces a *voiced* guttural noise.

"*Listen*," I say, then I repeat the phoneme, use the Hand Cue to prompt Mom to imitate, and then give Chris a turn. It is important for the child to know whether his production of the phoneme is right or wrong. The use of his mom's voice improves Chris's attention to the speech sound (a different voice adds additional cues). If he does not respond correctly, I may give a kinesthetic cue, such as having him feel the breathstream on his hand, but then we all take turns producing it repeatedly *through listening* to develop the auditory-feedback loop. This practice will enhance Chris's future perception and production of the phoneme.

I hand Chris the balls and, in order to practice a single-item auditory task, ask him to put four on the game.

We reinforce unvoiced /p/ /p/ /p/ /p/, which Chris produces well, and then alternate unvoiced phoneme /p/ with /m/ to improve the perception and production of voiced versus unvoiced speech sounds.

Mom says, "/p/ /p/ /p/ (pause), mmm," /p/ /p/ mmm," and Chris imitates.

This time I give him six balls and tell him to give them *to Mommy*. As this is not the obvious thing to do, he does not understand, so Mom says, "*Give them to me*," a few times, and I glance in her direction. If we give Chris a directional cue, we repeat the verbal request a few times to confirm what we are asking.

Chris's production of the phoneme /m/ is weak in the initial position, and he frequently substitutes /b/, probably because of lipreading. Previously when Chris relied on lipreading, the phonemes /m/, /b/, and /p/ looked similar on the lips. Because he could not hear them, he often interchanged these speech sounds. I model for his mom to produce /m/ in the final position as I give her the balls to the game to continue the speech babble with her son.

His mom covers her mouth and says: "*ummmm, um.*" Chris listens and produces it well.

I whisper to Mom to try *ummmm-mu* to move the phoneme /m/ into the middle position. Chris produces the /m/, but follows it with a nasalized vowel.

I say, "Try an /h/ before the second vowel: *ummmm-hu.*" This works! We continue the game.

We put the rest of the balls in the center and use lots of natural language during play (e.g., "I want the green hippo," "Wait for Mom to say 1, 2, 3, go," "How many balls did you get?," "Do you want to play again?," "You dropped a ball. It's under the table").

Parent Guidance

- The incidental language that you use while preparing the activity is often more important than the activity itself, as it shows how to integrate targets into whatever you do during the day.

Photographs

I have many personal photographs to use for a variety of listening targets such as descriptions, question forms, prepositions, and sequence stories. Children often prefer them to commercially prepared materials. My cat has been photographed while wearing a Santa hat, drinking water, hiding under the table, and crouching in a paper bag!

While looking at a photo hidden from the others' view, I say, "*Shhhh, Daddy's sleeping.* What do you see, Mom?" She looks at the photo and repeats the phrase. Chris listens and tries to imitate, "*Shhh.*" Once we have reviewed four pictures and they are spread on the table, I ask Chris to listen to a short phrase and select each one to put away. There are many reinforcers that can be used; for example, paper clips can be attached to each photo and the pictures can be picked up with a magnet.

Discussion

Discussion between the therapist and parent occurs throughout the therapy session. If there is a family concern, discussion may consume the whole session while the child plays. The parents' level of understanding and feelings of competence are paramount in helping their child learn. The therapist teaches, guides, and supports the family in creating a listening, language-enriched, communicative environment inside and outside the home.

In her notebook, Chris's mother records the activities that she practiced and the targets outlined during the session. Thus, she has a good understanding of the objectives.

Parent Guidance

Audition:

- Continue *one-item memory tasks* as outlined in this session's goals, but choose meaningful new vocabulary to highlight throughout the week. Once Chris knows a word or phrase, always expand it to include some new information.
- Begin *two-item memory* in its simplest form, two nouns or verbs in repetition (e.g., "Where's the *cow* that goes *moo, moo, moo* and the *car* that goes *brrbr-rrrrr?*"). You might use two separate containers of water or two circles of playdough so Chris sees that there are to be two items, one for each container. Model with someone else first and remember to have the person confirm what he or she heard. Practice this game in a formal way as well as integrating it into daily routines (e.g., "Get the *spoons* and *cups,*" "Where are your *shoes* and *hat?*"). To ensure Chris's success in listening, the objects requested must be part of his known vocabulary.
- Expand your sentences to describe objects a little more (e.g., "The dog is drinking water; oh, he's wagging his tail. Look at his tail").
- Expect Chris to turn and respond to his name. Reinforce him for doing so by saying, "Good, you heard me call you. Do you want some *hot chocolate?*"

Speech:

- Keep speech babble practice brief and motivating. If Chris experiences difficulty with certain phonemes, then do not reinforce them. Record the problems and wait until the next session. Otherwise, you will be reinforcing incorrect production.

- Produce /m/ in the medial position and move to initial position (e.g., *ummu, mmhu, mmu, mmu*).
- Beginners often require more auditory input to produce the higher-frequency phoneme /i/ than the lower-frequency vowels, so do not be concerned if this takes more time. Just provide many opportunities for Chris to hear the vowel /i/ as in *ee, ee, ee* for a monkey, *squeak, squeak, squeak* for a mouse, *wheeee* as he goes down a metal or wooden slide (not plastic, as static electricity can erase his cochlear implant's MAP). At this stage, listening is more important than production.
- Alternate /b/ and /p/ with different vowels that he can already produce (e.g., "*ba, ba, ba* [pause and change direction of pitch]*; boo, boo, boo; puh, puh, puh... po, po, po*").
- Develop /h/ in long duration to differentiate it from /p/ (whispered): *hhhhh, hhhhh.*

Language:

- Continue to record and assess new vocabulary that Chris develops through listening, and check that it contains a variety of parts of speech. We do not communicate by nouns alone. By developing varied parts of speech, Chris will gain the foundations for spoken language. Stress the pronouns *mine* and *me,* beginning routine verbs, early developing adjectives and adverbs, and the prepositions *on* and *under* (contrast acoustically).
- Once Chris comprehends short, meaningful phrases, encourage their expressive use in everyday experiences. In therapy sessions, Chris can play the role of teacher and ask Mom to select a picture depicting a phrase of his choosing. She may understand his phrase only by the rhythm and vowel content, but this is fine at this stage.
- Do not press Chris for clear speech at this time.
- Practice listening to and identifying family names, as we did not have time to work on this activity. A structured activity you might try is to put out photos or figurines that depict Mommy, Daddy, and Chris's siblings including the baby, Elizabeth. From a cloth bag containing interesting objects, pick one, conceal it, and say, "Baby wants it, where's baby?" Once Chris shows you the baby, have him put the object on or near the baby. This is preparation for two-item auditory tasks (e.g., *Daddy is washing,* as Chris puts a little play man in a bathtub).
- Reinforce family names all day long.
- Use the same highlighting techniques in speaking to other family members as you would to Chris. The baby will benefit from the language stimulation, and there is a lot for Chris to learn while you interact with others.

Communication:

- Practice and reinforce turn-taking skills. Chris cannot hear his vocalizations if he is trying to monopolize the conversation at the same time.

Turn-taking is best practiced in games. If Chris doesn't wait until you have finished talking, turn away from him while you talk, using a Hand Cue in front of your mouth to indicate you are talking. When you finish talking, turn back, and indicate that it is now his turn.

- *Catch him listening and talking!* Reinforce the behaviors that you want. Listen actively: stop what you are doing and reinforce his verbal attempts. We will deal with his attention-getting behaviors later, when he has learned to talk.
- Continue to provide phrases as substitutes for his signs. It is your goal that signing gradually be replaced by verbal communication as Chris gains confidence in listening and talking.

Session Summary

This session focused on using Chris's newly enhanced auditory potential to build his confidence and competence in learning through listening. A variety of goals were set in audition, speech, language, communication, and cognition, with extensive parental guidance intended to reinforce listening in daily interactions.

One year after this session, Chris was conversing in intelligible speech via audition only, and was attending a mainstream class in his local school. On a standardized test of language, he scored only one year behind his hearing peers. His parents' choice of a cochlear implant and the auditory-verbal approach provided Chris with his own choice of communication strategies.

SESSION PLAN #5: SARA (AGE 6)*

Born to talk! Sara is the most gregarious person I have ever met. Sara has undoubtedly been outgoing since birth, but she has not been a verbal child for very long. Born in Lebanon, she was diagnosed at 3 months of age with a profound hearing loss but did not have access to hearing aids until she came to Canada at age 2. Her older brother also has a profound hearing loss. Initially in a Total Communication program, Sara appeared, at that time, to have no useable hearing, and use of amplification was suspended. At age 3, she and her family joined our auditory-verbal program. She was using several signs, understood fewer than 20 spoken words, and used fewer than 10. She did not use her voice when she spoke.

One of our first challenges was to get earmolds to fit Sara's tiny ears. This took a couple of months and several remakes. Soon thereafter, she started to use her voice more consistently and to develop a few Learning to Listen Sounds, containing relatively easy-to-hear, low-frequency vowel sounds and simple rhythm patterns. Lessons were a bit of a struggle, as Sara was extremely visual

---

* By Pamela Steacie, M.Sc., Cert. AVT®. Adapted from W. Estabrooks (Ed.), *Cochlear Implants for Kids.* Washington, DC: Alexander Graham Bell Association for the Deaf and Hard of Hearing, 1998. Used with permission.

and very distractible. Her mother has always worked with admirable consistency, effectiveness, and determination to develop Sara's speech, language, and listening skills, as well as those of Sara's brother. As English was her mother's third and not very fluent language, she took English classes and volunteered at her son's school to increase her own language competency.

Sara was given an FM system for home use to enhance listening further. Even so, she was still unable to process high-frequency sounds and found listening difficult all the time. Sara's audiologist and I met with her parents to discuss a cochlear implant, but they were reluctant to pursue it at that time. When Sara was 4, she received a frequency-transposition hearing aid to help process high-frequency information. Soon, she began to detect /s/ and /f/, although she could not discriminate between them. She still was not able to hear place differences among front plosive consonant /p/, mid plosive /t/, and back plosive /k/. She seemed to have more difficulty identifying low-frequency vowels /u/ and /a/ than she had with her ear-level hearing aids. Distance listening improved in that she could hear her name being called from up to 8 feet away.

Over the next year, Sara's speech and language progressed more quickly, but it was clear that her limited residual hearing made spoken communication laborious. After much soul searching, her parents chose a cochlear implant for Sara, which she received at age 6. Prior to her implant surgery, vocabulary comprehension, as measured by the *Peabody Picture Vocabulary Test*, was at the 2-year, 5-month level. Understanding and use of language as measured by the *Zimmerman Preschool Language Scale—3* were at the levels of 3 years, 1 month and 3 years, 2 months, respectively. Sara expressed herself using short phrases of four to five words. By concentrating very hard, using listening alone, she could decode three-word phrases containing very familiar words when the context was known and limited. She needed to lipread to understand conversational speech.

Introduction to the Therapy Session

One week after it was switched on, the cochlear implant was giving Sara excellent listening potential. To exploit that potential fully, we needed to begin with listening all over again, pinpoint baseline diagnostic information, and then reinforce skills at that level. The lesson that follows—the first after activation of the implant—is heavily weighted with listening goals. Previously mastered speech and language goals are reinforced here through audition, and thinking skills are reinforced incidentally.

Goals

Audition:

- Phoneme detection; Ling Six-Sound Test.
- Phoneme identification of /bababa/, /a/, /ʃ/, *brbrbr* (car sound), and /m/.
- Responding to her name, i.e., turning towards the person calling her.
- Identification of familiar phrases: *Shut the door!; Ow, that hurts!; Sit down; Put it in the garbage.*

- Identification of familiar verbs *Sit down; Sh! Go to sleep; Go up, up, up the stairs; Wash, wash, wash, wash (your hands, the car, the floor).*
- Identification of familiar nouns *baby, hat, shoe, flower.*

Phoneme Detection

This is usually checked as soon as the first complete MAP is established, while the implant is still plugged into the MAPping computer. The Ling Six Sounds (/m/, /u/, /a/, /i/, /ʃ/, and /s/) are used because they cover the full frequency range of spoken language. The same toys and the same procedure are used for this task as for conditioned play audiometry during audiological testing and cochlear implant MAPping.

Parent Guidance

- Point out a variety of environmental sounds to Sara. Point often to your ear and cue her to *Listen!* Keep a daily note of the environmental sounds to which she does and does not respond.
- Perform the Ling Six-Sound Test with Sara daily. If she is unable to hear a sound, cue her to listen. Repeat the sound, closer to her and/or more loudly and/or more prolonged (e.g., *mmmm* rather than /m/). Again, keep a daily record of the speech sounds detected or not. This information will be useful in refining Sara's cochlear implant MAP.

Phoneme Identification

Phoneme detection is simple compared to the more complex tasks of discrimination (differentiating between two sounds, syllables, words, or phrases, e.g., /f/ versus /s/) and identification (telling which one of several possible sounds, syllables, words, or phrases has been said). Through phoneme identification tasks, I determine which sounds Sara can identify. As she can read a bit, I use a small number of printed letters and a happy-face stamp for this activity. I use the staccato /bababa/; "ah" with a long, slowly rising, then falling, intonation; "sh" for the blowing, fricative sound; and "brbrbr" ("raspberries") for the car sound. These sounds are very different from one another in rhythm, intonation, and consonant and vowel content.

- I say each of the target sounds two or three times and then print each one on a piece of paper. Sara repeats each sound as I print it.
- I say each sound and ask Sara to repeat it and then stamp a happy face beside the corresponding letter(s).

Sara identifies all sounds except /m/, which she confuses with /a/, so we practice discriminating /m/ from /a/. For this task:

- I say the sounds /m/ and /a/, and then print the letters *m* and *a*.
- I give Sara a felt marker and ask her to print the sound she has heard.
- She listens, repeats the sound, and then prints the appropriate letter.

Sara is able to perform this task correctly. Using the same task format, she is also able to discriminate /ʃ/ ("sh") from /s/.

Parent Guidance

- Every day, do the *a/m* discrimination task as a warmup, followed by the phoneme identification task with all suggested phonemes, including /s/. If mastered, add whispered /p/ /p/ /p/ and /i/ ("ee").
- Use the *auditory sandwich* technique (audition/vision/audition) if Sara is unable to identify a sound by audition alone:
  - Say the sound a few times for Sara to process by audition alone, then ask her to repeat it.
  - If she is unable to do so, use a visual cue such as lipreading or printing the sound while saying it. Ask her to repeat the sound.
  - Say the sound again immediately for processing by audition. Encourage Sara to repeat it.
- Use familiar words containing target sounds. For example, to reinforce /m/, use *Mama, mine, me,* and *more.*

Responding to Her Name

The goal of this activity is to help Sara learn to identify when her name is being called. I use a pop-up stacking toy with six rings. This procedure is similar to the Ling Six-Sound task:

- Sara holds a stacking ring up to her ear and then I say, *Listen!* I mime to her that when she hears *Sara* and turns towards me, she can put a ring on the pop-up toy.
- From a distance of 1 foot behind Sara, I call her name.
- She turns to me. I congratulate her and give her a stacking ring.
- We repeat steps 2 and 3 as I call her from 2, 3, 6, 8, and finally 10 feet away.

Sara celebrates by activating the lever that sends the rings flying up into the air. Since she turned to her name even at a distance of 10 feet, to increase the level of difficulty, I try calling her name unexpectedly. She is less consistent at this unless I am very close, about 1 foot away. I also make the original task more difficult in a different way, by turning it into a discrimination activity with the words *Sara* and *Mama*, as follows:

- I place five beads in front of her mother and five in front of Sara.
- I explain and demonstrate: "When I say Sara, you put a bead on the string, and when I say Mama, Mama will put a bead on."
- I call their names in random order.

- Each person places a bead on the string when her name is called, until all beads are strung.

Sara performs this activity successfully.

Parent Guidance

- From behind, about 2 feet away from her, call Sara's name unexpectedly. If she turns to you, congratulate her, and then call her from slightly farther away. If she does not turn to you, try again at 1 foot. If she does not respond at this distance, tap her on the shoulder, tell her you were calling *Sara!*, and call her name again at this distance while she is turned away from you. Repeat at distances of 2–3 feet. Praise her lavishly when she turns to you. As a rule, it is best to have a good reason for calling her, such as a forthcoming treat, an outing, or a meal, so that she doesn't decide to tune you out for being annoying.
- Since Sara was able to discriminate *Mama* from *Sara*, add the name *Papa* with whispered, exaggerated *p*'s. If Sara is able to choose correctly among these three, add *Abdallah* (Sara's brother), using a sing-song intonation for his name.
- Frequently, call other family members within Sara's earshot. Also have her call them, when appropriate.

Identification of Simple Expressive Phrases

I use a set of cartoon drawings that represent a variety of common phrases, mounted on construction paper, designed specifically for this activity. As a reinforcer I use a mechanical apple from which a worm darts to grab a penny. I have chosen the phrases *Shut the door; Ow! That hurts; Sit down;* and *Put it in the garbage,* which have different rhythm and intonation patterns. To make these phrases still more different from one another, I use acoustic highlighting techniques such as lengthening the "sh" of *Shut the door* and the *Ow!* of *Ow! That hurts,* using a sing-song intonation for *Sit down,* and emphasizing the staccato rhythm of *Put it in the garbage.*

- Hiding each drawing, I say the associated phrase a couple of times, showing Sara the drawing and asking her to say the phrase. She then places a penny on the drawing. I introduce the first two drawings this way, and then her mother introduces the others.
- I cue Sara to *Listen!* and then say one of the phrases.
- Sara repeats the phrase, then removes a penny from the corresponding drawing and feeds it to the worm.
- Mother or I continue the second and third steps until the activity is completed.

Sara is able to identify these phrases correctly, so I add a very abrupt *Stop!* and a long, enthusiastic *Hi!* She begins to confuse *Stop!* with *Sit down,* so I ask her to discriminate between an even more curt *Stop!* and a slower, more singsong *Sit down.* She is probably confused by the newly salient /s/, which she has been unaccustomed to hearing well in these expressions. When I highlight other features of these words, as above, and reduce the number of choices to only two, Sara is successful.

Parent Guidance

- Practice the same task at home, using the cartoon drawings provided.
- Make a point of using these expressions frequently during the day. Post these and other targets on your fridge or in some other convenient spot.
- As soon as Sara can identify a word or phrase by listening in a structured exercise, expect her to do this by audition throughout the day in as many settings as possible. When necessary, use the auditory sandwich technique (audition/vision/audition). Tell her, for example, *Shut the door* through audition alone a couple of times. If she does not respond appropriately, use lipreading, with or without a gesture if necessary, while saying *Shut the door* again. Finally, say *Shut the door* once or twice again through audition alone. In this way, you are providing visual support while still reinforcing audition. As Sara acquires more auditory experience, she will be more likely to identify phrases by listening alone.

Identification of a Few Basic Verbs

I use a colorful toy furniture set and a toy girl. Sara has to make the girl *Sit down; Sh! Go to sleep; Go up, up, up the stairs;* or *Wash, wash, wash, wash* upon request.

- I say each verb once, then I ask Sara's mother to say the target verb once. I produce the appropriate prop and encourage Sara to repeat the target verb.
- When the chair, the bed, the stairs, and the sink are all in front of Sara, I cue her to *Listen!* and I say, *Go up, up, up the stairs.*
- Sara indicates which verb she has identified by repeating it after me, then chooses the right prop and makes the girl perform the appropriate action.

Sara has no difficulty with the first three verbs except *wash.* She tends to confuse it with *Sh! Go to sleep.* She is probably hearing the "sh" sound much more strongly than before her implant and is distracted by it. I make the two verbs as acoustically different as possible by lengthening the "sh" of *Sh! Go to sleep* and by saying *Wash, wash, wash* as rhythmically as possible with no extra emphasis on the "sh." Sara is then able to identify *wash* correctly.

Parent Guidance

- Practice this structured activity every day. Use real or toy props. Gradually try to shorten the "sh" of *Sh! Go to sleep* and reduce the number of repetitions of *wash.*
- Use these verbs at every opportunity during the day. If Sara does not identify them, use the auditory sandwich technique.
- Play a variation of Charades: take turns ordering each other to mime a particular verb.

Identification of Familiar Nouns

For this activity, the materials are rubber picture stamps, an ink pad, and a large piece of paper on which I have drawn the outline of a house and a few pieces of furniture. The target words are *baby, hat, shoe,* and *flower* because their different vowels, consonants, and number of syllables make them easier to hear. I acoustically highlight: for *baby* I use a sing-song intonation; I lengthen the /h/ in *hat* and both the "sh" and "oo" of *shoe*; I lengthen *flower*, using a gently rising, then falling intonation.

- Hiding each stamp, I say the target word a couple of times, with Sara's mother following suit. I produce the stamp; Sara repeats the target word, is handed the stamp, and then places it in front of her.
- When all stamps are displayed, I cue Sara to *Listen!* and ask, *Where's the...?*
- Sara repeats the target noun and then selects the appropriate stamp. I ask her where she is going to put it and why. She then stamps it wherever she chooses in the house picture.

Because Sara selects all nouns correctly, I will next increase the difficulty of the task by exaggerating the words a bit less and/or increasing the set size from four to five or six nouns.

Parent Guidance

- Play Memory (also known as Concentration), using pairs of the target words, to give Sara experience listening to them. A customized, homemade version can be made with file cards cut in half and pictures drawn or glued on.
- With crayons and paper in front of each of you and a barrier such as a tray between you, take turns telling each other, "*Draw a...*" while drawing one of the target nouns on your paper. Compare drawings.
- Add more challenge by increasing the set size to six nouns, adding, for example, *apple* and *man*, and/or reducing exaggeration of the target words.

Reassessing Speech Goals

Sara has already mastered most vowels and simple consonants. In this session, the main focus is to reinforce a selection of previously mastered speech targets in order to give her practice listening to them with her new implant. These include nasal consonant /m/; fricative (blowing) consonant /s/; vowels /a/, /u/, and /i/; and diphthongs /aʊ/ (*Ow!*) and /ʌɪ/ (*eye*). I chose /m/ because it is one of the sounds Sara had trouble with in the phoneme identification activity, and /s/ because it is a new sound for her. She had been able to detect it with her frequency-transposition hearing aid, but now it will sound quite different. Finally, since accurate identification of vowels has always been a problem, we're practicing front vowel /i/, mid vowel /a/, and back vowel /u/ to ensure that Sara acquires lots of experience listening to them.

First, I ask Sara to imitate several series of repeated babbled syllables containing the target sounds. As she is very fashion-conscious, I use a create-your-own-outfit puzzle (Amanda's Closet™ from Discovery Toys), which she assembles piece by piece after each set of a few babbled syllables.

Speech Targets

- /s/
  - Sara listens to /s/ in isolation, then repeats after me.
  - Sara listens to *sasasa* or *seeseesee* or *soosoosoo,* then repeats after me.
  - I reinforce Sara's correct imitations with verbal praise and by providing a puzzle piece for her to place.

Had she been unable to repeat a particular babbled syllable string I would have used the audition/vision/audition (auditory sandwich) technique, followed by reinforcement.

- /m/
  - Same procedure as for /s/, using babbled syllables *mamama, meemeemee* but not *moomoomoo,* as the acoustic similarity between /m/ and /u/, known to be problematic for Sara, would likely cause her to fail at this syllable string.
  - Sara tends to confuse /m/ with /w/, a liquid sound very similar to /u/. To focus on the difference between /m/ and /w/, I use a discrimination task. I print *mamama* and *wawawa* on a piece of paper, saying each one as I print it. I lengthen the /m/ and use a more sing-song intonation for the *oo-ah* of *wa.* I then say *mamama* and *wawawa* in random order.

Sara repeats each syllable string after me and successfully puts a check mark under the appropriate letters.

- /u/, /a/, /i/ in isolation
  - I encourage Sara to imitate a single /u/ or /a/ or /i/. I use slightly rising, then falling intonation for each one.

She confuses /u/ with /m/ until I specify that we are working on vowels only.

- /u/, /a/, /i/ in babbled syllables
  - Same procedure as for /s/ in babbled syllables, using *bahbahbah, booboo-boo, beebeebee.*

Sara correctly imitates all syllable strings with /b/. She has more difficulty with the /ʃ/ syllable strings *shahshahshah, shooshooshoo,* and *sheesheeshee.* I first say the "sh" in isolation to cue Sara to the consonant sound. Then I slow down the syllable strings and lengthen the vowels. Sara is then able to imitate them.

- ah-oo and ah-ee in isolation
  - Same procedure as for vowels in isolation.

Sara produces *ah-oo* as *ah-m* until I print the two target diphthongs for her. She then discriminates them correctly.

- /aʊ/ (*ah-oo*) and /ʌɪ/ (*ah-ee*) in babbled syllables
  - I use *bowbowbow* and *byebyebye.*

Sara has difficulty here, so I slow down, lengthen the diphthongs, and place more emphasis on the "oo" and "ee" parts of each one. Sara then correctly achieves them.

Word Games

For the word games, I use a board game and incorporate the target speech sounds /m/ and /s/ into it by means of a set of articulation cards (Articucards™ from Communication Skill Builders). Before rolling the die each time, Sara turns up a card and says, "*That's a...*" (using an m-word such as *man, mouse, mitten, moon, mask* or an s-word such as *sun, school, sock, sandals*).

Parent Guidance

- Play a board game that requires Sara to imitate a babbled syllable string or use a target m- or s-word in a sentence before each turn.

Reassessing Language Goals

Sara had already acquired many language skills before she received her cochlear implant. In this session, the goal is to help her identify easy-to-hear, beginner-level language targets. The long-term objective is to progress grammatical item by grammatical item, following a developmental hierarchy, occasionally adapted to ensure that targets are audible. For example, if /s/ was not yet detected, we would postpone working on the plural noun marker /s/.

Language Targets

- To discriminate *in* from *under.*
- To identify question forms *What's he doing?* and *What's that?*

Discriminate *In* from *Under*

I use my favorite activity for teaching basic prepositions. The materials include beanbags, a large toy car, and a playhouse.

- I put the toy car on the table, point to it, and then ask Sara to put a beanbag *in.* Then I ask her to put another beanbag *under.* To emphasize the difference between the two words, I exaggerate and lengthen the /n/ of *in* and vary my intonation from a high *un-* to a low *-der* with *under.*
- Then I ask her which one is *in.* She selects it and then gets to throw it into a tub far across the room. I replace the *in* beanbag and ask which one is *under,* followed by the same reinforcer. I ask which one is *in/under* a few more times.
- For variation, I repeat the same overall procedure with the house instead of the car. By the end of the activity Sara is able, with close listening, to discrim-

inate *in/under* consistently, so I will increase the level of difficulty to *in the car* versus *under the car*, or add a third preposition, *beside*.

Identify Question Forms *What's He Doing?* and *What's That?*

I reinforce these question forms separately several times first, then mix and match them. For the question form *What's that?*, I use picture cards and a feely-meely bag containing corresponding objects.

- I show Sara six pictures, asking "*What's that?*" Each time Sara answers correctly, I place the picture on the table.
- As Sara reaches into the bag, I ask, "What's that?" She identifies the simple objects by feeling them and says, "*That's a...*" She removes the object from the bag to see if she has guessed correctly.
- Her mom or I take a turn, alternating with Sara until all objects have been identified.

For the question *What's he doing?*, I use the verb cards from Creatures and Critters™ (available from Communication Skill Builders). These cards portray cute frogs and turtles performing human activities.

- Sara picks a card from a pile.
- I cue her to *Listen!* and then ask, *What's he/she doing?*
- Sara answers the question.
- Her mom or I pick a card, listen to Sara ask the question, and then one of us answers it.
- We continue until we have used up five cards.
- For the combined activity, we continue with the verb cards using the same procedure, occasionally asking each other, *What's that?* to identify one of the frog's or turtle's quirky accessories.

Sara requires a bit of prompting to listen to the question asked, as opposed to the question expected.

Parent Guidance

- When you are reading a picture book to Sara, often ask her these two target questions.
- Throughout the day, ask her these two questions whenever an opportunity arises.

Mom's Notebook

As Sara's mother has now attended Auditory-Verbal therapy sessions for 3 years, she has the knowledge and experience to carry out therapy goals at home. Between activities throughout the session, I provide activity suggestions, and Mom jots them down in a small notebook. At the end of the session, we briefly review the assigned targets.

Session Summary

Sara's implant has now been switched on for about one month. After two weeks of wearing it, her ability to understand familiar words and phrases, through listening alone, reached her preimplant level. Her ability to identify high-frequency sounds /s/ and /f/ is superior to her preimplant levels. She is beginning to make the hard-to-hear place differentiation among front-plosive consonant /p/, mid-plosive /t/, and back-plosive /k/. Sara can now identify most vowels and diphthongs. We continue to work on identification of low-frequency phonemes /u/ and /m/ because they are still confused. Distance listening is dramatically better in that Sara can hear her name being called from across a 20-foot room or even from an adjacent room. Her ability to understand spontaneous spoken language through audition, at the time of this lesson, was as weak as before she received her cochlear implant.

To date, Sara's performance with her cochlear implant has been excellent. With further refining of her implant MAP and continued listening practice throughout the day, her parents and I are optimistic that she will eventually be able to understand most spoken language through listening.

SESSION PLAN #6: AUDREY (AGE 6)*

At the time of this session, Audrey had just celebrated her sixth birthday with her triplet siblings, Aaron and Michael. Her brothers have typical hearing, but Audrey was diagnosed at 14 months of age with a bilateral moderately severe to severe sensorineural hearing loss of unknown etiology. Immediately following diagnosis, Audrey was fitted with behind-the-ear hearing aids. A month later, she and her parents began Auditory-Verbal therapy.

During her first year in therapy, Audrey made impressive gains in spoken communication. Her voice sounded natural, and she developed most speech sounds expected for her chronological age.

In her 26th month of Auditory-Verbal therapy, Audrey had difficulty detecting /s/, /f/, and /θ/ ("th"). Listening tasks became "hard," and she would promptly tell the therapist to "ask Mommy!"

Subsequent visits to the audiologist revealed that Audrey's hearing loss had progressed to the severe to profound range. Investigation for cochlear implant candidacy began, and at 4 years, 10 months, Audrey received a cochlear implant.

Introduction to the Therapy Session

At the time of this session, Audrey had had 1 year of listening with her cochlear implant and was achieving excellent auditory-verbal development. She was integrated into a large kindergarten class at her local school, used a personal FM

---

* By Karen MacIver-Lux, M. A, Aud.(C), Reg. CASLPO, Cert. AVT®. Adapted from W. Estabrooks & L. Birkenshaw-Fleming, (Eds.), *Songs for Listening! Songs for Life!* Washington, DC: Alexander Graham Bell Association for the Deaf and Hard of Hearing, 2003. Used with permission.

system in the classroom, and received support from an itinerant teacher 3 hours a week.

As I approach the waiting room, Audrey is reading a book with her mother while four other children are chattering excitedly. I call Audrey's name amidst the noise. After I have called twice, Audrey looks up and smiles shyly. I tell her I am pleased that she heard me call her name. I tell her that we are going to do the Hokey Pokey today. Audrey is interested in funny words, and her mom loves the idea.

Goals

Audition:

- Identify objects based on related descriptions.
- Follow directions containing several critical elements.
- Extend auditory memory and sequencing.

Speech:

- Sing songs with imitation of suprasegmental features.
- Enhance production of /s/ in final position of words.

Language:

- Enhance use of plurals, articles, and conjunctions.
- Formulate requests (e.g., *What would you like?*)
- Use the pronouns *her/him, she/he, they/them.*
- Ask questions (e.g., *What did he/she do?*)
- Request repetition and/or clarification.

Cognition:

- Reinforce *right* and *left.*
- Continue developing higher-level auditory–cognitive concepts.

Ling Six-Sound Test

I introduce Mr. Pokey (a potato head), "who invented the Hokey Pokey." Audrey and her mom sit at the table across the room (about 12 feet away) with Mr. Pokey. Mom holds a basket of Mr. Potato Head™ body parts, clothing, and accessories. For each sound I make, Audrey places the item on Mr. Pokey. Her mom helps Audrey correctly identify each of the basket items and its color by giving her related descriptors ("It gives Mr. Pokey *sight,* and it's the *same color as the sky,* and guess whether it's in my *left* or *right* hand").

Parent Guidance

- Use the words *right* and *left* throughout the day. Audrey can survey friends and family members (e.g., "Are you left-handed or right-handed?").

- Discuss various parts of the body and their functions. Books such as *Hands!* (Kroll, 1997) and *From Head to Toe* (Carle, 1997) contain short, catchy rhymes about parts of the body.
- Create games to reinforce left/right. Hide a treat in one hand and request others to guess "right hand" or "left hand." This will help Audrey use questions, practice left/right, listen for answers, and request clarification and repetitions.

Preparing for Mr. Pokey's Party

I tell Audrey that Mr. Pokey is having a "Hokey Pokey party" for four of his potato-head friends. Each potato head needs to be *dressed to impress.* I say "Audrey, you can help the guests get ready for the party."

I present a box full of bits and pieces (arms, lips, eyes, hats, shoes, purses, and glasses). I ask Audrey to "put on purple eyes, pink lips, and yellow shoes." We switch roles, and I whisper directions to Audrey for her to relay to her mother. Audrey omits /s/ and /z/ in the words *lips* and *shoes.* I use acoustic highlighting to elicit correct production. Audrey substitutes /f/ for /θ/ in the word *mouth.* As "th" was a speech target in previous lessons, I just lean towards Audrey with a quizzical look, and she quickly repeats her sentence using the correct production. We include concepts such as *without, similar, first,* and *last* throughout the activity. When the activity is finished, Audrey names each one of Mr. Pokey's guests. Mom and I encourage her to remember their names.

Parent Guidance

- Extension of auditory memory can be incorporated into everyday routines (e.g., laying out Audrey's clothes, preparing her lunchbox). Introduce sabotage such as *sandals* instead of *boots* during the winter, or *ice cubes* instead of *pudding* for dessert in the lunchbox. Discuss why those items don't belong.
- Children's literature can help extend auditory memory. Read *Teddy's Secret* (Warren, 1998); it is a perfect follow-up to our session.
- Reinforce *without, similar, first,* and *last.*
- Tell Audrey real-life stories of when the triplets were born. You could use a picture album and talk about who was born *without* hair and who was born *first/last.*
- Acoustically highlight /s/. Whispering the word makes /s/ easier to hear.

Mr. Pokey's Dinner Party

I coach Mom to ask Audrey to seat each of Mr. Pokey's friends at the dinner table. I use such phrases as *head of the table, to Mr. Pokey's left/right,* and *between.* Audrey places the guests.

I present a small picnic hamper of "party foods" (French fries, cookies, bananas, hot dogs, ice cream, cake). Audrey guesses some of the party foods and places them on the table. I describe some for her ("It's cold, you can lick it, it comes in a cone").

Audrey will help Mr. Pokey serve the guests, so we practice such questions as "What would you like to eat?" and "What can I get you?" Mom says, "The guests are very hungry and want six things to eat" (e.g., "He wants a *hot dog* and some *French fries*, a *banana*, a *cookie*, *ice cream*, and *cake*"). We switch roles, and Audrey practices asking questions, recalling six items, and making requests for clarification.

Parent Guidance

- Enhance word-retrieval skills and expand vocabulary by playing the game Outburst Junior™. The object of this game is to practice word retrieval. Each player has a limited time to think of as many items as possible that are associated with a category (e.g., fruits, forest animals, vehicles). The player who names the most items listed on the question cards wins.
- Review new concepts such as *head of the table*.
- Play the Restaurant Game (pretend-ordering at a restaurant) for question development and turn-taking skills.

Partying with Mr. Pokey

With Mr. Pokey in my hands, I sing the song "Hokey Pokey." I help Mr. Pokey do the actions. I ask Audrey and her mother to pick a potato head and join in. Audrey and her mom both manipulate the parts of their potato heads as I change *in/out* to *up/down* and *shake it all about* to *wiggle, jump, march, stomp all about.* Then we listen to the CD (Estabrooks & Birkenshaw-Fleming, 2003). I sing the song and encourage Audrey to sing. Then her mom and I follow the directions as Audrey sings. Audrey sings by herself, and we model the past tense for her (e.g., "He *put* his left hand in and *shook* it all about"). Mom asks what my potato head did in the song, and I prompt Audrey to ask Mom.

Musical Suggestions

- This is an action song that all children like to sing and act out. The Hokey Pokey is performed by raising both hands up in front of the body, palms out, and moving them left and right. Turn once and then clap the rhythm of the words, "That's what it's all about."
- When the song is well known, vary the tempo to maintain interest and challenge listening.

Parent Guidance

- Listen to the CD of "Hokey Pokey."
- Sing "Hokey Pokey" all week. We will do it again next week.

- "Hokey Pokey" is excellent for developing auditory memory.
- To help reinforce formulation of prepositional phrases, read the book *Snake In, Snake Out* (Banchek, 1978).

Session Summary

A "Hokey Pokey party" theme was used to work on targets in audition, speech, language, and cognition. The song, the poem, and play within a rich linguistic environment helped both Audrey and her mother develop confidence in their auditory-verbal development.

CONCLUSION

The examples of Auditory-Verbal therapy given in these session plans for preschoolers are intended as guidelines. In all cases, an individualized treatment plan has been tailored to the child's and family's interests, following the natural sequential development of children with typical hearing (Estabrooks & Samson, 1992). Both natural and contrived play are encouraged, together with direct structured intervention. Parental carryover into daily activities is crucial for optimal stimulation and achievement of agreed goals in audition, speech, language, cognition, and communication.

REFERENCES

Amanda's Closet™. Livermore, CA: Discovery Toys. <www.discoverytoysinc.com>.

Articu-cards™. San Antonio: Communication Skill Builders. A Division of The Psychological Corporation, 555 Academic Court, San Antonio, TX 78204-2498.

Banchek, L. (1978). *Snake In, Snake Out.* New York: HarperCollins.

Call the Plumber™. Grand Toys International. <www.grand.com>.

Carle, E. (1997). *From Head to Toe.* New York: HarperCollins.

Caruso, T. (1998). "Lesson Plan for Heather." W. Estabrooks (Ed.), *Cochlear Implants for Kids* (pp. 186–200). Washington, DC: Alexander Graham Bell Association for the Deaf.

Creatures and Critters™. San Antonio: Communication Skill Builders. A Division of The Psychological Corporation, 555 Academic Court, San Antonio, TX 78204-2498.

Estabrooks, W., & Birkenshaw-Fleming, L. (Eds.) (2003). *Songs for Listening! Songs for Life!* Washington, DC: Alexander Graham Bell Association for the Deaf and Hard of Hearing.

Estabrooks, W., & Samson, A.B. (1992). *Do You Hear That?* Videotape. Washington, DC: Alexander Graham Bell Association for the Deaf.

Fox, M. (1992). *Hattie the Fox.* New York: Simon and Schuster.

Kroll, V.L. (1997). *Hands!* Honesdale, PA: Boyds Mills Press.

Houston, K.T. (1998). "Lesson Plan for Chase." In W. Estabrooks (Ed.), *Cochlear Implants for Kids.* Washington, DC: Alexander Graham Bell Association for the Deaf.

Hungry Hungry Hippos™. Pawtucket, RI: Milton Bradley. A Division of Hasbro Inc.

Ling, D. (1976). *Speech and the Hearing Impaired child: Theory and Practice.* Washington, DC: Alexander Graham Bell Association for the Deaf.

Ling, D. (2005). "The Six-Sound Test." *The Listener* (Special Silver Anniversary Edition), 72–74.

MacIver-Lux, K. (2003). "Hokey Pokey." In W. Estabrooks & L. Birkenshaw-Fleming, L. (Eds.), *Songs for Listening! Songs for Life!* Washington, DC: Alexander Graham Bell Association for the Deaf and Hard of Hearing.

Martin, B. (1992). *Brown Bear, Brown Bear, What Do You See?* New York: Henry Holt.

Mr. Mouth™. Pawtucket, RI: Milton Bradley. A Division of Hasbro Inc. <www.hasbro.com>.

Mr. Potato Head and his Li'l Potato Kid™. Pawtucket, RI: Hasbro Inc. <www.hasbro.com>.
Operation™. Pawtucket, RI: Hasbro Inc. <www.hasbro.com>.
Outburst Junior™. Pawtucket, RI: Parker Brothers. A Division of Hasbro Inc. <www.hasbro.com>.
Probe!™. Pawtucket, RI: Parker Brothers. A Division of Hasbro Inc. <www.hasbro.com>.
Silverstein, S. (1974). *Where the Sidewalk Ends.* New York, NY: HarperCollins.
Simser, J. (1998). "Lesson Plan for Chris." In W. Estabrooks (Ed.), *Cochlear Implants for Kids* (pp. 174-185). Washington, DC: Alexander Graham Bell Association for the Deaf.
Steacie, P. (1998). "Lesson Plan for Sara." In W. Estabrooks (Ed.), *Cochlear Implants for Kids.* Washington, DC: Alexander Graham Bell Association for the Deaf.
Warren, A.C. (1998). *Teddy's Secret.* Brookvale, NSW, Australia: The Book Company.

CHAPTER 7

Auditory-Verbal Therapy and School

Dorothy Boothroyd-Turner, B.A., M.E.D.
Wendy Sheppard, B.A., B.Ed.

When children go to school, society has ambitious expectations for them. These include literacy, academic and communicative competence, social and emotional well-being, intellectual curiosity, and growing independence. Meeting these expectations is a challenge for all children, but especially those who are deaf or hard of hearing. In our experience, children who have learned to listen and to speak at an early age have good potential to meet these expectations with their hearing peers in a mainstream school setting.

This chapter considers some theoretical and practical aspects of the mainstream support program for children who are deaf or hard of hearing who attend public schools within the Toronto District School Board. Parents and professionals elsewhere can generalize this information and apply it to their own child or student.

INCLUSION

Inclusionary education suggests acceptance versus exclusion; it embraces each individual child in all aspects of the classroom and the wider school community, and promotes growth in this context (Little, 1992). Proponents of Auditory-Verbal therapy have been on the forefront of advocating for inclusionary education since the pioneering work of Helen Beebe and Doreen Pollack (see Appendix G [Position Statement on AVT in Schools]). These two professionals had a vision of what children who are deaf or hard of hearing could accomplish with the opportunities provided through Auditory-Verbal therapy. Improved hearing technology, such as digital hearing aids and cochlear implants, and legislation have converged with Auditory-Verbal therapy to make inclusion within the mainstream classroom viable for the majority of students who are deaf or hard of hearing. Inclusion, however, is not possible without long-term commitment and proactive intervention on the part of all stakeholders. This intervention must occur through state-of-the-art mainstreaming practice.

Mainstreaming is defined as "making ordinary education special" (Little, 1992). It entails making whatever changes are necessary in the typical classroom environment to facilitate growth in all areas of development. For the child who is deaf or hard of hearing, these changes may involve accommodations, alternative curricula, curriculum modification, or a combination of these. Accommodations might include acoustic considerations, preferential seating, appropriate lighting, assistive devices, extra resources, more time to complete assignments, and individualized instruction. Alternative curricula might include speech, listening, and developmental language. Curriculum modification might include reduction in the number and complexity of learning expectations of the typical classroom. The impact of deafness on the ability to perceive, process, and acquire speech and language presents a significant challenge, even for a child who is equipped with the most recent technology and who has had intensive Auditory-Verbal therapy since a very early age. Simply placing the child in a classroom with hearing children is not enough (Boothroyd-Turner, 1990; Ross, 1990; Ross, Brackett, & Maxon, 1982). Adequate support systems must be in place to ensure that each child is developing cognitively, academically, communicatively, socially, and emotionally.

KEY STAKEHOLDERS

The key stakeholders in any successful mainstreaming model include the parents, the itinerant teacher, the school principal, the classroom teacher, and the child, among others (Figure 7.1).

The Parents

Parents have been their child's primary case managers from the time they first suspected a hearing loss. Through an Auditory-Verbal therapy program, they have become their child's primary teachers as well. The parents' role shifts when the child goes to school. This may be the first time his or her learning is independent of them. The parents are not in the classroom, nor do they participate in most tutorial sessions the child attends with the itinerant teacher. Instead, communication usually occurs through the home–school book, telephone calls, or brief discussions when the child arrives at or leaves from school. Giving up complete control is difficult for some parents; it is a relief for others. In our experience, mainstreaming a child who is deaf or hard of hearing works best when the parents remain the ultimate case managers, but when they appreciate the role of a new advocate for their child—the itinerant teacher.

The Itinerant Teacher

The role of the itinerant teacher is multifaceted: collaborating, informing, educating. He or she must be proactive, flexible, persistent, diplomatic, sensitive, knowledgeable, and skilled. The itinerant teacher usually integrates the key stakeholders' efforts and attempts to keep the lines of communication open. This consultative-collaborative model clearly benefits the mainstreamed child who is deaf or hard of hearing (Little, 1992).

The itinerant teacher provides in-service assistance to the school community and, specifically, to the mainstream classroom teacher. Parents often want the

Figure 7.1 Key Stakeholders in the Life of a Schoolchild Learning Through the Auditory-Verbal Approach

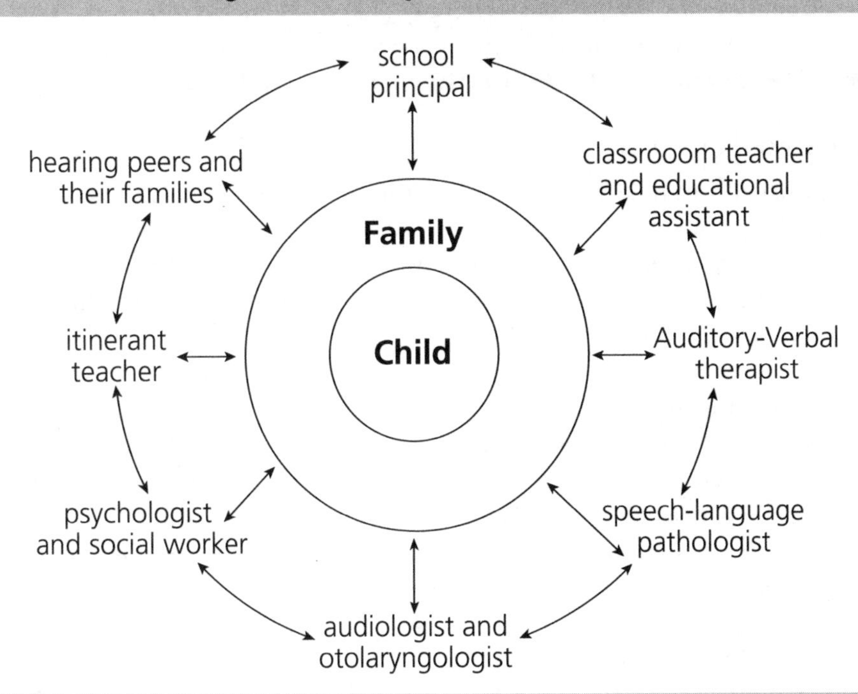

classroom teacher to learn about hearing loss, cochlear implants, auditory-verbal goals, and their child's individual needs in the spring prior to his or her arrival at school the following fall. We have discovered, however, that most teachers find in-service that occurs early in the fall of the current academic year to be more practical and meaningful, as the teacher is better able to comprehend it in the context of the child who is now in the teacher's classroom.

The timing and style of successful in-service are very important. The itinerant teacher gives the classroom teacher information on such matters as hearing loss, hearing aids, cochlear implants, FM amplification systems, Auditory-Verbal therapy, speech and language development, adaptive teaching strategies, closed captioning and note taking, a little at a time. He or she provides this information both verbally and with materials and handouts that can be referred to at a later date.

Most importantly, the itinerant teacher plans and carries out the child's mainstream support program. In collaboration with the school and in consultation with the parents, an Individual Education Plan (IEP) is prepared each fall (Government of Ontario, 2004). This document clearly delineates the child's strengths, areas of need, and current levels of achievement. The IEP establishes annual goals and realistic learning expectations for both the classroom and tutorial sessions. The extent of curriculum modification, required equipment, and necessary accommodations for teaching and assessment are clearly stated in the IEP, so that parents and school personnel alike have a clear understanding of the child's program (Government of Ontario, 2000). Assessment and evaluation are ongoing, and formal review of the child's placement, with parent and school participation, is required (*Education Act*, 1990).

The School Principal

The principal's attitude is critical to the child's success in the mainstream. Each principal sets the tone for the entire school community. He or she is often the first person whom parents meet when they visit their neighborhood school. Parents report that the principal's initial reaction has a profound impact on their level of comfort and confidence.

The best school principals support the parents, the child, the classroom teacher, and the itinerant teacher. They greet and chat with the child on a regular basis; they make themselves aware of his or her strengths and areas of need; they understand and respect individual differences; they are aware of their legal responsibility to implement and monitor the Individual Education Plan; and they help find solutions if the child is at risk. In short, they are positive, yet realistic, advocates for the child.

The Classroom Teacher

The classroom teacher is responsible for delivering a specific grade curriculum to a heterogeneous group of children, some of whom may have learning exceptionalities. This task is not an easy one. The classroom teacher deserves the utmost respect.

In our experience, most teachers welcome the child who is deaf or hard of hearing into their classroom and consider his or her presence a challenge rather than a burden. They are generally willing to wear the FM transmitter, if required; implement curriculum modifications and accommodations into their teaching; and work with the team of parents, itinerant teachers, and others. Occasionally, a teacher may have difficulty with this challenge. If this difficulty persists after a reasonable amount of in-service and encouragement, it is probably best to consider a change of classroom. Perpetuating a negative situation is not good for anyone concerned, least of all the child who is deaf or hard of hearing.

When the classroom teacher understands, respects, and welcomes individual differences, this attitude permeates the classroom and is absorbed by the children. It is in this environment of acceptance that the child who is deaf or hard of hearing has the best opportunity to thrive in all areas.

The Child

Much has been said about what others need to do for the child who is deaf or hard of hearing in the mainstream. Little is ever said about what the child must do. The child must be an active participant in achieving the goals that were originally set by his or her parents, and must assume these goals as his or her own at some point. This is a significant undertaking when the goals include learning to listen and to speak, and attending school with hearing peers. In our experience, most young adults who have had extensive Auditory-Verbal therapy report that mainstreaming was indeed the best route for them, and that it was worth all their efforts. Some, however, did not identify with the goals, and felt out of place.

Clearly, a mainstream education is not for all children who are deaf or hard of hearing, despite early Auditory-Verbal therapy, their parents' best intentions, and a great deal of support. Attending school requires tremendous concentration, determination, ability, and self-confidence. It requires more time at work and less time at play. Parents and professionals can support and enable, but the responsibility for achievement is ultimately the child's.

CHILDREN WITH COCHLEAR IMPLANTS

Recent years have seen a notable increase in the number of cochlear implant users in the mainstream. Of well over 100 students in the Toronto District School Board who currently receive direct instruction withdrawal support, approximately a quarter are cochlear implant users. Ten years ago, only a few itinerant teachers worked with a small number of children with cochlear implants; today, most itinerant teachers have at least one student with a cochlear implant on their caseloads.

Another notable change has been that children are receiving cochlear implants at a much younger age, offering them enhanced opportunities during the critical early years to listen and learn. Bilateral cochlear implants are emerging now, and may further improve listening and learning potential.

In Toronto, English is not the first language of an increasing number of children. This adds complexity, as English remains the language of instruction in the classroom.

GOING TO SCHOOL

The Challenge of the Typical Classroom

A good classroom is a complex and exciting learning environment. It requires readiness and attentiveness to receive incoming sensory input of an auditory, visual, and tactile nature. It requires receptive processing and attaching meaning to the incoming sensory input. This involves decoding, organizing, associating new information with what is already known, and storing information in memory. The classroom also requires higher-level processing during which the child integrates information across all sensory modalities in order to produce an active expressive response.

All stakeholders have an important role to play in meeting the challenge of the learning environment. Sometimes we encounter parents who initially feel that an itinerant teacher is unnecessary, as they do not wish any special attention directed towards their child. In our experience, however, an itinerant teacher who is regularly on site provides enormous benefits. In addition to providing extra tutorial support, the itinerant teacher, in collaboration with the classroom teacher, monitors the participation and success of the child in the classroom.

When the itinerant teacher has a workable, ongoing communication system in place that is inclusive of parents and other team members, he or she can discuss and make suggestions on how to respond to any of the child's changing needs. Generally, we find that most children who have had Auditory-Verbal therapy function remarkably well in a controlled, quiet setting. In the typical classroom, however, they can become overloaded and "turn off." Large group lessons and discussions pose greater listening challenges than smaller, controlled groups and individual lessons. Despite best intentions, listening conditions in the classroom may not always be optimal, and as a result, incidental language may not be heard. At times, the contributions of the child's peers may be inaudible. Even teacher-directed instruction, presented clearly, may be difficult to process if it includes a great deal of abstract language or is delivered too quickly.

Tutorial Support

The Toronto District School Board provides tutorial support to mainstreamed students who are deaf or hard of hearing through individualized direct instruction under optimal listening conditions. These students need specialized instruction in the areas of listening, speech, and overall language development. This does not mean that the itinerant teacher works in isolation. He or she frequently weaves specific listening, speech, and language goals into the regular work of the classroom. In addition, the itinerant teacher can pre-teach and re-teach language that is not always accessible in the large classroom. A student who is familiar with vocabulary or subject matter prior to its introduction in the classroom is much more likely to be able to follow and comprehend the lesson. The itinerant teacher relates his or her program not only to the child's life at school, but also to the child's home life. This tutorial model has its disadvantages. It can foster dependence rather than independence, and can lead to egocentric behaviors. The itinerant teacher tries to address these concerns by working creatively and collaboratively with the classroom teacher.

There are times when the itinerant teacher may work directly in the classroom with the mainstream teacher. In this way, the itinerant teacher can observe the expectations and interactions of the entire classroom first hand. Sometimes the itinerant teacher may work with a small group withdrawn from or within the class. Along with his or her peers, the child who is deaf or hard of hearing can practice planning, listening, turn-taking, discussing, and respecting the views of others in a structured yet nonthreatening environment. The advantages for all students involved are substantial.

Access to the Curriculum

In the province of Ontario, the classroom curriculum is based on the Ontario Curriculum, which sets out key areas of study. The focus of the mainstream support program in the Toronto District School Board is developmental rather than remedial. The goal is for the child who is deaf or hard of hearing to learn the skills he or she will need for current and future endeavors in school, as set forth in the curriculum. While some children may require learning expectations that are modified from the grade-level curriculum, many can master the curriculum's concepts and skills but need accommodations to do so.

Older Students

In the Toronto District School Board, itinerant teachers continue working with mainstreamed students who are deaf or hard of hearing throughout the high school years. The balance between developmental and remedial work shifts as the child grows older, learns to read and write, and becomes a more competent and confident communicator. In the later years, specific subject content is the main focus of tutorial sessions. The itinerant teacher further encourages the student to become a more independent learner by suggesting organizational and self-help strategies. Lessons for students at the intermediate and senior levels may involve essay writing and proofreading, oral presentations, interpreting Shakespeare and other literary works, or preparing for tests and examinations. In short, the expected outcomes of the mainstream school curriculum drive the core content of the itinerant tutorial lesson.

AUDITORY-VERBAL THERAPY IN THE MAINSTREAM SCHOOL

Anita Bernstein, Cert. AVT® and Tina Olmstead, Cert. AVT®

As children learning to listen and speak through the auditory-verbal approach enter the school system, their parents expect continuity of auditory-verbal services. Parents who have been involved in and committed to Auditory-Verbal therapy are requesting that their child be seen by trained auditory-verbal professionals and that they continue to be able to participate in these sessions.

In Ontario, families and professionals have been working collaboratively and tirelessly to ensure that auditory-verbal services are available. Auditory-verbal programs have developed both at the preschool level and for the school population. Although some programs have received government support, most evolved without such funding. Parental demands led to the growth of many of these services.

With universal hearing screening now the standard, families have access to government-funded audiological services and auditory-verbal intervention for a period of two years post identification. Auditory-verbal services are provided in clinical settings, in private practices, and through home visiting programs offered by some school boards.

Certified Auditory-Verbal therapists who work in mainstream schools continue to provide programs that incorporate the principles of auditory-verbal practice in the following ways:

- delivering a one-on-one, diagnostic intervention program based on assessment data in the areas of audition, speech, language, communication, and cognition (Ling, 1989; Duncan & Dodson, 2001), using the school curriculum as the vehicle to develop these skills. The student's development in all these areas is carefully monitored, and intervention services are provided according to need. As diagnostic teaching reveals that a student reaches competency and age-appropriate functioning, this intervention is correspondingly reduced.
- playing a key role in optimizing the acoustic signal in the classroom and maximizing audition in a variety of situations. Since the Auditory-Verbal therapist's focus is to develop language through hearing, properly functioning hearing devices are of paramount importance. Auditory-Verbal therapists work as part of a team with the clinical or educational audiologist by providing information on the student's functional use of hearing in school. They are current in their knowledge of technological advancements and are responsible for monitoring students' amplification systems and assistive devices.
- developing skills in the areas of listening, language, speech, cognition, and communication, which the student will require to learn the curriculum. This development requires the integration of specific goals with the curriculum, as opposed to using a parallel program (e.g., listening hierarchy vs. auditory skills development curriculum).
- utilizing the academic and social demands of the mainstream school as vehicles for continued diagnostic teaching in skill development. Duncan (2001) provides a framework for facilitating the development of communication competence and complex skills development in the areas of pragmatics, semantics, syntax, and phonology. The framework is based on experience with students who are deaf or hard of hearing, aged 6-14. According to Duncan, progression through complex skills development is critical to independent adulthood.

As increasing numbers of children who are deaf or hard of hearing enter mainstream schools, the need for school-based Auditory-Verbal therapists also increases. To facilitate the child's integration, the Auditory-Verbal therapist creates individualized programs based on results of assessments (Duncan & Dodson, 2001), plans the program, teaches the child, guides the parents, evaluates, and maintains accurate records of progress.

The auditory-verbal program at school includes classroom teachers, administrators, other school personnel, and the child's peers. All help to create opportunities for social interaction to foster positive social relationships. School-based auditory-verbal programs that address all these factors facilitate the successful mainstreaming of children who are deaf or hard of hearing (Eriks-Brophy, Fitzpatrick, Durieux-Smith, Olds, Whittingham, Duquette, & Capelli, 1999).

ASSESSMENT AND EVALUATION

Student achievement must be evaluated to determine whether defined outcomes have been met and to plan future instruction. It is the responsibility of the itinerant teacher to assess the child's baseline competencies in listening, speech, language, and cognitive development. Ideally, the itinerant teacher will work collaboratively with the child's audiologist, Auditory-Verbal therapist, and parents to gather, interpret, and report this information. It is the responsibility of the classroom teacher to assess and evaluate the child's ability to master the learning expectations of the mainstream grade curriculum, with any accommodations and/or modifications noted on the IEP. This evaluation is documented on the child's report card three times annually.

Clearly, development in listening, speech, language, and cognition provides the underpinning for participation and success in curricular endeavors.

The classroom placement is deemed appropriate when the child's overall performance is comparable to that of his or her classmates. If this is not the case, the reasons must be determined, and additional accommodations, modifications, or a change of placement considered. Some professionals and parents may feel that social integration is reason enough to continue a mainstream placement. It is not. Children cannot maintain a good self-image if they know they are significantly lagging behind their hearing peers academically and if they cannot communicate effectively with them. In such a situation, the children are not socially integrated or even accepted for long. While the principles of auditory-verbal practice include "mainstreaming and integration of children with hearing loss into regular classes to the fullest extent possible" (Auditory-Verbal International, 1991), auditory-verbal proponents do not advocate compromising a child's emotional, social, and academic well-being by perpetuating a placement in which the child is not thriving.

CONCLUSION

Under the auditory-verbal approach, going to school with hearing peers is a natural and logical step for children to take. Parents have been preparing them for this since making an initial commitment to the principles of auditory-verbal practice. The process of mainstreaming is a challenging one that requires substantial effort by the key stakeholders.

Mainstreaming children who are deaf or hard of hearing is only a means to an end. The end is inclusion. This is the dream when children who have learned to listen and speak through the auditory-verbal approach go to school.

REFERENCES

Auditory-Verbal International. (1991). "Auditory-verbal position statement." *The Auricle, 4*(4), 11.

Boothroyd-Turner, D. (1990). "Mainstreaming into the nineties." In M. Ross (Ed.), *Hearing-Impaired Children in the Mainstream.* Timonium, MD: York Press.

Duncan, J. (2001, Fall). "Facilitating complex skills development for students with hearing impairment: A practical framework." *The Listener,* 27–29.

Duncan, J., & Dodson, C. (2001). "Why is Auditory-Verbal therapy referred to as diagnostic?" In W. Estabrooks (Ed.), *50 FAQs about AVT.* Toronto: Learning to Listen Foundation.

Education Act, RSO 1990, c. E.2, O. Reg. 181/98 (Identification and Placement of Exceptional Pupils).

Eriks-Brophy, A., Fitzpatrick, E., Durieux-Smith, A., Olds, J., Whittingham, J., Duquette, C., & Capelli, M. (1999). "A study of factors which facilitated the integration of adolescents with a hearing impairment: Implications for policy and practice." *OSLA Connection,* 26(2), 3–4.

Government of Ontario. (2000). *Individual Education Plans—Standards for Development, Program Planning, and Implementation.* Toronto: Ministry of Education.

Government of Ontario. (2004). *The Individual Education Plan (IEP)—A Resource Guide.* Toronto: Ministry of Education.

Ling, D. (1989). *Foundations of Spoken Language for Hearing-Impaired Children.* Washington, DC: Alexander Graham Bell Association for the Deaf.

Little, D.M. (1992). "The muddle of mainstreaming: Cross-Canada currents—Policy and practice of inclusive education." *Exceptionality Education Canada, 2*(1 & 2), 9–48.

Ross, M. (Ed.). (1990). *Hearing-Impaired Children in the Mainstream.* Timonium, MD: York Press.

Ross, M., Brackett, D., & Maxon, A. (1982). *Hard of Hearing Children in Regular Schools.* Englewood Cliffs, NJ: Prentice Hall.

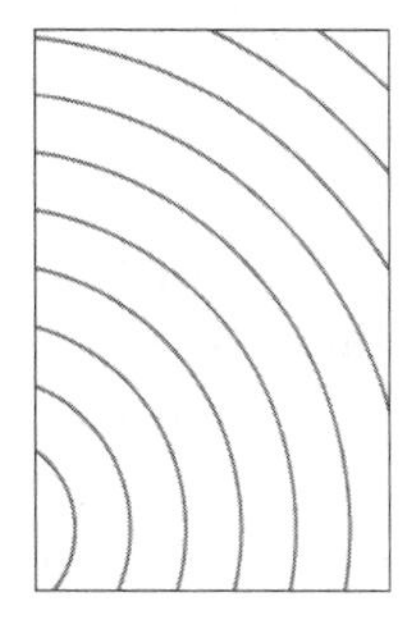

CHAPTER 8

The Family–Professional Partnership: A Parent's Perspective

Ariella Blum Samson

Parents who discover their child has a hearing loss arrive at the process by accident, having anticipated nothing less than a perfect child. They experience confusion, anger, despair, and frustration, together with an inevitable mourning process. Many professionals whom they will meet have elected to devote their careers to the needs of children who are deaf or hard of hearing and their families. These professionals believe that the sooner they can identify and diagnose a problem and initiate therapy, the more promising the outcome will be (Estabrooks, 1993; Ling, 1989; Pollack, 1970, 1985).

There is, however, a gap between parents and professionals regarding the delivery of services. Even the most experienced professionals cannot assume they always have a successful relationship with parents. Any one program for children who are deaf or hard of hearing cannot meet all the needs of all the children and their families, even with the full participation of parents.

OUR SON

Jonathan, who is presently 34 years old, was diagnosed at 11 months with a profound hearing loss, averaging 105 dB in his better ear. I first suspected his deafness the day we came home from the hospital. He was five days old. Our new nursery was still in transition from sewing room to baby room. As Jonathan looked about peacefully from his crib, the ironing board crashed to the floor, startling me from my tranquillity. Jonathan, however, slept on undisturbed! The first seeds of doubt were firmly planted in my mind. Still, this was our first baby, and I was not yet ready to face the shattered dreams ahead. As long as I did not talk about it, I could pretend the problem did not exist.

It took almost 2 months to muster up the courage to open up to my husband. I waited for reassurance that I was just imagining it. Jules, however, must have been doing his own dance of denial during this time. When we finally talked, we could no longer hide in our own protective corners. Yet, on our next visit, the pediatrician convinced us that we were neurotic, overanxious parents, expecting too much from our firstborn. A month before his first birthday, in a crowded narrow hospital hallway, the otolaryngologist blurted out that Jonathan was profoundly deaf. The actual jargon used was that Jonathan "had a 90% hearing loss." That particular verdict launched us into a tumultuous relationship with many different professionals.

Our next contact was with the audiologist, who made earmold impressions and booked a return appointment for Jonathan's hearing aid fitting. Approximately half an hour after the official diagnosis, we left the hospital; no further information was volunteered, no materials were dispensed for study at home, and no hope was extended to us.

Nevertheless, aside from our initial numbness, the predominant feeling that day was relief: relief that what we suspected was finally confirmed, relief that Jonathan was not retarded but only deaf, and relief that we could begin to do something. Yet we knew nothing about deafness!

Thus, armed with our ignorance and the impetus to do something, we went to the university library for a stack of books. We then visited the local school for the deaf after finding the address in the yellow pages of our telephone directory.

After school hours on this particular Friday afternoon, the three of us were left to our own devices in the empty building. We walked about, peeked into classrooms, and perused the walls that lined the hallways. This was our first confrontation with academic expectations for the deaf. We were appalled.

In the weeks that followed, Jonathan was confirmed to have a left-corner audiogram with a 105 dB hearing loss in his better ear. With no discernible hearing in his right ear, Jonathan was fitted with one body hearing aid. It would be 8 years before ear-level aids were powerful enough. I read every book in the field that I could find. Having read *Educational Audiology for the Limited-Hearing Infant* (Pollack, 1970; rev. 1985, 1997), I knew that Jonathan ought to have the benefit of a second hearing aid. That was to be the first of the many differences of opinion between our family and professionals. Soon afterwards, I realized that my role was to be Jonathan's advocate—in today's lingo, his case manager.

As parents, our goal was fairly single-minded: we not only wanted the best for our children, but we also wanted the best from them. We wanted Jonathan to learn spoken English. My husband, Jules, and I each speak three languages. English, our common tongue, is the only language spoken by both sets of in-laws, albeit awkwardly, when together. That is why we felt an auditory-verbal program was the best choice for Jonathan and our family. Thus we began our odyssey: weekly sessions at the Hospital for Sick Children for 8 years, then a further 7 years at the Learning to Listen Foundation.

We went to our weekly therapy sessions and worked in a structured session once daily, but most learning took place during play and regular daily activities. Everything we saw, experienced, and heard was pointed out and talked about in as many ways as possible. Although we did not designate separate lines of duties, a specific pattern emerged in our family, beginning at Jonathan's diagnosis—I became the teacher. I planned the daily lessons and worked through any structured session with Jonathan, while Jules took on the supportive role of reinforcing the language during playtime. More importantly, he was my support in times of stress. As our other children came along, Jules took on the basic caregiving of bathing, dressing, and feeding, while Jonathan and I retired to a quiet corner for our regular work.

At other times, the family worked as a unit and everyone joined in. During the early years, both Jules and I learned to use the generous support of grandparents who would come in for a day or two and allow us a quick getaway totally to ourselves. We were a self-contained unit, not uncommon with a family facing crisis.

When Jonathan began school, his language and communication skills developed more, and we began to feel comfortable in utilizing the support of a larger network. In time, the support of our local parent group became crucial to us, as did our local parents' sharing group which met occasionally on a more intimate basis to discuss early problems, doubts, and concerns. As we began to give more of ourselves, subtly, we got much in return.

School Days, School Days

At the age of 3, Jonathan went to a mainstream nursery school, and at 5 he joined all the other children in our neighborhood public school, where he stayed until 6th grade.

Throughout the primary grades, I was Jonathan's intermediary within the school system. I would introduce us to each new teacher, give some brief background information specifically about Jonathan and generally about hearing loss, and give the teacher some useful handouts. I tried not to be overbearing and usually focused on our part in Jonathan's education.

I spent a lot of time at the school, volunteering as class mother for many school trips or assisting at tutorials for students requiring individual help with reading or writing. This helped me keep close tabs on Jonathan's academic and social progress. I could spot potential problems early and relieve the teacher from some of the pressure of having a child in the class who might require a lot of extra time.

As Jonathan moved from one grade to the next, the issue of extracurricular and after-school lessons became a greater concern. Much energy, time, and effort went into teaching language. The little spare time remaining went into recharging my own batteries, and unstructured playtime for Jonathan. I was concerned, however, that he spend his time in the company of other children his age who would be role models for language and social behavior. But each year, it seemed more difficult to get our small group of friends together. Inevitably, as the children grew older, they were involved in activities such as art classes, skating, music lessons, or computer courses.

Eventually we too succumbed to this "executive syndrome." It seemed the only way to surround Jonathan with playmates. We too enrolled, though not so much for the lesson content as for the child content! When friends went to computer classes, swimming, Children's Symphony, and ballet, we went too, and Jonathan thrived.

After 4 years of going to the ballet, Jonathan *suddenly discovered,* through peer pressure, that ballet was really only for girls, and he hated it! Initially disappointed, I soon became delighted. Finally, here was an abstract concept that did not originate at home!

At the age of 6, Jonathan began to learn Hebrew, which he continued for 10 years. At 13, he confidently recited his Torah bar mitzvah portion in Hebrew. When Jonathan turned 7, he began asking for piano lessons. Outwardly, we were enthusiastic and encouraging, but inwardly, I again felt all the initial pain of diagnosis and loss. How was I to tell my son to lower his goals and select a more realistic and attainable interest?

With great trepidation, I put Jonathan's request on mental hold. His confidence and determination, on the other hand, never lagged. When he reached 9, we finally capitulated. He deserved the same opportunity to succeed—and more importantly, the opportunity to try and even possibly fail—as any other child.

We found a music teacher willing to teach Jonathan to play the piano and to forgo the piano theory. The rigors of daily practice and weekly lessons began. Subsequently, Jonathan's brother and sister each took piano lessons, and the ritual nagging about practice permeated our home. Jonathan continued piano lessons for 8 years and was the most musically inclined of our three children; his repertoire was mostly classical, with the occasional Broadway or popular tune.

He stopped studying piano when he was in 12th grade with a very heavy workload. (He did, however, take computer keyboarding as a high school credit, and not only received an "A" in it but acted as a peer tutor in the subject.) I know I learned more from these music lessons than Jonathan. I learned to give my son room to grow, flourish, and excel, but more importantly, to stumble occasionally. I learned that not all children master all they set out to do. I know Jonathan will never be a concert pianist, but he enjoys the quiet, contemplative private time that the piano allows him, as well as the general pleasure we all get from listening to music.

Once Jonathan was in junior high, I spent less time at the school. The itinerant teacher's role, however, widened. Jonathan's needs grew, and itinerant services were provided for 3 hours a week during junior high school, down to 2 hours in the first years of high school, and finally 1 hour in his last year—a gentle and natural weaning process. The teachers were very helpful during this 3-year period. There were different teachers for different subjects, but unlike high school, the students stayed together and moved about as a unit from one class teacher to the next.

Junior high was Jonathan's first exposure to social isolation. He left his small neighborhood elementary school, where all the children knew each other from kindergarten and played together in the neighborhood. Now, he found a less homogeneous group who paradoxically seemed less tolerant of anyone who was somewhat "different." He had a very small group of children that he called "friends," but whom we recognized were only acquaintances. Lunch periods during this first year in the new school were most often spent in the computer room, rather than alone at the lunch table, or as a bystander on the sports field.

This was also the year for a new itinerant teacher, of whom Jonathan was very critical. In these early prepubescent years, the FM system became his focus of rebellion. Sensing his new teacher's insecurities, he centered all his energies into sabotaging this area, and became quite accomplished. The FM was conveniently forgotten in the locker or left at home. To divide is to conquer, so classroom teacher, parent, and itinerant teacher were all given different stories. When actually forced to wear the FM, he regularly reported intermittent problems that his itinerant teacher was not equipped to detect on the spot, thereby gaining 2–3 weeks of "repair time." He concentrated all his boundless energies into the demise of the FM system, and eventually succeeded. By the time he began high school, we conceded defeat.

Most of the time, however, Jonathan was the loner in the group. When he discovered baseball, the computer room gave way to the baseball field, and Jonathan found it much easier to interact with the guys. Girls were far less tolerant of him; Jonathan was the topic of many a curious conversation, which he observed through lipreading.

The most painful time came when his "best friend" announced he could no longer be friends. Many of his "friends" were ridiculing him for his friendship with a boy who was deaf! How we blessed Jonathan's openness at that time. We could not take away his pain, but we had given him the tools to communicate his feelings. More importantly, he had the trust and comfort to talk to us. We had shared many wonderful experiences in the past. Now we shared a painful one!

High school was a total change. For the first time, Jonathan was directly involved in the choice of school, taking the initiative in talking to teachers before classes began, introducing himself to each class teacher, identifying his needs, and periodically meeting with teachers to evaluate his progress. Though at first reluctant, he experienced numerous benefits from this new obligation; his confidence grew, he felt a sense of comfort with the staff, and he learned new interactional skills.

While many of his junior high peers moved on to this high school, Jonathan met them on fresher grounds. A circle of new friends grew, and old friends became real friends. High school was a difficult adjustment for Jonathan. Classes rotated, and there were new teachers and students for each subject. Even though exposed to a greater number of people, Jonathan seemed to thrive. His grades improved dramatically, he achieved the honor roll, his self-esteem flourished, and there was a healthy respect between him and his peers.

French is required coursework for a high school diploma in the Canadian school system. It was also Jonathan's most hated subject. Throughout elementary school and junior high, he maintained an average grade in French, but continued to dislike it intensely. In 9th grade, Jonathan discovered a loophole for special-needs students and quickly negotiated a release from this compulsory subject. Principal and student finally agreed to exchange the French credit for music, to be followed by 3 years of Latin. To this day, I don't think the principal realized the discrepancy in this unique release: a student with a hearing loss dropped his compulsory unwanted subject on the grounds of his disability,

Jonathan Samson (left) and family, 1994

and exchanged it for music and another language! At the same time, Latin proved to be an excellent choice. Since Latin is studied predominately in written form, Jonathan was at no disadvantage and achieved grades in the high 90s, becoming a peer tutor again.

Life has a strange way of coming full circle. My mother, who had suffered from cancer for over 10 years, came to live with us. Her condition deteriorated drastically, and she now required daily care. After an operation, one of her vocal cords had to be severed, and she now had a tracheotomy tube. Her most difficult adjustment centered around communication.

Though she was housebound for years, she retained her friends through personal visits and extensive telephone use. Now, she was only able to whisper. As my mother's best friend had developed a severe hearing loss due to old age, the telephone became a particular problem in mother's life.

We, however, are an innovative family. Now Jonathan, with his expert lipreading skills, became the oral interpreter (in reverse)—voicing for his grandmother, while her friend replied at the other end. The TDD became my mother's newest gadget. She would "type" to her friend and then lift the receiver to hear her friend reply.

When her friends who were hard of hearing came over, she used a hand-held microphone and amplifier that was originally intended for use with unamplified hospital patients who were deaf or hard of hearing. The device amplified my mother's whisper through a Walkman-type headset worn by her friend, who would talk back naturally. With one of them unable to talk and the other unable to hear, they lovingly referred to each other as "the odd couple"!

When my mother's condition deteriorated, our family rallied. Her place was with us and not in a nursing home. Her addition to the fabric of our family was by far richer than the few mundane chores required from each of us. Much of this attitude inadvertently came our way through raising a child who is deaf or hard of hearing.

BRIDGE TO PARTNERSHIP

Over the past three decades, our family has come into regular contact with pediatricians, doctors, otolaryngologists, audiologists, hearing aid dispensers, hearing aid sales representatives, psychologists, social workers, school and medical administrators, educational specialists, itinerant teachers, school principals, a stream of classroom teachers, private tutors, numerous bureaucrats, and two Auditory-Verbal therapists.

Like most parents, we came into this experience having to make many adjustments. Most of our first year was spent learning to accept, to understand, and to cope with this devastating news. We secretly hoped to discover that it was all a big mistake. This searching on the part of parents, however, is quite normal. It gives us time to recover from the diagnosis. Denial allows us the necessary time to heal, regroup, and eventually to keep on going. We take steps to seek alternatives and answers, and the act of the search itself facilitates our acceptance and adaptation and gives us a small sense of control over our lives. This initial pursuit, however, often puts parents and professionals at odds with each other in the earliest contacts. Alternative medicine and second opinions are acceptable in most medical areas today, yet searching parents are sometimes unfairly perceived and labeled as "capricious."

We parents experience different stages of mourning and different degrees of guilt. The anger that we commonly feel towards the professional is often the anger that comes from our own helplessness and our need to feel more in charge. Unconsciously, we redirect this energy into obtaining the best possible service for our child.

We come into the field of hearing impairment as total amateurs. Unlike the professional, we don't choose this domain, but we are faced with the reality of a great deal to learn. The professional is able to walk away from the problem or situation or just see it as another appointment. He or she remains detached and, consequently, can bring fresh vibrancy and enthusiasm into the arena. But this is a luxury never afforded to us as parents.

The professional, furthermore, may have only one client to deal with during a session or appointment. The family, on the other hand, has a variety of problems and dynamics. We must deal with all our children and our own mourning, as well as the different stages of grief and acceptance among our siblings, grandparents, relatives, friends, and neighbors. Finally, we find ourselves stuck with the newly created and unasked-for job of public awareness and public relations.

In these early years, many parents find it difficult to reach out and ask for help. Going to meetings or even lifting the telephone can be emotionally draining. We feel helpless and alone within the community and, occasionally, within our family. In our own way, however, and at our own individual pace, we slowly master the situation as our lives gradually return to normal. We are compelled to create a new and different way of life because of the hearing loss. In time, old routines find their way back into our lives. Some of us choose to go back to work or find new careers. Some of us stay at home with our child and, maybe, have another. As we feel more empowered, we also feel more comfortable in the company of professionals.

During those early months, whenever someone told me what our son could never do or attain (as they often did), my guard always went up, and I dismissed these harmful comments. In fact, these comments spurred me to prove the professional wrong. When the otolaryngologist delivered the initial diagnosis to us, he concluded that Jonathan would probably "never learn to speak." Strangely, that prognosis was actually the most helpful one; it became the mechanism that helped us succeed. That same verdict, however, could also have had the opposite effect on our family. This is why professionals need to be *very careful* with the prognosis they give to families.

Looking back, I perceive our initial contacts with professionals as challenges. However, they can and ought to be alliances in which the professionals become our colleagues and allies. The control that professionals can wield is immense. When we deal with them, our child might be just a commodity, another statistic, or another audiogram. Professionals, like parents, need to separate the child from the hearing loss in order to appreciate the youngster as a child first who happens to be deaf or hard of hearing; to see the cup as half full instead of half empty; and to focus on the abilities, not the disabilities.

Many professionals' training and educational background directly center on children, with little emphasis on counseling families. Conflicts can emerge over differences between the parents' and professionals' assessments of the child's needs. Professionals can help by making adjustments in their services to the families' real and current needs. Professionals need to recognize the value and importance of the parents' perspectives. Differences in values will always exist. Good professionals encourage families to make their own choices, even though they might encounter priorities, outlooks, and values that differ greatly from their own.

It is the parents' responsibility also to act professionally. Some parents are guilty of poor attendance, being late for appointments, or not following through on a required action. Such behaviors can frustrate the professionals. Good professionals do not bypass clashes. They acknowledge them and endeavor a reconciliation by working together. The child cannot be treated in isolation from the family. Ultimately, both parents and professionals want only success for the child and the family.

Unfortunately, parents and professionals sometimes fail to communicate effectively, resulting in misunderstanding over each other's definition of success. One professional's view of success may mean a child with a healthy self-esteem. To a parent of a young infant, self-esteem may still be an abstract concept at a time when all concentration is on teaching language in the hope that the child will eventually be understood by playmates. Since goals may be prioritized differently, we must discuss the services we need for our child and define our goals out loud.

The responsibility for our child's education falls directly on us, the parents. We must negotiate effectively to get the services our child needs. It is, therefore, up to us to acquire the knowledge to coordinate and monitor services (Simons, 1987). This is a time-consuming task, and some parents find it easier to do than others. One useful strategy is to think of it as our profession. When a task seems impossible, or we feel too embarrassed to ask, it helps to remember that it is our job to ask, to talk to the professionals, and if necessary, to get them to talk to one another. Finally, I also remind myself that although they may know the programs and services better, I know my child better.

Few of us find our ongoing daily interactions with professionals as gratifying as we would like them to be. Parents and professionals may make comments about each other such as:

"They don't answer our questions."
"They don't listen."
"They don't make time to help us."
"They talk to us in unusual ways."
"They keep information from us."
"They insist that we make the decisions."
"They don't think about child behavior the way we do."
"They don't ask our opinion." (Niagara Children's Services Committee, 1990).

Looking back, I now see conflicts as inevitable and essential, but at that time, they were a constant source of pain. My husband, myself, and the professionals did not always realize that we were working with different agendas. Our goals often differed, our needs for services varied, and we often focused on a different aspect or definition of success. Nevertheless, there are many things that we, as parents, can do to make the relationship more productive, satisfying, and rewarding:

Good Communication

All parents can develop better communication skills. It is in our interest to invest time and effort in our relationship with professionals; it may prevent antagonism. If we communicate positively and with respect, we can prevent a stalemate and make it easier for professionals to give us what we need.

Learn to Listen

We must learn to listen actively and be open minded. It is easy to complain. Talking and sharing information is a two-way exchange. Often, we are so busy waiting our turn to speak that we tune out others. If we don't listen to the professionals, how can we expect them to listen to us? We need to assess new information and allow ourselves time to absorb it and then act. In time, we might even come up with a fresh perspective.

Stand Up for Our Rights

We can learn to be assertive without being aggressive. We need to concentrate on the issue at hand, not on the individual. We can express opinions with firm conviction, not indignation. We can talk it out. We are part of a team! We want the professional to hear what we have to say, not back them into a corner.

Professionals need to remember that parents are individuals too, with individual styles and personalities, and will present different mannerisms and skills.

Keep Records

If we have a particular concern, we can prepare notes on the situation in advance. This will help the professional to deal with it, and will help us document our concerns. We can compare notes with other parents. We often hit a plateau or feel depressed at our slow progress. It is hard always to be enthusiastic. As parents, we face a lifetime of challenge requiring tremendous physical and emotional stamina. These records plot our progress, which often goes unnoticed while we are going through it.

Be Prepared—Keep Informed

We need to get the most out of our appointment by doing our homework. If we make a list of questions before the meeting, we arrive prepared. We also expect that preparation from a professional. We, too, are professional, so we can use our pen and notebook to record questions, information, and terminology exchanged during appointments. If possible, obtain permission to use a tape recorder at meetings with professionals. This is a helpful tactic for nervous parents, especially in the early years. It is particularly useful for reviewing new information and technical terminology. We can keep our own files. We don't need to be afraid to ask questions or for explanations. We don't need to feel intimidated. We never need to proceed or to leave unless we understand what has been said.

Establish or Use Available Support Networks

Parents are often intimidated at the prospect of meeting a roomful of professionals. Anxiety can cloud our thought processes as well as our memory. Most parents can relate to the experience of hearing something for the first time, only to be told by the professional that the issue had already been discussed. We might take along a tape recorder to a meeting, explain its presence, and ask for permission to use it, so we can later review the information. We might be amazed at how much we miss when we listen to the tape again at home, and we have the added advantage of sharing the information accurately with our spouse and family.

We don't need to go alone to school or hospital meetings. We can bring a spouse, friend, therapist, or itinerant teacher. There is strength in numbers, even if only one person does the talking. The tag-along friend can help replay the events of the meeting, and may have a more objective point of view.

Learn the Lingo

We need to learn to use the correct terminology that the professionals use. This takes time and effort, but knowledge is a powerful tool. We gain confidence and respect along the way.

Access Information

We can ask for all copies of reports, tests, and audiograms. We have a legal right to such information. By learning to be comfortable with the information we acquire, we will become more familiar with the issues, learn to ask relevant questions, and research new areas.

Stay On Track

We need to stay within the subject matter. It is even helpful to keep a mental or written agenda to prevent us from digressing during a scheduled appointment and, consequently, running out of time. By verbalizing all our concerns, we can help the professionals see our own agenda as well as lead us through it. We must also understand the importance of selecting the right time for a specific discussion or confrontation. We will be better prepared at the next meeting if we have time to ponder and analyze the situation.

Stay Calm

We need to be level-headed and in control. As parents, we tend to bring emotional baggage into the room. Most professionals understand that most of the time. Still, being emotional can be counter-productive and may cost us our credibility, which undermines our efforts. Unleashing anger doesn't work. We have a right to talk about what is bothering us, but we have a much greater chance of being heard and getting some or all of what we want if we wait until the heat of anger passes. Some professionals will ignore us and may even mentally dismiss us; the more rational we can remain, the more likely it is that they will listen. If being calm, cool, and collected is not part of our personality, it often helps to explain our shortcomings to the professional and may help defuse the situation with humor.

Trust Our Expertise

We have our own area of expertise—our child. It is up to us to share information. We see sides of our child that professionals never see. We need to trust our instincts about what our child needs. Even though it is not easy to convey that kind of information to a professional, we need to be listened to and we deserve respect for our opinions. We need to remind ourselves frequently that we will remain the most consistent support for our child. A professional usually enters our lives for short periods of time, while we have the greatest investment in our child. We have to listen carefully to all opinions, but remember that opinions are all that they are. We are the ones who will have to live with the consequences. We need to get the best medical therapeutic advice we can, and then determine as a family what course of action makes the most sense for us.

Be Objective

If a problem or a special need occurs, we need to remain objective. We need to be as realistic as possible and, if necessary, reevaluate our goals and objectives. We need not be afraid to take a risk or recognize a mistake. We need to set our own limits if necessary. Sometimes, we even have to compromise.

Be Assertive—Remain Polite

This is the backbone of professional conduct. If we disagree, we need to speak up. If we are not sure or would like a second opinion, we need to say so. No one can read our mind! We need to learn to persuade, not antagonize. Disagreement is difficult for most of us to deal with and for professionals to accept. We need to separate the issue from the person. Parents and professionals both need to be courteous and respectful of one another.

Get a Second Opinion

Second opinions are common in the medical field. We are entitled to them! We can ask the professional for more information or literature on the subject, whether another professional might feel differently, and how the professional might deal with the situation if it were his or her own child. We all accept the fact that therapy is an ongoing diagnostic and ever-changing process. We need accept no less from our relationship with any professional. Our goal is to form an alliance—a potential partnership. We, as parents, bear part of that responsibility. It is advantageous for a professional to work with parents who can advocate effectively, make decisions, and solve problems by themselves or in a partnership.

Express Our Appreciation

We all need to be appreciated and complimented. It is not easy for a professional to say, "I don't know" to a parent. Yet the professional who says, "Maybe I can help you find out or find someone who knows the answer" can inspire a greater degree of confidence and be reassuring and helpful. This atmosphere of freedom is conducive to working things out.

Keep Expectations Realistic

Schools or doctors may tell us that our expectations are unrealistic or too high. This is a common source of conflict between parents and professionals. We must learn to trust our own intuition about what are realistic expectations for our family. Our backgrounds and value systems may differ; what is realistic for one family may not necessarily work for another.

Trust Our Instincts

Sometimes a school system perceives itself as the expert. Such an attitude can shake our confidence and lead us to question what is best for our child. These professionals may spend more time focusing on past failures than reflecting on future potential and see the proverbial half-empty cup! School personnel work with hundreds of children, whereas we are working with just one. They may look at what is wrong instead of what is right. They may tell us what our child cannot do instead of what our child can do. Most of us can set goals for our children better than anyone else. Even though some professionals don't want to expose the child to failure or put too many stresses or demands on the family, there is dignity in risk. We have a right to try, a right to succeed, and the right to fail.

If parents and professionals cannot agree on a course of action, we must at least establish the proper protocol for resolving our differences. The parent needs to move up the ladder of authority only as required. If we work with the professionals instead of antagonizing them, our disagreements can often be resolved. Sometimes, no matter how well prepared we are, we run into a brick wall in the form of a professional. All parents have a list of such encounters; if we are lucky, the list is short. These are times when we get stuck and feel that there is no way out but to shoot them. There are, however, alternatives!

- *Reevaluate the situation.* There are always alternatives, and we can always learn new ways of dealing with problems.
- *Renegotiate whenever possible.* One of the most important things we can do sometimes is to get a second, or even a third, opinion. It is also our right.
- *Recognize the bright side of every situation.* We keep growing. When our son had an inadequate itinerant teacher, I told myself that I was responsible for the work, and we would have a new teacher next year—and we did!

The professional needs to create an atmosphere of exchange. By facilitating parent participation in the entire process, the child remains the focus. Professionals must recognize the specific requirements of every parent in receiving information, to refrain from using excessive professional jargon, and to furnish necessary information while remaining sensitive to the grieving process. Professionals have to provide opportunities for parents to experience success while remaining cautious about positive reinforcement. The parents' and professionals' concept of "doing great" may differ and may cause conflict. By using active listening skills, the professional could demonstrate willingness to implement a parent's plan of action instead of his or her own if it is possible. Professionals need to provide legitimate program options while remaining focused on the process and the outcome, which is where most parents are focused (Luterman, 1991; Raver, 1991).

CONCLUSION

There are many rewards to a true partnership between parents and professionals. What began as a rather negative and difficult impact on our family slowly became positive. If necessity is the mother of invention, our family unit grew in a way we could not have predicted. We became self-reliant, closer, and stronger, and learned new skills and problem-solving techniques. People are resilient and, as parents, we can and do learn to cope in a variety of difficult situations. Whether out of practice or necessity, we become more adaptable and better able to meet the next challenge—more than we ever thought possible.

I believe the role of a good parent is to eventually do oneself out of a job. The goal that we work towards is achieving independence for our child so that we are no longer needed. Having a child with a disability certainly intensifies that role. We did not choose to enter the world of those who are deaf or hard of hearing; it was thrust upon us. As our son's primary agents, we learned to advocate effectively, make all the necessary decisions along the way, and solve problems for him and our family. We taught the teenaged Jonathan the skills of managing his own life; as a young adult, he absorbed these lessons and learned to work in a respectful and effective partnership.

In order to establish a successful and caring program for a child who has a hearing loss, it is important that a genuine alliance be formed between the parents and the professionals. We parents need to be respected as the primary players on the team, because we have the ultimate responsibility for our child's future. Even though a communication gap exists between some professionals and some parents, it is more a gap of style than of intent. By parents and professionals planning initiatives together, the gap can be bridged and lines of communication can be opened. Parents and professionals both want success for the child and for the family. For parents, success affirms parenting skills, and for professionals, success justifies their careers. Our family crossed the bridge and formed many partnerships. Today, some of my best friends are indeed the professionals who have entered and enriched our lives.

A positive parent–professional relationship can be achieved only by responsible sharing of information, feelings, attitudes, and values. Trust, integrity, creativity, innovation, the respect of individual differences, acceptance of responsibility, and accountability are essential ingredients for the making of such a relationship. A successful relationship between parents and professionals is always changing and always maturing.

UPDATE

In 1998, Jonathan began to think seriously about getting a cochlear implant. The immediate impetus was his deteriorating hearing loss and his progressive listening frustrations, especially in his work environment. I became his sounding board as he tossed about the pros and cons of going forward with his plan. There was, however, no mistaking the fact that this was his plan.

It was now his turn to become a professional. He began his quest, first by contacting as many cochlear implant users as he could, directly and through the Internet. He kept meticulous notes and searched out many answers to the various issues and questions.

He then attended a cochlear implant conference in order to meet consumers as well as therapists, audiologists and, especially, the manufacturers; he was diligent in talking to everyone. Finally, he decided to attend a cochlear implant medical conference. With his investigation complete, he was able to move forward with his decision with full confidence.

Jonathan, Tania, and Jacob Samson today

Jonathan received his cochlear implant in 1999. Although the immediate adjustment was difficult, he has benefited incredibly. He initially went through 6 months of intensive auditory rehabilitation twice weekly in the clinic, and he practiced almost daily at home. I became his teacher once again—but at his urging rather than mine.

The impact of cochlear implantation on his life has been dramatic. Today, Jonathan relies mostly on his hearing, with very little need for visual cues. He has become proficient on the telephone for the first time in his life and no longer requires oral or technical support.

My job as his parent is done. I have watched my son acquire and synthesize some very advanced and complex auditory skills and transfer them usefully into his life.

A year after receiving his implant, Jonathan met his future wife, Tania, at a conference. Encouraged by his benefits, Tania too decided to get a cochlear implant shortly after they married.

Deconstructing the Parent

Their story only begins there. In 2002, their infant son, Jacob, was diagnosed almost immediately following his birth with a profound hearing loss. Can you picture our extended family? Jonathan and Tania with their new baby and two sets of parents and their combined years of expertise!

We knew, however, that as parents and grandparents, our new role would be that of a support network for our children, but it would be a secondary role. It was time to back away. The role reversal was complete, and our young couple was in charge.

Jacob received his cochlear implant at the age of 9 months, and his parents have dedicated themselves to his ongoing education. My current perspective is that of a grandparent—the parent once removed. It is the new parents who have brilliantly assumed their partnership with the professional community.

REFERENCES

Estabrooks, W. (1993). "Still listening: Auditory-Verbal therapy for older children." *The Volta Review, 95*(3), 232–252.

Ling, D. (1989). *Foundations of Spoken Language in Hearing-Impaired Children.* Washington, DC: Alexander Graham Bell Association for the Deaf.

Luterman, D. (1991). *When Your Child Is Deaf.* Timonium, MD: York Press.

Niagara Children's Services Committee. (1990). *Parents in Case Management.* Thorold, ON: Consumer Subcommittee.

Pollack, D. (1970, 1985). *Educational Audiology for the Limited-Hearing Infant and Pre-schooler.* Springfield, IL: Charles C. Thomas.

Raver, S.A. (1991). "Effective family-centered services: Supporting family choices and rights." *Infant–Toddler Intervention: The Transdisciplinary Journal, 1*, 169–176.

Simons, R. (1987). *After The Tears: Parents Talk about Raising a Child with a Disability.* San Diego: Harcourt Brace Jovanovich.

CHAPTER 9

The Family Stories

The following stories by parents of children who have learned to listen and speak through the auditory-verbal approach initially appeared over a decade ago (Estabrooks, 1994). Now, these same parents generously offer updates of their children's lives.

CELESTE

Judy and Charlie Mance

Celeste Jewel was born on October 24, 1990. Needless to say, her arrival lit up our lives. But the joy and excitement of having her was soon tempered by my vague sense of anxiety that *something was wrong*. My anxiety grew stronger when she was 6 months old. I had devised a little afternoon ritual with her to keep myself busy while my husband was in school. Just after Celeste's afternoon nap, I would sneak up close to her crib and, wanting to surprise her, would call her or sing to her while out of her sight. Soon, I came to dread this game. It only seemed to confirm my earlier suspicion—Celeste was hearing impaired. She didn't turn towards me no matter how loudly and persistently I called her name. My singing never seemed to soothe her; neither the sound of the musical mobile nor the rattle appeared to attract her attention.

"Honey, do you think Celeste can hear me?" I would ask Charlie, nonchalantly.

Pausing briefly from writing his term papers, my husband would reply, "Of course she can, Judy. Don't worry if she's not paying attention to you. She's just too busy looking at all those toys in the crib."

But my fear never went away. Soon, I started mentioning my concern to my friends. Like my husband, they dismissed my anxiety as symptomatic of the "paranoia typical of first-time mothers."

I would feel relieved each time I talked to Charlie or our friends. They all seemed very positive that everything was fine with Celeste. Once, a malfunctioning smoke detector, just above the entrance to Celeste's room, went off at 4:00 in the morning—it was one of those huge, old, electrically operated smoke detectors designed to wake up the whole neighborhood. It took Charlie nearly 20 minutes to figure out a way to stop it. Celeste slept through the event soundly. It was at that point that my nagging anxiety turned to fear. But unconscious denial pre-

Celeste Mance (center) and family, 1994

vented Charlie and me from seriously discussing the possibility of Celeste's hearing impairment and, hence, from seeking medical help for her.

In the summer of 1990, about a month and a half after the incident with the smoke detector, we went back to Malaysia and the Philippines for holidays. Celeste got sick a number of times. During one of the visits to a pediatrician in Malaysia, I voiced my concern. Her clinic was not equipped to perform hearing evaluations, but she quickly improvised a test using rattles. Perhaps not wanting to alarm us unnecessarily, she said that it looked as though Celeste had some hearing deficiency. "She's a rather active baby. It's really difficult to tell if she is reacting to the sound or not," she added. She advised us, nevertheless, to consult a specialist immediately. We cut short our visit to Malaysia and flew to Singapore, where we consulted a well-known ear, nose, and throat (ENT) specialist. An auditory brainstem response (ABR) test was done, and it was determined that Celeste had a severe to profound hearing loss. Charlie and I were devastated. My mother followed us to Singapore. She was the best person to offer us comfort because she, too, had raised a child who was hearing impaired—my eldest brother, William. Late into her pregnancy, my mother contracted rubella; as a result, William was born with a profound hearing loss. My parents sent William to a special school in Australia where he learned primarily by lipreading. Later, he learned to use sign language when he went to the United States for his university education. As I look back, it was perhaps my experience of having a brother who was hearing impaired that has made me unusually sensitive to Celeste's special needs.

Three days after we returned to Canada, we moved from the small city of Regina, Saskatchewan to the bustling metropolis of Toronto, where my husband was slated to begin a year-long church internship to fulfill the academic requirements for his degree from the seminary. A physician, who was an elder of the evangelical church where Charlie was serving, heard of Celeste. He immediately referred us to the Learning to Listen Foundation, where Celeste underwent further testing. Her hearing impairment was confirmed again. We were resigned that Celeste would learn sign language.

At the Learning to Listen Foundation, we were introduced to the auditory-verbal approach for children who are deaf or hard of hearing and their families. We met the clinical staff for an interview. At that first meeting, it immediately became apparent to Charlie and me that Auditory-Verbal therapy would require a tremendous commitment from us. We would not only work closely with the therapist, but would make a long-term investment of time, hard work, and patience. It was emphasized that the therapy sessions were meant primarily for the parents. The primary responsibility for the therapy would be on our shoulders, and we wanted that.

The clinical staff gave us some literature about hearing impairment, hearing aids, speech therapy, audiograms, and Auditory-Verbal therapy. We spent the next few days poring over these materials. At about the same time, we were contacted by other people introduced to us by our new friends in Toronto, who told us of the other promising programs they thought might be best for Celeste.

Soon, we were suffering from an overload of information, which subsequently produced a bout of depression. We were unsure about which program to choose. But all this was to change when the clinical staff of the program at the Learning to Listen Foundation invited us to observe some of their therapy sessions. The children, many diagnosed as profoundly deaf, were not only listening but talking—and they were talking very well! That visit was a milestone.

I remember telling my husband on our way home, "This is exactly what I want for Celeste. I want her to listen! I want her to talk!" What attracted us most to the program was its philosophy of encouraging children who are hearing impaired to attend mainstream schools. We strongly felt that Celeste's participation in the hearing world of the mainstream school was the best gift we could give her.

Celeste was fitted with a pair of hearing aids in early December 1992. There were marked changes in her behavior during the first few days she wore her hearing aids. She just sat at a corner of the table with a bewildered look on her face. Normally very active and playful, she suddenly became passive and frightened, especially in public places. During the first 2 days, we were inseparable; she spent a good part of each day clinging to me. She rarely cried, but when she did, it was very softly. Even her own crying appeared to startle her. Obviously, her transition into hearing was not easy. But Celeste can be commended for one thing—never once did she pull out her hearing aids.

A week after she got her hearing aids, Celeste started therapy at the Learning to Listen Foundation. There were just two sessions before the Christmas break, but we were overwhelmed by what we felt we needed to learn. During the holidays, we started to teach Celeste by ourselves. We scoured toy shops for specific toys to teach her specific sounds. Among the first ones we bought was a tiny toy jumbo jet to teach her "ahh" and a red London double-decker bus for "bu, bu, bu." Soon, we had a huge tote box filled with toys ranging from apples to zebras.

The novelty and thrill of teaching Celeste soon gave way to the sobering realization that it was a Herculean task. In short, it was a 7-day-a-week job! Our every waking moment was a teaching opportunity to be seized. *The classroom was everywhere.* As long as she was cooperative, she had lessons in the car, in the kitchen, in the church, at the grocery store, in the parking lot, at the airport, in the park, in the bathroom—just everywhere. Charlie and I are not native speakers of English, and we are not talkative by nature. My first language is Mandarin Chinese and Charlie's is Tagalog, the Filipino national language. This added to the challenge of Celeste's learning to communicate.

Nothing really dramatic happened until late January, when Celeste surprised us with her first vowel: "ahh." By March, she would call out "baba" whenever she saw either Charlie or me. I knew she meant mama; Charlie insisted she said papa. By summer of that year, she would yell, "Buy!" repeatedly if we ran out of her favorite cereals. Then, "Mine, mine, mine!" became her favorite expression. A year after she started therapy, she could recite little lines from "The Cares Chorus," which was to become her favorite song. Missing a word here and there, she would say in her own unique way, "I cast all my cares upon you... I yay [lay] all [of] my burden down at your teet [feet]... And any time I don't know what [to] do... I [will] cast all my cares upon you." She had become a child who listens.

Teaching a child who is hearing impaired is a serious and demanding job. But what is perhaps a more difficult task is dealing with the parents' own expectations. The more Celeste made exciting headway in speech, language, and listening, the more inflated our expectations became. For instance, at one point, her "e" was very nasal despite our persistent effort to correct it. Adjustments made on her hearing aids did not help. The problem, which later proved to be transient, nevertheless caused us sleepless nights. When faced with such a difficulty, which was just one of the many to come, Charlie and I tended to overlook the astounding gains she had made at her young age! Celeste taught us that the worst principle in measuring her progress was the law of diminishing returns. As we go through our ups and downs, Celeste seems to be always reminding us, "Please be patient with me. God is still working in me."

One of Celeste's strengths is that she is extremely talkative. My parents, who recently visited from Malaysia, had a taste of this. We spent one weekend with them at Niagara Falls. On the 2-hour trip back from Buffalo to Toronto, Celeste regaled them non-stop with her stories, nursery rhymes, and songs, interspersed with her incessant complaints, demands, and reminders to Charlie, who was driving. She was the quintessential backseat driver, constantly yelling, "Don't drive too tast [fast], Daddy!" or "Stop, Daddy, stop! It's red, 'ready [already]!" This was something my parents did not expect; they last saw her when all she could say was "ahh." Before they left, my mother told me that she planned to hold a worship service in our hometown in Malaysia as a gesture of thanksgiving to God for Celeste's progress.

Indeed, Celeste's progress has been wonderful. With guidance, patience, and encouragement, and her insatiable love for books, we continue our journey together. It is not uncommon for me to read eight to 10 books to her before she goes to bed. This past summer, we set the goal of teaching her 80 new words and phrases; she ended up learning 320! Charlie, who has been so diligent in keeping track of her vocabulary, has finally lost count.

Just this morning, Charlie and I took Celeste to her day care center for the first time. We decided to stay awhile to see how she would manage in an unfamiliar setting. As she played and chatted with the other children and followed the teacher's instructions, we felt an immense sense of pride in having given her a solid foundation for communication. We left the place with a warm assurance in our hearts; our little girl was just like so many other kids.

Lately, she loves singing, "Are you sleeping, are you sleeping, Brother John, Brother John? Morning bells are ringing, morning bells are ringing, 'tinky dong, 'tinky dong." There is little melody to her singing, and she needs to get that last line right. But it is the sweetest-sounding music to our ears. Hearing Celeste sing reminds us how grateful we are to our family, friends, therapists, teachers, mentors, and fellow travelers in this challenging but rewarding journey of hope for Celeste. It also reminds us that, with God, all things are possible.

Update

Charlie Mance

The fall of 1991 and the fall of 1996 are like bookends that hold between them the volumes of an incredible story that happened in Toronto, Canada.

It is the story of a 1-year-old baby with a hearing impairment, Celeste Jewel Mance, now a teenager, and her therapist (whom she fondly calls Uncle Warren even today, as do the other members of our family). In the early days, our story ran the gamut of difficult emotions: despair, as we discovered that Celeste's hearing loss was profound; hope, as we spoke to the therapist for the first time and heard promising things about Auditory-Verbal therapy; frustration, as Celeste initially made little progress; elation, on the morning we heard her say "bu, bu, bu" as she played with her red toy bus; perseverance, as we restructured our lives around attending weekly therapy sessions and the search for toys to help us teach specific sounds; exhaustion, as we did endless teaching at home, in the park, and out in the backyard; and frailty, as we in our humanity struggled with impatience at the snail's pace of progress.

Celeste Mance (left) and family today

The next 6 years of therapy went by very quickly. And it went exceedingly well! It was a triumph of hope over despair, elation over frustration, and perseverance over frailty. Celeste made remarkable strides in her ability to say specific sounds that became the building blocks of words, phrases, sentences, and then, conversation. These sounds were music to our ears—melodies that surpassed those of the great classical composers!

We knew the tables had turned when, 4 years after the start of Celeste's therapy, the problem at home was no longer getting her to talk but stopping her from talking too much. The house was never quiet with our lovely and energetic 4-year-old loudly reciting Rebus Rhymes from kindergarten and singing Barney songs she had picked up from TV. Then, at her request, she started piano lessons just before her sixth birthday.

The fall of 1996 concluded our stay in Toronto. By the spring that year, I was done with my seminary education, and the following November, we left Toronto for Calgary, where I had accepted a position as pastor of a church. We will always remember how deeply saddened we were to see the Auditory-Verbal therapist for our last meeting. The other bookend in our decade-long story was set in place at that last of our weekly Wednesday afternoon sessions in therapy—the conclusion of those fruitful years as we patiently taught Celeste skills that would equip her to face a hearing and speaking world. As we say in our church, "It was a 'God thing'"! To have crossed paths with the therapist and Auditory-Verbal therapy was also a God thing!

Judy Mance

I felt so insecure moving to Calgary with no more therapist to teach Celeste or guide us. However, the public school board in Calgary was wonderful in providing help as we put Celeste into a mainstream school. She got a good itinerant teacher starting in 1st grade. She was also fitted with an FM system, which the school board maintained and promptly upgraded almost every year. Her need for itinerant support, however, gradually diminished so that by the time she was in 6th grade, the school and we felt it was no longer necessary. In fact, it was starting to hinder rather than help her studies.

In 2004, Celeste was enrolled in 8th grade in a small class in a private school, where she was enjoying the close support of her teachers and classmates. She has been doing well in academics and shows strength in languages and sciences. She is thinking about becoming a medical researcher. To her, Tuesdays from 6:00 to 7:00 p.m. is a sacred slot: *American Idol* time. She still plays piano and has switched to contemporary pieces. Loud Christian rock music is the backdrop to her homework time. She's our typical teenager.

For about a year, she did not want to use an FM unit, but the September she started 8th grade, she changed her mind. So we purchased an FM unit, and it is helping her learn much better. Celeste is still getting used to the habit of carrying her FM unit from class to class and giving it to her teachers. She has turned her hearing aids into a fashion accessory. A few years ago, she had bright red hearing aids with bright pink earmolds. Later, she switched to baby blue hearing aids with matching blue earmolds!

Aside from school, she enjoys the youth activities offered by our church. A couple of months ago, she surprised us by singing in the youth band on Youth Sunday. She helps edit the youth newspaper and is also one of the best hip-hop dancers in the church.

We are hopeful that Celeste will continue to do well in school and succeed in all her undertakings. Auditory-Verbal therapy has given her a good foundation in speech and language, and we are confident that she will be what she wants to be with God's help.

We count it as a privilege to have been part of an Auditory-Verbal therapy program. Programs such as this should be fully supported by governments. We hope that auditory-verbal programs are made available to every part of the world so that many more children can be given the opportunity to learn how to listen and talk.

In 2006, Celeste was 15 years old and attending 10th grade in Calgary, Alberta, doing online home schooling after finishing junior high in a private school. She is interested in break-dancing, playing the guitar, reading fiction, listening to her MP3 player, writing poetry, and doing calligraphy, and plans to attend a high school for the arts.

LOGAN

Peter Enright

"Logan happy!" says the beaming 3-year-old. But before the words have registered with me, I see his sudden attempt at a full-stride, 90-degree turn fail miserably. He winds up as a heap against the wall. "Ouch!" he says, rubbing his head and looking back at me for attention and comfort. A minor argument with a wall. Nothing special. After all, it's a commonplace event for a 3-year-old, replayed literally thousands of times a day throughout the country. But for me, it's something very special. And when I see and hear events such as this, I try to have the presence of mind to pause, to think, and to appreciate.

Logan Enright (right) and Family, 1994

After all, these are *words* he's using. This, from a child who for a solid year verbally communicated only in varying degrees of screams. This, from a child so frustrated by his inability to make himself understood that he habitually banged his head against the floor. And in truth, this from a child who is just beginning his adventures in the world of verbal communication.

I try to hang on to the moment, because I feel, fleetingly, that it gives me a precious bit of perspective. But it's gone like quicksilver, and my life with Logan moves on to another involvement. Is there any other way with a 3-year-old who is hearing impaired and who is learning to listen and to speak? Not really.

Our life with Logan was destined to be emotionally charged even before he was conceived. At that time, my wife, Joy, and I were the proud parents of a 3-year-old girl named Devon. And we were the bereaved father and mother of Matthew, our son who lived only 1 day and died in our arms of genetic problems. Within a few months of Matthew's death, Joy and I had a hard decision to make. Even though the doctors said Matthew's genetic problems were a fluke, a 1-in-3000 chance, we had to decide whether we were going to try for another baby and if we were going to put Joy through the amniocentesis. The only reason to do that would be to terminate the pregnancy. If something were wrong, we decided that we would keep and love, as best we could, any baby that came along. So, no amniocentesis—we would fly blind! But fly we would!

We had been warned that a child who comes after an infant death is a special child. You cherish the child so much that you can easily wind up spoiling him. We fully intended to spoil Logan. We loved and cherished him. A few months would soon demonstrate to us just how special he really was.

When Logan was born, everything seemed normal, to our great relief—except for a little jaundice, which resolved after a couple of days under lights. Joy said to me, "Well, we have our precious baby and everything's fine." And for some reason, I replied, "Yes, everything is fine so far." I don't know why I said that, but it came back to haunt me when Logan was diagnosed with a profound hearing loss.

Our knowledge of Logan's deafness came to us mostly in stages too subtle for us to be aware of them. In retrospect, I could have been suspicious the very day we brought him home. It was the kind of hot summer afternoon where the humidity hangs in the air like a blanket. Clouds were building, and it would not be too long before a vicious thunderstorm hit. We just got Logan inside the house and asleep in his crib when the storm struck. The thunder was so violent, it shook the house. Logan did not stir. But he was a new baby, they all have their own characters, and I thought he was merely a sound sleeper. As the months went by, the feeling of uneasiness grew, at least subconsciously. But there were hints that nagged us into awareness, such as how hypersensitive he was to touch. Noise would not wake him, but with the touch of a tip of a blanket, he was instantly awake.

At one of Logan's regular check-ups when he was about 6 months old, we asked the pediatrician to check his hearing because our uncertainty had become defined enough for Joy and me to broach the subject with each other. I remember the conversation very well. It took about 5 seconds. I said, "Do you think he hears very well?" and Joy tersely answered, "I don't know." The answer was so clipped that I knew I had touched on something serious.

The pediatrician told us to keep an eye on things. We did for about 2 months, up to the time that Joy discovered Logan holding a toy telephone to his ear and moving his mouth—without making any sound whatsoever. Joy immediately realized that such non-verbal behavior was what Logan thought all people did with telephones. That could only mean Logan was deaf.

Months of frustration followed as we tried to get Logan diagnosed. We had understood that he needed to be properly diagnosed before hearing aids could be prescribed. Two attempts at a brainstem test were inconclusive. Our visits to the downtown hospitals were not only non-productive, they made the Mad Hatter's Tea Party seem the height of reason. And all the while, time ticked by. This was all the more frustrating because we knew from our reading on deafness that time was of the essence in getting some sort of therapy program underway.

After finally getting Logan hearing aids, we set out to determine the best program for him. After initially favoring Total Communication, we settled on the auditory-verbal approach. Our reasoning was straightforward. Our goal for Logan was to open as many options as possible so that the widest range of lifestyle choices would be available to him later in life. Had Logan been born a hearing child, our approach to raising him would have been the same. We reasoned that any program that set the goal of mainstreaming children in society would fit our primary goal. If deafness did not need to mean segregation, then we would do everything possible to promote integration.

After reading the materials from the Learning to Listen Foundation and listening to Auditory-Verbal therapists Louise Crawford and Warren Estabrooks, we knew that our single biggest investment would be our time. Although Warren was to be Logan's therapist, we would be his teachers. For there to be enough teaching going on, either Joy or I would need to quit work. This was one of our toughest times. It made the most economical and logical sense that Joy end her career in advertising to be with Logan. Although there was no question that Joy loved Logan more than her work, it was painful to give up a career she also loved. And so the lessons began, and our house became a teaching center with Post-it™ notes all over the walls, the mirrors, and the furniture... reminding us to communicate consistently and constantly with Logan. The Learning to Listen Sounds punctuated our conversation, whether we were alone or with company. This family habit produced more than one startled look from a friend when, upon seeing an airplane flying by, we stopped our adult conversation in mid-sentence, pointed to the sky, looked at Logan, and said in unison: "Ahhhhhh."

Soon, Logan began to respond. The therapy seemed to be working, but the evening before Logan was to see Warren was always a time of some anxiety because we felt (and still feel) keenly responsible for how well, or how poorly, Logan does in his lessons. As Logan became older and came up to the 3-year mark, his communication steadily improved. He had a vocabulary of about 700 words, of which about 60% were understandable to "outsiders" to an auditory-verbal program.

By the fall of 1992, that brief period of equilibrium was soon to erode. Logan was about to start school. It's well known that, for many parents, the start of schooling for their children is one of those highly significant rites of passage. For parents of children in Auditory-Verbal therapy, it's a time for anxiety—at least, that was our experience with Logan. It was the first significant life event that would challenge the wisdom of choosing Auditory-Verbal therapy. Logan would be moving from his home world, the one that we had carefully constructed and used to nurture and protect him, to a world where we would not be directly involved. We believe that the whole point of Auditory-Verbal therapy is to integrate the child into society, and now the integration was about to begin. Joy and I would not be there to guide Logan every step of the way. In a very powerful way, the wisdom of opting for Auditory-Verbal therapy would be tested. And sure enough, it did turn out to be a test.

Logan would be going to two schools; in the mornings, he would travel to the Integration Support Unit in North York, Toronto; in the afternoons, he would attend the neighborhood school across the street. We felt very fortunate that we lived in a place where Logan could go to such a unit. The Metro Toronto School Board had set up an intensive program for kindergarten-age kids who are part of an Auditory-Verbal therapy program on the condition that the children also attend a regular kindergarten class in their home school. Logan would be in class with three other students and a qualified teacher of the hearing impaired with an assistant. However, North York is some distance from where we live. Logan would be taking a cab to the school, returning by cab to a neighborhood baby-sitter to have lunch, and then he would go to the local school in the afternoons. Joy had returned to work some months earlier as a college instructor.

I found events, once again, reminding me that teaching your child to listen and to speak is tough stuff—not only for the child, but for the rest of the family as well. This toughness is not restricted to the therapy per se. We subscribe to the underlying philosophy of doing everything possible to open doors for Logan, and choosing Auditory-Verbal therapy has become embedded in the other decisions that we make. For example, most children of Logan's age go to school for only half a day, as this is the usual limit of their endurance. But because of our "open all doors" approach and the rules set down by the school board, Logan was going to school all day, being integrated into two separate situations, and commuting by cab! Not easy stuff for Logan or the family. When Joy saw him get into the cab that first day of school, he looked so small—too small to be facing all these challenges.

The transportation became an issue in itself. Because Logan was going to a small school for special purposes, the school board arranged for a cab to transport him and one other student to the Integrated Support Unit. That was great, wonderful! But... the cab company sent a different driver to the door every day. Not only was this difficult from a tactical point of view (the drivers never seemed to know where the school was), but we had been painstakingly teaching Logan to not go off with strangers. Here we were now, doing precisely the opposite 5 days a week—yet another thing to sort out. We were reminded how being involved with Auditory-Verbal therapy encourages parents to become negotiators and advocates for their child. We dealt with the school board and the transportation company in order to get a consistent driver for Logan. Happily, everyone saw the problem and was willing to help.

Logan's first year in school was a mixed success. His experiences in the Integrated Support Unit were gratifying. At first, it was so unusual to have him saying something that we had not taught him. Up to that point, every word in his head seemed to be there because we had taught it! Now he was saying things and relating experiences that were new to us. At first, it felt weird, then exciting—our boy was starting to grow and develop independently from us! It's what we were striving for when we first chose Auditory-Verbal therapy.

Unfortunately, Logan's experiences at his local school were not going so well. The problem seemed to come in three parts: his hearing impairment, his personality, and the teacher's classroom management. Putting the three together produced a situation in which the teacher could not cope and Logan was unhappy.

We were prepared for problems associated with the hearing issue. Parents of older children in Auditory-Verbal therapy had warned us that we would, at least occasionally, run into teachers who would not wear the FM system or who would have difficulty accepting that children who are hearing impaired should be in a mainstream school. We had not really expected a situation where the teacher honestly professed acceptance of integration but, in practice, could not execute it. Logan is an energetic and sometimes controlling child. His teacher dealt with this by attempting to invoke rules and yet more rules, which Logan had difficulty even understanding. When he did understand the rules, he rejected them because of his personality. We felt this left only one area where a workable solution could be found, and that was that the teacher needed to adjust her style of teaching and supervision. This particular teacher could not achieve this goal, and so we had a problem on our hands. Once again, luck was with us, as the professionals at the Integrated Support Unit rallied around Logan's cause and arranged for him to attend school there in the afternoons as well as the mornings.

From this experience, we learned at least two significant things. First, Logan could integrate fairly well in a small group setting. His experience with one-on-one therapy at the Learning to Listen Foundation and at the Integrated Support Unit worked well. I was very pleased with his rate of learning and his happiness. When he was in a much larger group, however, requiring conformity of behavior, things went wrong quickly. Logan would hide under tables, lock himself in the washroom, or lie on the floor and fall asleep. Second, we learned that without the support and flexibility of professionals who would go the extra mile for Logan, we could run into dead ends within a matter of weeks.

It was becoming quite clear that our life with Logan was going to be ever changing. One of the consequences of choosing Auditory-Verbal therapy is that you really are on the "road less traveled." Most others do not know where you are. (Why are we not teaching sign language? Why don't we send our child to special schools?) In truth, you can't always depend on knowing where you are yourself. Surprises, some of them nasty, can be just around the corner. Logan's subsequent hearing tests are a case in point.

In mid-December 1993, Logan had a routine unaided hearing test. Because he did poorly compared to previous tests, another one was scheduled for the next week. Again, a poor test resulted. Logan was cooperating fully with the testing, so something had happened. Somewhere along the way, he had lost up to 15 dB in the middle frequency range of one ear and the audiologist didn't know why! Perhaps it was the result of illness! Perhaps it was a progressive loss! It could be Mondini syndrome (incomplete development and malformation of inner ear)! All I knew at the time was that I felt sad for Logan, depressed for myself and our family, and angry at the situation. Also, I was scared. What if his loss was progressive? What implication would this have for Logan and Auditory-Verbal therapy? If Logan's destiny was to become 100% deaf, what was the point in pursuing the therapy? Had it all been a waste—a well-intentioned, so far effective, but ultimately misguided effort? A blackness descended on Joy and myself.

The pre-Christmas environment only served to sharpen the pain. Surrounded by best-of-the-season sentiments and the holiday's focus on children, I found it impossible to look at Logan and not feel that he had been robbed. He is such a fighter, and the whole family had been spending over 3 years fighting for him. Logan wants to talk so much! There has never been a problem with his motivation. Doubt, anxiety, and confusion were once again our companions. It was just the way it was when Logan was first diagnosed. Emotionally, we could do without a repeat visit to all this. But the situation had to be faced.

A subsequent opinion from an ENT specialist indicated that the loss was not due to Mondini syndrome but probably to an attack of chicken pox, which had hospitalized Logan. This was good news and not such good news. We wanted to cheer that the loss appeared not to be progressive, but we became even more wary than we already were. If Logan's residual hearing was that fragile, what about the next infection? What about the next fever? Were we still facing the specter of gradual loss? There's no answer to questions like these. There are few facts, fewer probabilities, and absolutely no certainties. And so we are left with faith.

We will proceed as before, but we're digging still deeper into this strange stuff called faith. In retrospect, our life with Logan has always meant an exceptional series of adjustments compared to those required with children who can hear. The effects of Auditory-Verbal therapy on the family could all be regarded as too exhausting, too disruptive, and too emotionally expensive except for two key facts: the auditory-verbal approach works for Logan, and it is involving.

Even with his recent extra 15 dB loss, Logan's a boy with a profound hearing loss who hears, listens, and communicates verbally. His therapist continues to be pleased with his progress, and his teachers are likewise enthusiastic about his growing communication abilities. Despite everything, Logan continues to progress. For example, when he got himself lost in a large store recently, he was able to tell the staff that his daddy was named Peter and his mommy was Joy. As we frantically searched for him, I heard the announcement, "Will Peter or Joy please come to the jewelry counter to claim your son." When we briefly left Logan alone in his hospital room when he had chicken pox, we found him talking to a doctor, trying to negotiate his release: "I want to go home now; spots are all gone. I'm better now," he pleaded. Sydney, his taxi driver, understands his speech as well as we do. In fact, I think Logan gives a better description of the day's school activities to Sydney than he does to us, because he sees Sydney first.

To say that Logan is involving is an understatement! Life with Logan is definitely not a spectator sport. I can see no possibility of ever being distant from my child. The bonding between parent and child is very tight, because the intense need to communicate is always with us. There's no middle ground. One either quits or devotes oneself. To our surprise, we have found that friends and family members fall into one of these two camps. Some have remained with us and become involved with our more demanding lives; others quickly became distant. I feel that children in Auditory-Verbal therapy provide a rare opportunity to give and receive love. But seizing that chance requires putting forth effort and an acceptance of discomfort. (Logan is very loud; he interrupts without hesitation. Adult conversation gets strained easily and quickly.) So those relationships that turned out to be mere acquaintances, or friendships of convenience and habit, didn't stand up to that kind of irritation.

An unexpected benefit of the program is that it asks parents to pay attention to the small things in life. Life in the auditory-verbal approach is a constant "listen and tell" exercise—you actively look for things to support the lessons. The commonplace becomes special, the focus of an instant lesson, and a source of active experience for both parent and child. Opening cans, filling the car with gas, and shoveling snow have all become subjects for vivid demonstration and animated communication. There's a lot less of doing things on automatic pilot in our life.

Upon reflection, I have found the primary effect of Auditory-Verbal therapy on families is one of magnification. Everything seems to come in bolder strokes. It's tough, with sadness and setbacks, but it's also often rewarding. On the basis of faith we have found that we strive for growth—with no guarantees for the future. We have learned to expect the unexpected.

I've given up grieving about the past and the fact that Logan is hearing impaired. I'm not going to worry so much about the future, as I clearly can't control it. Rather, as a family, we'll concentrate on celebrating the present and play whatever hand is dealt to us to the best of our ability. With the assistance of good professional guidance, help from others, and a bit of luck, our future continues to run on hope. Our choice of the auditory-verbal experience has done much to make such hope both justifiable and realistic. And that, to put it in Logan's words, makes "Daddy very happy."

Update

In 2004, when Logan was 15, his hearing age was 13 years, 6 months, as he was 18 months old when first fitted with hearing aids and started Auditory-Verbal therapy. He still had a profound bilateral hearing loss and was undergoing candidacy testing and interviews for a cochlear implant at the Hospital for Sick Children in Toronto.

I had thought that the emotional roller coaster rides were over. But I was wrong. When it comes to dealing with serious hearing loss, I realize that I should have known better.

For the previous 10 years, Logan's hearing had been stable, with no further deterioration. He had responded well to Auditory-Verbal therapy as a child and

Logan Enright and family today

carried good comprehension and verbal skills into his teenage years. Although he was seen as different by teachers and schoolmates, he formed friendships, attended local schools, and did well in some subjects while continuing to be a high-energy, active guy.

Because of this overall progress and the stable nature of his hearing loss, it appeared that our key tactics of reinforcement and perseverance would continue indefinitely. In my mind, I had conveniently pushed aside some potential longer-term issues, such as the reduction of Logan's hearing acuity as he grew older or, when he gets his first real job, how he will cope with telephones and fast-paced conversations in noisy environments. Then there would always be the possibility of injury, as Logan is an extreme-sport devotee. I had settled into the mindset of not worrying about things I could not control and that might never happen. So we all lived nicely together in our auditory-verbal niche, one that was, by now, very familiar to us.

Then the snowball hit.

Logan was walking by a group of boys in the schoolyard, and out of nowhere a snowball hit him square on the ear. The result was severe and apparently caused permanent tinnitus in his left ear. This condition makes using a hearing aid impossible. With that unlucky blow by a snowball, everything changed. We'd been ejected out of our comfortable niche.

Logan was essentially now relying on lipreading, something he does not do well, and his learning at school instantly nose-dived. All the associated frustrations were kicking in. Hopefully, he would soon be able to receive a cochlear implant.

I'm relating this turn of events for two reasons: it puts into context what I'm about to relate of Logan's experiences over the past decade, and it serves as a reminder that when one addresses auditory-verbal issues, one is dealing with something that is inherently changeable—sometimes quite abruptly. The child's age and functional stability don't matter.

Parents of older listening and talking kids clearly remember what they went through in getting their child diagnosed, choosing AVT, going to therapy, and learning to live with hearing impairment within the family unit. Sometimes, parents need to be prepared to go through much of that all over again. Things can always change. Being deaf will always be a challenge.

Sports

Logan has developed a typical teenager's love of sports, the more extreme, the better. This is ironic in that in his younger years, we despaired at his terrible sense of balance. At age 18 months he still was not walking, and seemed to have no potential for doing so. At that point we were convinced that he would never walk, hear, or talk. Yet, here we are a decade later, making repeated visits to the hospital because he broke his knee. Why a broken knee? From doing delicately balanced stunts on his BMX bike at a skate park! The injury could have occurred just as easily through his keen passion for snowboarding, wakeboarding, hockey, and skateboarding. In short, anything that seems predisposed to breaking bones, Logan loves. And in this there is a point for his mother and me. Although we knew that Logan is at risk for a hearing injury via a blow to the head, and our strong inclination is to protect him at all costs, we let him engage in these sports. Obviously, we insist on his using protective headgear, but otherwise we let him do his thing. This is just part of our overall philosophy of opening as many doors as possible for him. This belief led us to choose Auditory-Verbal therapy as a communication approach for our son. His great pleasure, however, is matched only by our nervousness.

Safety issues present themselves often. We are lucky enough to have a cottage and boats. Logan continually pushes for independence by badgering me to let him take the 10-horsepower boat out on his own. My concern has always been that with a howling motor operating just inches from his ear, Logan would hear nothing; and although hearing isn't the most important sense when boating, it still has a significant role in safety.

Logan needs to learn to look around more than other kids out on the water. He needs to operate against his naturally impulsive character and exercise judgment over enthusiasm. We see this as more than a boating issue. In the near future, Logan will begin agitating to start driving lessons, so we need an approach that will work equally well for this eventuality.

Joy and I decided to take a phased approach. First, Logan had to study and pass his boating exams. Next, we started him off with a very small motor, and he was allowed out on the water only as far as we could see him. He proved himself over time, so we let him travel farther. But we alerted our neighbors to let us know if he did anything unsafe. He knew about this and understood that his boating privileges would be withdrawn if he transgressed. After he passed this stage, we let him use the 10-horsepower boat. We have generally found that this phased approach gives Logan the time he needs to learn to compensate for his hearing loss—for example, taking a moment for additional observation and attention.

Education

In 2004, Logan was in 9th grade. We had been warned by other parents of older kids who had learned via the auditory-verbal approach that mainstreaming such children requires constant vigilance and intervention on the part of the parents. This turned out to be true. Nevertheless, there were some surprises along the way.

For example, mathematics is a significant challenge for Logan, partly due to basic lack of skill (learning the multiplication tables took him forever). More significantly, mathematics has its own language; algebra, in particular, has a unique terminology that builds the foundation for understanding abstract concepts. Logan missed learning these terms completely, partly because he couldn't comprehend the teacher's verbal explanations. The concepts being taught might just as well have been in Greek, as far as he was concerned.

We responded by hiring an adult tutor, who also happened to be an itinerant teacher with the school district, to help Logan. We also brought the issue forward at his annual IPRC meeting (similar to the IEP meeting in the United States) with the request that Logan be assisted with mathematics by the itinerant teacher on the days when he was withdrawn from class. The initial reaction at the IPRC meeting was that math was not within the scope of itinerant help, since the purpose of such assistance was to deal with language and communication issues. We had to explain that one big area of Logan's math problems was his lack of understanding of the language of math. Once that point was clarified, help was promised.

I wish I could report that the tutor and the additional help did the trick. Not so. Logan had slipped too far behind, and his ongoing lack of basic "math sense" had made it impossible for him to keep up with the curriculum. We also discovered that the tutor and Logan's math teacher had different views on what constituted a correct math answer. I strongly urge parents of early grade school kids who are deaf to keep a close eye on math comprehension. If there's a problem, intervene early and don't focus on only the numeric issues. The language component may need attention, too.

Another issue was the changing of classes for almost every subject in junior high school. Logan had to have several teachers who needed to be oriented to his auditory needs. To say that the teacher response has been varied is an understatement. A few understood, used the FM system, and seated Logan appropriately. Some had the ability to change their teaching style, to slow down a bit, and to face Logan as often as possible. However, we found that many teachers would not, or could not, "get it." The result is that Logan's marks can vary wildly from year to year and from subject to subject, solely because of the teacher.

Our intervention with the junior high school teachers was less effective than at the grade school level. It appears that some teachers are not willing to make changes for just one student who is struggling within a large student population. Another factor is that teachers are very busy in the classroom and often simply forget to adapt.

We found good allies in the school's guidance counselor and the itinerant teacher. They intervened as best they could, and having such advocates within the school system is invaluable. Parents need to do everything possible to build such internal support as will be needed.

Telephone and other equipment

Like his teenage peers, Logan loves music. What's hot in the season's TV lineup is apparently a life-and-death matter! And, of course, the telephone is indispensable for arranging biking expeditions and other life-altering activities. Naturally, Logan wants to do everything that his friends do, and the auditory-verbal approach supports that desire. But there are extra challenges in making all this happen. We have devised some strategies to help Logan.

On the telephone, Logan gets no useful signal through the telecoil, regardless of the brand of hearing aid used. A speaker phone with an adjustable volume control has worked best, although a parent must still hover in the background to help with interpretation. (Most teenagers seem to mumble when they're not shouting.)

With television, Logan is lost without closed captioning. We discovered that the more he got involved with the program, the closer to the TV he sat. He explained that the character-height of the closed captioning was too small. We saw that the caption height is affected by the physical size of the screen, so we upgraded to a projection-sized TV with excellent sound. Now Logan can read the captioning while sitting back from the TV, and the enhanced sound helps him appreciate music and sound effects. A large TV would not have been a priority in our lives, yet here we are with this huge television. A parent does what a parent has to do.

One big surprise with Logan's development is his love of music. It's rock, and the harder the rock, the better. Although he sometimes puts earphones over his hearing aids, he does not prefer this approach. He'd rather take off his aids and use an in-ear headset. The problem with this is that he sometimes falls asleep at night with the CD still going strong. I'm personally not fond of seek-and-find exercises at 3:00 in the morning!

Character development

As Logan moves towards adulthood, the challenges continue. His maturity level is 1 to 2 years behind his chronological age—consistent with the delay in having his hearing loss diagnosed when he was a baby. He continues to overtalk in conversations and attempts to control his auditory environment by being the one who's doing all the talking. When he is with his peers, he continually strives to be the center of attention. He resists changing these habitual behaviors.

He requires constant, and at times exhausting, reminders about turn-taking in conversation and keeping his stories short. He tends to ramble and doesn't realize that the listener has tuned out. We attempt to curb his enthusiasm for being the class clown. We realize that this is part of his character, but we also see it as a control mechanism that has worked well for him. The difficulty now is that what was acceptable when Logan was a child is not acceptable in a teenager. His friends are less tolerant of these behaviors, and adults lose patience. One of our tasks is to help Logan understand that people's expectations of his behavior are changing as he gets older. He doesn't get that concept yet, so currently, he's often confused by the reactions of others.

The future

These are just a few of the many issues that we have dealt with as our son grows. Despite the frustrations and challenges, we are strong advocates for the auditory-verbal approach. Our basic philosophy remains the same: do whatever can be done to open up as many opportunities as possible for Logan. Auditory-Verbal therapy has been a fundamental part of our philosophy. If Logan gets his cochlear implant, we will be back into therapy again for auditory rehabilitation. We see it as a wise investment for Logan's future.

In 2006, Logan was finishing high school, where he has been very involved in sports, especially wrestling. He is currently trying to determine whether he will attend college or take up a skilled trade. Fortunately, his parents seem to have persuaded him that he can't make a living at wakeboarding, his real passion.

TRISTAN

Christine Hall

After Tristan had been swimming with a group of children at the beach on a vacation in St. Petersburg, Florida, I handed my 7-year-old son his hearing aids. He put them back in my hand and reported, "No, they are broken." A thorough check revealed nothing wrong, and I presented them back to him only to be refused again. "The batteries are dead," he said. "Tristan," I said, "the hearing aids are fine. Do you have water in your ears?" He was lipreading. "No," he replied.

After 10 minutes, I tried a third time. This time I put them in his ears myself. He yanked them out and said, "No, Mom. They are broken. I don't want them." I closed my fingers around his two vibrant blue hearing aids with fluorescent orange earmolds, and my heart sank. "Tristan, why don't you want them?" I asked. "Because," he finally confided, "I can hear."

For one tiny, fleeting moment, I was tempted to hope that a longed-for miracle had occurred, but that was quickly dashed when he added, "Because I want to be the same as all the other children." I knew then that it was only his wishful desire. After a long hug, we talked about how no two children are exactly the same. Some are tall, some are short, some wear glasses, some wear hearing aids. Some, like Tristan, are happy, outgoing, confident, and ever so special, but no two are exactly alike.

Tristan Hall (front right) and family, 1994

At 7 years of age, Tristan had already begun to search for his place in the world. His desire to belong is powerful. One day he will hold the world in the palm of his hand and he will do that with or without me. The gifts I have to give to him are his hearing aids and the power to communicate through spoken language so that he is free to share his joys and sorrows, his successes and failures, with whomever he chooses.

Reflections on the Past

It is difficult for me to remember these past 7 years. They have been very busy. August 17, 1986, the day of Tristan's birth, was as joyous as that of his brother Julian's 2 years earlier. Tristan arrived right on schedule without difficulties or complications. His Apgar scores were perfect.

The first weeks at home were happy ones. Tristan was a delightful baby. By 4 months of age, however, we noticed that he could not hold his head up very well. Trying hard to control my anxiety, I took him to a pediatrician who placed him in a physiotherapy program. Nobody seemed too concerned, but by 9 months of age, our baby could not sit up and a nagging voice told me that something more had to be done. Through a friend, I learned that Toronto's Hospital for Sick Children had a developmental assessment clinic for babies and young children, but the waiting list was long. Why hadn't anybody sent us earlier?

I was no longer able to suppress my mounting frustration and sense of helplessness. With much persistence and many phone calls, we finally got an appointment, and Tristan received a short examination from a pediatric neurologist. Without further explanation, we were told that Tristan had a "neurological disorder" and that we would be contacted by the hospital for further tests, including vision, hearing, and an EEG. We were to continue weekly physiotherapy sessions.

As we waited for a call from the hospital to arrange further appointments, I began to quiz Tristan's physiotherapist. Was he more than just a slow developer? What could be done to help him? Sensing my desperation, the physiotherapist suggested the Hugh MacMillan Medical Centre, a facility that services children who are physically challenged. I called immediately and was able to book an appointment in their child assessment program.

Tristan was assessed by a team that included an occupational therapist, a physiotherapist, a speech pathologist, a social worker, a psychologist, and a physician. They spent an entire afternoon listening to his history and my concerns. I was given his diagnosis that same afternoon: cerebral palsy with a suspected left hemiplegia. Tristan was 12 months old.

The news was not good, but at last, we had a diagnosis. Our initial distress was quickly overcome by the need to learn what we could do to help our son. We were relieved to know that his condition was neither progressive nor life-threatening for, by this point, my imagination had begun to interfere with my sanity. The waiting had been difficult, but now we were able to begin an intensive therapy program, which helped us during those early, heart-rending months. One year later, we still had heard nothing from the neurologist who was to have set up vision and hearing tests. Fortunately, these tests were carried out at the Hugh MacMillan Centre. Tristan was 18 months old when the audiologist explained to me that he had some hearing loss, greater in the high frequencies. It was difficult at first to find meaning in her words, because Tristan already had his share of problems. Surely he didn't need any more. What could be so bad about missing a few high frequencies? Ignorance is bliss, but not for long!

Once Tristan was fitted with two hearing aids, we were touched by the full impact of what a hearing loss might mean. The final diagnosis showed a severe to profound bilateral hearing loss—a devastating setback. The cerebral palsy with which I had been so obsessed up to this point began to take a backseat to the enormous challenge of learning to communicate. Tristan's physical development began to show improvement, and we were encouraged that, by the time he was nearly 2, he had learned to sit up by himself.

Learning to Walk, Learning to Talk

When we learned of Tristan's hearing impairment, we knew nothing about Auditory-Verbal therapy. Coincidentally, the same week of the diagnosis, our audiologist suggested we watch a Canadian Broadcasting Corporation (CBC) television documentary called "The Children Who Learned to Listen." We were elated to see many teenagers who are hearing impaired listening and talking. These children all lived at home, attended mainstream classes at their local schools, articulated clearly, and had good command of the English language. Their successes provided inspiration while giving us a goal to pursue. We respected their parents enormously. They had not had the benefit of observing graduates of an Auditory-Verbal therapy program to provide them with the knowledge that many children who are hearing impaired can learn to listen and talk.

Before "The Children Who Learned to Listen" was over, we knew that Auditory-Verbal therapy was the choice for our family, as it appeared to offer Tristan the best chance for a "normal" life. If we were to bear the heavy responsibility of making a decision that would affect him for the rest of his life, at least we were choosing an option on his behalf that fostered the fulfillment of his true potential. It would be up to him to make his own choices in the future.

The once-a-week therapy session with the Auditory-Verbal therapist at the Learning to Listen Foundation was encouraging. At home on our own, it was not easy to fit all the listening work into an already busy schedule of physiotherapy, audiological assessments, and doctors' appointments. I had many days of doubt and despair. Could I help him learn to walk? Could I teach him to talk? I wasn't prepared for this, and I never wanted to be a teacher! Countless times, I wished I had someone else to do the work for me. Many times, I felt like giving up. But Tristan loved to hear and began to learn to listen. We were elated to see him look up at the sky and say "airplane" when he heard a jet thunder overhead. Still, it seemed that for every word he learned, there were a hundred more to teach him.

For a long time, Tristan's development alternated between his physical skills and learning to listen and talk. When he was listening, physical movement was limited because he was sitting at the table with me. When he was trying to walk, the physical exertion was so great that his little mouth clamped shut with the effort. These two activities did not happen simultaneously. It was just too difficult for him to learn to walk and talk at the same time. Tristan was nearly 3 when he took his first awkward steps.

It was at this point that he also began learning concepts. We could see that his expressive language wasn't developing well because he should have been using two- and three-word utterances. We decided that he should be assessed by a specialized speech-language pathologist who diagnosed his difficulty in speaking as due to dysarthria, a condition related to his cerebral palsy. We believed that, in time, just as he had learned to walk, he would continue to improve his speaking skills as he gained control of his oral peripheral muscles.

Mysteriously, we had another unexpected setback when Tristan began to lose hearing in both ears. This unexplained loss of hearing occurred over several years and left Tristan with a profound 90 to 105 dB loss in his right ear and a profound 95 to 120 dB loss in his left ear with no measurable hearing past 1000 Hz in the left. Despite these setbacks, we were convinced he was an auditory child as he continued to use his residual hearing to its fullest potential. We remained committed to Auditory-Verbal therapy, which was now supplemented with two speech therapy sessions per week.

Meeting the Challenges of School

When Tristan began school, I was exposed to the language of his hearing peers, and I had to remind myself that he is hearing impaired. When I heard the expressive language of his peers who are hearing impaired I had also to remind myself that he has additional physical difficulties. If he had only a hearing impairment, he would be speaking in sentences, clearly expressing all those concepts on which we'd worked so hard together. At nursery school, he knew what he wanted to say, but putting more than three words together was a tremendous effort. His tongue was on one side and his chin was always wet. He was still unable to use the washroom by himself—a basic requirement of mainstream schools that nearly prevented his enrollment. After much searching, I found a very understanding teacher.

In kindergarten and 1st grade, Tristan's frustration level was high, especially at times when he was not understood by others with whom he so desperately wanted to communicate. It has been frustrating for me to tolerate adults and children who do not take the time or make the effort to communicate with him in return. There were many occasions during the first two years of school when Steve and I had extreme difficulty in convincing school board officials that Tristan belonged at the neighborhood school with his brother and friends. These are just two of the many little challenges we continue to encounter every day. After observing Tristan's remarkable progress over the years, the little things no longer have the power to shake my belief in the future. We have learned to be patient.

For Tristan, learning to read was the key to a new world. Although we always read to Julian and Tristan when they were little, we decided to teach Tristan to read in therapy when he was 4 years old. By the time he had completed 1st grade, he could read fluently and phonetically. Now he often asks, "What's this word, Mom?" or, "What does this mean?" Tristan is becoming his own teacher and is teaching others. He taught Steve, Julian, me, and a few teachers as well that our expectations for him need to be high.

Today, in 2nd grade, Tristan attends public school in the town of Aurora, just outside of Toronto. Last fall, he had surgery to release his tight and foreshortened left heel cord and hamstring tendons that were causing him increasing difficulties with walking, dressing, and putting on shoes. (I don't want to even think about the winter boots!) He spent 8 weeks in a wheelchair. Now, although he will wear a leg brace for the next few years, Tristan's walking has dramatically improved. This winter he learned to ski with Ontario Track Three's skiing for the disabled. We were thrilled to watch him ski down the hill by himself while listening to directions from his instructor via his FM system. This summer will be the third season he has played on a soccer team.

We continue to attend physiotherapy, speech therapy, hydrotherapy, and Auditory-Verbal therapy sessions. We still do a great deal of work at home. At school, he participates with confidence and he is accepted, encouraged, and guided. He is also expected to solve problems and to accept consequences. He is making new friends and spreading around his unmatched enthusiasm for life. Conversations are commonplace now. In our family, there is an impending sense that it's time to get on with the "good stuff." We have waited a long time, and the reward is sweet. Life will always be hard for Tristan, and that makes me mad. There are still tears, as there always will be. Life can be unfair. But the tears are fewer, and for every tear of grief, there are a hundred tears of pride and joy.

Update

Can it really be 10 years? At 17, my son, Tristan, excels at just about everything he does. I barely remember some of the struggles and successes I wrote about when he was 7 and still learning to listen and speak. Others I remember as if they occurred yesterday. After shedding a few tears re-reading my words of a decade ago, I am happy that we are at the end of these 10 years.

I know very well about the challenges of teaching a child who was born profoundly deaf to listen and talk using hearing aids. Tristan would not have learned to listen and speak without them. But teaching a child who is profoundly deaf to listen and speak by this method takes many years and is anything but easy. Sometimes it was fun, but more often it was just hard work.

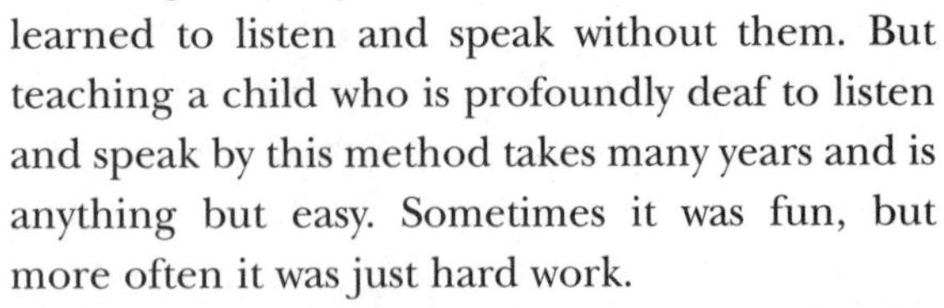

Tristan Hall today

When Tristan struggled to speak clearly as a result of not only his hearing loss but also dysarthria resulting from his mild cerebral palsy, I suffered from stress and guilt. I felt that somehow I might not be working hard enough with him. On the other hand, he was such a happy and charming little person that I didn't want to push him past the limit of enjoying his lessons. It seemed to take forever to teach him language, and he always lagged behind his peers at school.

Even with his FM system, I know he did not hear most of what was going on in the classroom. Every year he fell farther behind. I worried a lot. I admit now that if I'd had the choice 10 years ago

I'd have chosen for it all to go away. I persistently pushed ahead with Auditory-Verbal therapy and speech therapy, however, because more than anything I wanted Tristan to grow up to have choices, to make his own way in the world, and to have his independence. He deserved that.

Thankfully, miraculously, cochlear implantation in babies and young children has made all that struggling a thing of the past. It has given parents the opportunity to have fun teaching their children to listen and speak in a much shorter time, one that is comparable to that of children with typical hearing.

In Tristan's case, we did not have the choice of an implant; it was not available at the time. But in 1990, the first two Canadian children I knew through VOICE for Hearing-Impaired Children received cochlear implants in New York. Like Tristan, these children attended the Learning to Listen Foundation in Toronto. Each time we met these families at VOICE functions—which was often in those days, as we all needed support from other parents—I watched with envy as the children who had cochlear implants developed speech and language quickly while Tristan continued his struggle with his hearing aids.

It was amazing what those children could hear. I know; I watched very carefully. Unfortunately, Tristan, who was 4 years old in 1990, did not have a left-corner audiogram. Although his loss was profound, his residual hearing in the right ear continued across the frequency spectrum to 4000 Hz, and there was little research or consensus on the development of cochlear implants, unlike today. Of course, I didn't need research to tell me that Tristan would benefit from having an implant, but no implant center would listen to me. I tried.

Tristan had several implant assessments at the Hospital for Sick Children in Toronto, but all the years of Auditory-Verbal therapy had made him such a good listener that he did not fail the hearing tests. Once again I persisted, because I had seen at first hand the difference between Tristan's hearing and the hearing of other children with cochlear implants. I did not think it was fair that he should continue to struggle. We considered going to another Canadian city for an assessment, and also made contact with one of the cochlear implant centers in New York. Finally, Tristan was accepted as a candidate in Toronto at the age of 11. I feel now that I waited very patiently for 8 years until Tristan finally got his life-changing cochlear implant!

"Life-changing" is an understatement. Not a day goes by since Tristan's cochlear implant was turned on in 1998, just following his 12th birthday, that I don't think what an incredible thing this cochlear implant is. Sometimes I have to just say it out loud to somebody.

The implant has changed all our lives, but Tristan's especially. He went from being an 11-year-old with hearing aids—an excellent lipreader and active listener who still needed most dinner table conversation repeated several times—to a 12-year-old with a cochlear implant who overheard everything, even when he was in the next room. We, who spoke indiscreetly in the company of the 11-year-old, now had to learn discretion.

Recently, I attended a showing of a documentary produced by the Learning to Listen Foundation and Cochlear Americas called *Jacob's Journey*. The film depicts Jacob, age 1 and a cochlear implant user, at his Auditory-Verbal therapy session. He was even playing with some of the same toys that Tristan used. Jacob was listening and singing with the therapist and his parents. I was in awe. He was vastly ahead of where Tristan had been after his first year of Auditory-Verbal therapy. *Jacob's Journey* is a masterpiece that provides accurate and timely information about the cochlear implant and the auditory-verbal approach to prospective parents and to the general public in a very special, informative, and touching way. I met Jacob's father, Jonathan Samson, and his parents through VOICE for Hearing-Impaired Children. Jonathan was 17, and Tristan was a newly diagnosed baby. Jonathan played a big part in our choice of communication approach for Tristan. He was a great inspiration when the going was tough and we were unsure about the future.

In 2004, Tristan had become a wonderful young man of 17 who excelled in high school and was planning to attend university. He won prizes in history and geography. He worked during the summer as a camp counselor with young children.

Tristan loves to engage in public speaking. He has made enormous progress in the years since he received his cochlear implant. In 7th and 8th grades, after the activation of the implant, Tristan covered the equivalent of 6 years of elementary school. With the help of an outstanding educational assistant, he entered high school prepared for the new curriculum.

In high school he had the help and guidance of a wonderful hearing resource teacher who inspired him to love learning and to develop self-discipline, a great sense of humor, and a desire to succeed. What more could I ask for?

Throughout the past decade, three specific things gave me strength and helped me keep things in perspective. The first is a sign that was on the therapist's wall at the Learning to Listen Foundation. It read, "Tough times never last, but tough people do." The second is something my husband, Steve, always said when I despaired over how far behind Tristan was and about how well everyone else's kids were doing. He would say simply, "It's a long race." The third is something I read in a book by David Luterman, *When Your Child Is Deaf.* He referred to happiness as a time when you have someone to love, something to do, and something to hope for. He concluded that parents of children who are deaf have happiness handed to them on a platter! I couldn't agree more.

Did we make the right decisions on behalf of Tristan by choosing the auditory-verbal approach and a cochlear implant? You bet we did! Every day I am thankful for that. I am also thankful for the support of other parents and the professionals during our darkest moments. They believed we would succeed. Ten years and a cochlear implant made a wonderful difference in Tristan's life. The choices we made for him as a little boy have given him the power as an adult to become the master of his own destiny.

In 2006, Tristan was attending Trent University in Peterborough, Ontario, Canada. He is enjoying his studies in environmental science, politics, international development, geography, and history. He has note-takers for all classes, uses an FM system for lectures, and regularly chats with his parents and friends on the telephone. He loves the freedom and independence of living on his own.

ALEXANDER

Sharon Bergen

Our son, Alexander, is 10 years old and in 5th grade at our local school. He plays with his school friends and enjoys friendships with a wide variety of neighborhood children. He skis, plays soccer, swims, and skates very well. He's very stubborn and very curious about everything, and has always been that way. He wants to know things and makes sure he finds out. He has a very independent personality. Alexander also has a severe to profound hearing loss.

As we look back on his early years, especially those first years of therapy, we remember three stages: we learned to be teachers, we made school choices, and we watched Alexander become independent.

Stage 1: Parents Learning to Be Teachers

It was May 1985 when I took Alexander to the Learning to Listen Foundation for an audiological assessment. I was glad to be there because we were finally going to get some answers. Over the previous year we had to wait until his ear infections were better. We had to struggle with a doctor who felt we were "overprotective." But we were finally there. Alexander would be 2 years old in 2 months. After the assessment, we were told Alexander had a severe to profound hearing loss in both ears. We had no idea what that meant! This all happened at the time John was moving his ceramics studio from Toronto to Kitchener, in southwest Ontario, and I was pregnant with Gregory. So the Bergen family was undergoing some dramatic changes.

Fortunately for us, we were part of a very caring support system. Alexander received his first set of hearing aids. At that time, we met the auditory-verbal clinical staff, who gave us good information and the names of several people to contact when considering our options. We visited the clinic at the Learning to Listen Foundation and observed children who were around Alexander's age. We made our decision quickly following the visit. Auditory-Verbal therapy would be our first option.

Alexander Bergen (left) and brother Gregory, 1994

The decision was based on our feelings and intuition rather than on what we had read. If Alexander could learn to listen and talk, then that was what we wanted to try. We wanted him to be able to communicate with his grandparents, aunts, and uncles. We wanted to give him the educational opportunities that his cousins had. John and I both come from Mennonite backgrounds. Family and community are very important. Philosophically, we were not afraid of failure, and we were prepared to take a chance on what seemed the most logical choice. If it didn't work out, we were prepared to change course. Then came the hard part: we needed to learn to be good teachers as well as good parents! The weekly 1-hour commute to Toronto for lessons, the daily lessons at home, and the normal dealings with a 2-year-old were all big adjustments. These challenges meant less freedom for me, endless conversations with my son, and changes to my husband's routine involving specially organized games or activities in the evening.

Over the next 2 to 3 years, Alexander learned to cope with his hearing aids and his daily lessons. There were a lot of highs and a lot of lows, but he loved to hear sounds and seemed to us to be a keen learner. He enjoyed the one-to-one time with his mom and dad. We gave him as much time as we could.

Our best lessons seemed to develop out of our daily routines, such as going to the store. Alexander loved to touch everything, a habit that drove me crazy. I ran behind him, scooping up anything that might not make it back onto the shelf. He was a typical 2-year-old except that he had no language and no little friends—yet. If some little child might be around, he would take that child's toys. There were a lot of tears at this time. Alexander usually won the fight, but always ended up playing by himself.

Lessons were good, but they were often tough. We learned quickly that Alexander did not like to repeat the same lessons and games. He liked variety. So I had to be very creative in planning lessons. Sometimes it worked, and sometimes it didn't. Alexander and I spent 2 years of hard work developing ourselves as teacher and student as well as parent and child. I always started a lesson with a game or by drawing pictures. A game on the floor was a good way to introduce a lesson concept. Sometimes we just stayed on the floor.

I remember trying to teach Alexander the concept of "What's missing?" John, Alexander, and I were playing on the floor with his toys. I'd take a toy away and say, "What's missing?" He would say the name of the toy, and we'd give it back. It worked, but we couldn't do this too often or he'd get up and leave! Lessons were about 15 minutes in duration at this time. We tried doing about three mini-lessons a day at first. This schedule drove me crazy. I preferred to do it all at one time. By the end of his second year of therapy we were doing 1-hour lessons at a time, usually in the afternoon before Alexander's nap.

Prepositions were really tough concepts. We tried to teach them using drawings, pictures, and toys, but nothing worked; Alexander had decided he wasn't going to play any preposition games. Then, John built a 6-foot snow arch outside. He placed Alexander on the bridge, then we went *over* the bridge, *under* the bridge, and *beside* the bridge. He then took Polaroid™ pictures of the activity. This was a good lesson, and Alexander learned prepositions! I guess we'd made it important for him. He wanted to learn because that snow fort was important to him. Drawing was also a very important lesson tool. John could always intrigue Alexander with a cartoon or funny situation. We made elaborate, colorful word charts with pictures, and Alexander loved to look at them.

Around this time we started a daily journal, which we carried on for many years. It contained drawings and photos of the day's events. Later, we wrote stories to describe the pictures. This was an abundant source of new vocabulary. Alexander is and was a very strong-willed individual, and he needed things to be relevant. Obviously, we ran into a few power struggles. I recall the Auditory-Verbal therapist asking me whether I felt therapy was working for us.

After I had a good cry at home and found some tough new resolve, Alexander soon discovered that he wasn't going to bed until certain things were covered. As his parents, we were very firm about this because of his lack of language. Discipline was a constant problem.

At age 3, Alexander attended a small nursery school just a block from our house. He was surrounded by children who could hear. It took him and his classmates some time to adjust to one another, but by spring, he began to be a part of the group. His classmates were accepting him.

Stage 2: Making School Choices

Our first choice was not to send Alexander to a segregated public preschool for children who are hearing impaired. We didn't want him spending a large block of his time with children whose speech could potentially be a poor model. Secondly, the school's philosophy was that it was the primary educator, not the parents. So, Alexander went to a local nursery school in the morning and came home to have his lessons in the afternoon.

After 3 years of Auditory-Verbal therapy, we found ourselves again forced to make a choice. Which kindergarten program was best? Our choice was between two school boards. The public board encouraged us to send our son to a special school for children who are hearing impaired. The morning program was an integrated kindergarten, and there was a segregated enrichment program in the afternoon. This class consisted of children who were all hearing impaired and one child who was not. A full day seemed too much for a 5-year-old, and we were still making weekly trips to Toronto. Our local mainstream public school offered us an itinerant teacher only twice a week, and no more than that. If Alexander needed more support, we were advised to send him to the special-needs school. This board's philosophy was for parents not to take a chance on integration because of the possibility of failure—a point of view that conflicted with our attitude of "Let's not worry about failure when there is a chance for success."

We looked into the Catholic school system and were pleased with its attitude and experience with integrating children with special needs. Instead of centralizing care and resources, this board had a strong program in local schools for children with special needs. So we enrolled Alexander at our local Catholic school, and we feel strongly that this was the right decision. Alexander's brother Gregory also attends this school now. Attending school has been a very positive experience for Alexander and for us. School has given him interesting toys, a visually stimulating environment, children to play with, and, more importantly, independence.

Our routine at home continued with our daily lessons. Books were a constant part of our routine, and the Auditory-Verbal therapist taught us to use them in new ways! The therapist drew beautiful pictures that Alexander loved to copy at home, and soon he was creating the pictures while we told him the story.

When Alexander was in 3rd grade, I began to experience a strange new anxiety—I was becoming less important to his academic needs and to his successes. His itinerant teacher was working with Alexander three times a week. We created a team approach with his classroom teacher, the itinerant teacher, the school principal, the special-needs teacher, John, and myself. Alexander was in good hands. His teachers wrote a story about him and about what their students had learned by having Alexander in their class. This article appeared in our local VOICE newsletter and in *The Auricle*, a publication of Auditory-Verbal International. In the students' own words, they learned:

- Alexander needed hearing aids.
- Alexander liked to laugh with them.
- A lot about how much Alexander couldn't hear.
- Alexander needed them to be quiet when his group was reading.
- He sometimes needed to have the meanings of the words explained.
- Alexander's art was very good, and he often had terrific ideas.
- He did good work at school, and he could write in his journal and read like they could.
- He was smart and he was fun to be around, he liked to play with them, and he was kind.
- Even with his hearing aids, he couldn't hear directions or his friends talking on the playground if they were too far away.
- To speak more slowly.
- He shared his treats and toys readily.

Stage 3: Alexander and Independence

Alexander has learned to take responsibility for his own learning. He also has learned to tell us when he can't hear or understand. He asks "what" and "why" often. His fellow students help by teaching him valuable socially acceptable behavior. Alexander had trouble socially. He would take a soccer ball from a group that was enjoying a game, or laugh at kids who had difficulty, or talk out of turn in discussions. So the school developed a program of role playing and problem-solving. The Auditory-Verbal therapist also developed lessons that I could do at home. We were a real team—the school, the therapist, and us.

At the end of Alexander's fifth year of therapy, John and I began our own local chapter of VOICE. It began with a phone call to an Auditory-Verbal therapist at the Learning to Listen Foundation who was leaving full-time therapy for motherhood. We hired her one day a week to work with four children so that Auditory-Verbal therapy could be provided in our own town… no more long trips to therapy.

Seven years of Auditory-Verbal therapy have passed, and I am amazed how the time has flown. This baby of ours is now in 5th grade! He's a wicked skier, and loves jokes and reading R.L. Stine books. He still can't always understand what is being said, but his brother, Gregory, is an expert at interpreting for him. When they're not fighting, they're best friends. Our only problem is that Alexander talks too much! I like this problem! Over our recent Christmas holidays, we were all sitting around the table. Alexander was asking questions and talking non-stop to his cousins. When there was a pause in the dinner conversation, his cousin Joshua said, "Alexander, you talk too much." Alexander replied, "I like talking." Yesterday, he talked on the telephone to his school friend. I was on the extension phone in case interpreting was needed. His friend wanted to know about homework, and Alexander gave him all the information.

We discuss many things at this time. Recently, Alexander, Gregory, and I were driving home from school when Alexander asked a question we've never discussed at home. Perhaps it came from some discussions at school? We don't know. Alexander asked me why some people talked with their hands. This came as a surprise because we've never talked about sign language. I explained that sometimes parents make these choices for their children. Alexander paused for a minute, then said, "I like talking. If I talked with my hands then I couldn't talk to everybody, and I want to talk to everybody." We are glad Alexander likes talking to everybody. As parents, we have opened some important doors for our son. Now, it's up to him to open many on his own!

Update

One cold winter morning just before Christmas last year, my husband, John, and our 20-year-old son, Alexander, got up at 4:30 in the morning and headed for the international airport in Toronto. Alexander had been attending his second year at the University of Waterloo and had decided it was time for a break. He was heading for Panorama Ski Resort, just south of Banff, Alberta, on the border with British Columbia. For the next 4 months he was going to clean rooms and snowboard to his heart's content in order to earn money for his next term at school. We thought that the allure of helicopter skiing might impede this financial goal.

Alexander Bergen (center), brother Gregory, and dad John today

In 1994, when we first wrote about Alexander, he was 10 years old and in 5th grade. Today, he is 6 feet, 3 inches tall and attends the University of Waterloo in Ontario, Canada.

John and I have always believed that Alexander should be fully mainstreamed and that accommodations should be made only when needed. But this choice has not been without its challenges, and the road has had many bends.

Intermediate years (grades 5–8)

Alexander made steady progress during these years, and by 8th grade, he was on par with his peers. Regular Auditory-Verbal therapy had ended, and the itinerant teacher spent as much time with him on more complex listening behaviors and social skills as on academics. Alexander needed to learn how to listen attentively in group discussions, master clarification skills, and learn appropriate turn-taking. He had a wonderful group of friends whom he had known since kindergarten. Successfully communicating with a friend who was hearing impaired had become second nature to these young people. They would look directly at him before speaking.

Alexander had become a happy and confident self-advocate. During these intermediate years, he received itinerant help three times a week.

High school (grades 9–11)

Alexander had been schooled in the Catholic (separate) system because we preferred its policy of integration. When he reached high school we had to choose among three options: St. Mary's, the local high school; St. David's, the school across town, where most of his friends would attend; and another school that had a specific support network for students who were hearing impaired. We decided that the choice should be his. Alexander chose to attend St. David's along with his friends. We were pleased with this decision, because he would continue to work with the same itinerant teacher. He would also receive support in the special-education room and take an additional English class in lieu of French.

Alexander's English teacher was concerned that he might not pass the 9th grade curriculum. My husband responded by meeting with his teachers. John advocated for his son and helped the school develop strategies to enable Alexander to cope with the increased workload. We discovered that his teachers didn't fully comprehend his potential until they had known him for several months—a challenge due to the semester system. Teachers changed every semester; consequently, just as we all started working well together, it was time to break in anther group of teachers. So, every term, John would go to the school and give a talk about Alexander and his needs. We discovered that the special-education department did little to educate the teachers, who knew very little about hearing impairment. This also was a big challenge.

Once again, I became actively involved with Alexander's studies. We did homework together every evening. We devised a strategy for studying Shakespearean plays: we would get the movie first, then the abridged version of the play, and then we would read the full-length text. Somehow, it all worked, and English continues to be one of his best subjects.

During these 3 years, Alexander became overwhelmed in such a large high school. His marks began to slip. He received less itinerant help and less special education support, and his network of friends began to disperse. Alexander was becoming isolated and discouraged. We decided that something had to change.

By 11th grade, Alexander had experienced many disappointments. The children's camp that he loved to attend during his summer holidays had turned him down for a staff position. He struggled to find success in his academic subjects. Although he was passing, that was not good enough for him. He was losing self-confidence, he was always late for class in the morning, and he seemed depressed. I remember making many long-distance phone calls at that time to his childhood Auditory-Verbal therapists.

We again looked into alternatives for Alexander's 12th grade. We asked ourselves whether he should attend our third-choice school or a private Mennonite high school. The former had a great support program for students who were hearing impaired. The private school had small class sizes and was Mennonite. He could walk to the school, and he already had friends there, but it had no special education teachers. We made the decision to send him to the private school. We also decided that Alexander needed a camp experience in the summer.

Outward Bound

A profound change occurred for Alexander during the summer following 11th grade: he attended the Outward Bound adventure camp near Sioux Sainte-Marie in northern Ontario. It was a physically demanding course with intensive hiking, canoeing, and camping north of Lake Superior. At the end of this experience, Alexander's counselor said that he had been one of the best leaders in the group.

High school (grades 12–13)

Alexander's adjustment to his new high school was amazingly easy. He made new friends and had no trouble fitting into school life. We had gotten a little smarter by this time, and visited school at the beginning of the term to talk to teachers. I planned a special meeting for the entire staff with Alexander's former itinerant teacher. It was very successful. The combination of a strong peer group and small classes helped Alexander regain his confidence and begin to achieve his academic potential. His best subject, once again, was English, and he graduated with good marks. He was accepted at the University of Waterloo in the Recreation and Leisure Program.

University life

After working in a meat packing plant for the summer, Alexander went into residence at the University of Waterloo. Before the first week of classes, he and I went to the special-needs department and discussed his requirements for success at university. Alexander had student note-takers in each class, and his professors wore the FM system. It was a very difficult year for Alexander, and he passed only 7 of the 10 subjects. In hindsight, I think he had taken on too big a course load, the note-takers were inadequate, and even with an FM system the large, noisy lecture halls made it impossible for him to hear. He also found that living in residence was too noisy and distracting for studying.

Alexander was put on a probationary period for the fall term. A friend and professor advocated for him in the recreation program and the special-needs department. Consequently, his workload was reduced to three courses. We hired a tutor to help Alexander with his study habits and teach him how to prepare for essays and exams. Most importantly, the university hired a professional note-taker, a right Alexander had had in his first year—although, to our consternation, we had not been aware of that. Alexander's marks improved greatly. He is now looking forward to going back to school this summer and perhaps increasing his workload to four courses per term.

In 2002, Alexander was assessed for a cochlear implant. Unaided, he was definitely a candidate. His aided listening ability was too good because of his intensive Auditory-Verbal therapy. We still believe that Alexander would benefit from an implant, but he is reluctant to pursue this possibility further at this time. We agreed to revisit this issue in the near future. The decision is his to make.

As I write this, Alexander has just sent me an e-mail. He's looking forward to our visit to the ski slopes. He especially misses his father's good food, and regrets to report that no good snow has fallen in the last month.

Our wish was for Alexander to be integrated, to have friends, and to be able to pursue his choice of career. To our great joy, our wish has come true.

In 2006, Alexander was attending Brock University in St. Catharines, Ontario, majoring in geography. He obtained a cochlear implant in 2005, followed by auditory rehabilitation, with outstanding success. Alexander has continued to participate in Outward Bound and has traveled extensively on his own throughout Europe and North Africa.

NORA

Karen McKellin

"Mom, do I have to wear my boot today?" My 8-year-old is rummaging in the bottom of the hall closet. We live in Vancouver, and it's raining. "Boot*s*, Nora, boot*s*." I correct her automatically, stuffing brown lunch bags into two backpacks.

"Mom, do I have to wear my BOOT-S-S today?" Nora yells again. "Yes. Put them on now. Hurry up—You're late." I tie the hood of her raincoat more securely. Nora squirms, "How come I gotta wear the hood? Meggie's not wearing hers." Meg is Nora's twin. "Because she doesn't wear hearing aids and she's taking her umbrella and you lost yours—so hurry up!" I say with brisk mother logic.

"Aw, it... IT'S... not fair," Nora grumbles on her way out to the car where my husband, Bill, and Meg are waiting. You're absolutely right, Nora. It's NOT fair. It's not fair that you were born dwarfed, with short arms and legs, a curved spine, a cleft palate, and fused elbow joints. Why couldn't you have entered this world with the same strong and straight body as Meg?

Our children were born 8 years ago in Toronto. Bill and I expected twins. Our obstetrician expected the usual complications of a premature Caesarian delivery, but none of us were prepared for Nora, who was born with a still-undiagnosed form of dwarfism.

Nora McKellin (left) and family, 1994

I had trouble, at first, believing she was ours. Who was this tiny stranger lying in the bassinet next to pink and perfect Meg? But by the time we brought our babies home from the hospital, I loved them both with equal fierceness.

Nora fought to survive those first years. Her minor colds developed into severe respiratory infections that required hospitalization. She had plastic surgery to repair the hole in her soft palate. When a routine X-ray revealed her cervical vertebrae to be alarmingly unstable, orthopedic surgeons devised a protective neck-and-back brace that Nora wore all her waking hours. She didn't begin walking until she was 3 years old. Both girls were subject to chronic middle ear infections.

Although doctors had assured us Nora had normal intelligence, Bill and I were uneasy that, at 18 months, she was still not experimenting with sounds or responding to stories and music the way Meg was. In January 1982, audiologists at Toronto's Hospital for Sick Children confirmed our suspicions. We were told Nora had a severe to profound sensorineural hearing loss with an 80 dB loss in her left ear and a 90 dB loss in the right. The audiologist explained to us the noise level of normal speech, at about 25 or 30 dB, compared to the drone of an airplane or the roar of a lawn mower, and the range of Nora's hearing in comparison. Later, a tomogram showed that several of the concentric rings of the cochlea were missing. We were advised to have Nora fitted bilaterally with hearing aids as soon as possible. "Dear God, it's not fair!" I wailed. Why, on top of everything else, does she have to be deaf?

Powerful hearing aids were purchased and fitted, but Nora screamed every time we tried them on her. It took weeks of persuasion before she gradually consented to wear them. In my passionate desire for a quick fix for Nora's deafness, I assumed amplification and talking to her a lot would help her hear and talk. But the professionals advising us were unanimous in recommending that Nora begin some kind of systematic language training immediately.

We soon realized that there were several types of communication modes that deaf children could utilize and learn. There were sign language programs, oral programs, and Total Communication programs. Each one had a different philosophy and methodology and offered a range of services in the metropolitan Toronto area. During our research on these options, we contacted a local parents' organization (VOICE for Hearing-Impaired Children) and learned about Auditory-Verbal therapy. We attended one of the organization's monthly meetings and had an opportunity to meet some of the children who were enrolled in the auditory-verbal programs at the Hospital for Sick Children and the Learning to Listen Foundation. These children seemed to be able to hear to a remarkable degree, despite their hearing losses. The speech of the older children especially was intelligible, although a few spoke with the nasalized, muted quality I remembered from a film about Helen Keller.

What impressed Bill and me the most was the way these kids seemed at home in the everyday life of the hearing world—they could communicate with their parents, siblings, and hearing peers. Some of the kids were taking music lessons, they played hockey or soccer, and a couple of them had graduated from their local high school and were preparing to start university.

A sobering meeting at the Hospital for Sick Children introduced Bill and me to the rigorous requirements of Auditory-Verbal therapy. Put simply, Auditory-Verbal therapy consists of "coaxing a little hearing to go a long way." Children are systematically introduced first to sounds and then to words. Through amplified residual hearing, children can learn to listen and, by listening, can develop natural speech. We committed ourselves and Nora to a long-term, intensive program of weekly visits to a clinic and daily instruction at home.

With Bill being our primary wage-earner, the responsibility for teaching Nora rested on me. I didn't have much confidence in myself as parent–teacher, and neither Bill nor I could predict whether this communication approach would even work for Nora. But it seemed to us that other methods of language acquisition weren't options for our small daughter. She was always going to be short, way below lip-level, and her fingers had so little dexterity that signing would be difficult.

The program at the Learning to Listen Foundation was full. But to our great relief, an opening was created for Nora, and her multiple problems were accepted as a challenge. We immediately arranged as many sessions as we could squeeze in before the summer break. The Auditory-Verbal therapist acted as a coach, teaching us to teach Nora.

For the rest of that spring, all summer, and into the fall, I dutifully followed the therapist's instructions, bathing Nora in sound, talking to her constantly, and keeping up a running commentary on all our daily activities. Each day, I'd seat her in her high chair at the dining table and push a little toy bus back and forth in front of her. "Bu, bu, bu," I'd babble. "The bus goes bu, bu, bu." Then I'd walk a plastic black and white cow across the tabletop. "The cow says moo, Nora. Moo-moo-moo." I'd fly a little yellow airplane over her head and land it beside the bus and the cow. "Ahhh," I'd say. "The airplane goes ahhh." Nora appeared to be watching, attentive but uncomprehending, and then cry to get down. Every time we came across a picture of a cow, plane, or bus, every time we saw a real plane or bus, I'd point to it and repeat the sounds. Meg regressed and began referring to cows as "moos" and planes as "ahs."

It took a long time before Nora twigged to the meaning of the sounds she now heard. She made no significant response for months. Despite the therapist's repeated assurances, I was beginning to lose hope, until one morning, quite unexpectedly, Nora picked up the airplane when I said "ah." I tested her reactions to "bu, bu, bu," then "moo, moo, moo," and then "ahhh" again. She picked the matching toy every time.

I called Bill at work. I called my mother in Chicago, my mother-in-law, two friends, and Nora's therapist. "NORA CAN HEAR!" I whooped. "SHE CAN HEAR!" This was a major breakthrough, after which Nora's learning progressed more quickly. Within the year she was expressing herself in single words, later in phrases and, eventually, in whole sentences.

That's not to say that Nora didn't have good weeks and bad weeks, or that I didn't at times lose patience with her and grow weary. I found out the hard way the necessity of managing the stress and fatigue endemic to parents of children with special needs. Nora's needs had to be balanced with Meg's, Bill's, and my own. The one saving constant of our years of therapy was the auditory-verbal clinical staff. Their support for Nora and for me was unflagging. They were always positive, consistently prepared for every day's lesson. They knew when to pressure Nora and when to slacken the pace.

When Nora was 5, we enrolled her in the junior kindergarten of our neighborhood public school in Toronto. Equipped with an FM system, and with the help of an itinerant teacher twice a week, Nora moved on to senior kindergarten the following year. After four years of clinical sessions at the Learning to Listen Foundation, Nora, age 6, graduated from its program.

Nora is now in 2nd grade at our local public school here in Vancouver, where we have lived for the past 2 years. Her teacher reports that she is a B-average student and participates to the best of her ability in all school activities. The itinerant teacher of the deaf who visits her three times a week finds her speech "highly intelligible with good articulation; her stress and intonation are all satisfactory." In fact, Nora's so chatty that I sometimes (not very often!) wonder why we ever taught her to talk. She has taken a little ballet to improve her coordination, and she is now trying the piano, although her right hand can't span a scale. She's an exuberant, if unorthodox, swimmer. At this point, her social life, like Meg's, is busy with birthday parties and sleep-overs. How we prize as unique all that is ordinary in her! Those first traumatic years are over, but like other dwarfed children, Nora faces orthopedic surgery to correct anomalies in her spine. There are no medical cures for Nora's physical condition, but we are consoled by the words "steady progress" from her doctors and teachers.

It is not fair that one child in every thousand is born with a hearing impairment, or that many more are deafened by meningitis or other diseases. It's not fair that some children are born with severe disabilities that will force them to struggle to keep pace in this fast-moving, often indifferent, sometimes cruel world of ours. But fair or not, here they are. We who have been entrusted with their fragile and precious lives must forgo questions of fairness. As someone has said, there are no good answers, only good responses. Our first task, whether we are parents or teachers, doctors or therapists, friends or family, is wholly to accept these children among us and then be willing to accompany them on a journey of discovery and hope. For we have been granted the incomparable privilege of assisting in the miracle of a child like Nora, helping her to become all that she has the potential to be.

1994: Postscript

I wrote the preceding piece about Nora 5 years ago. Nora is now 13. We are still living in Vancouver (it's still raining) and Nora is still at Queen Elizabeth, our neighborhood elementary school. She will be finishing 7th grade this spring, and already we are considering which high school she will attend next fall.

Nora underwent massive reconstructive spinal surgery in 1990 and again in 1992. She spent many long and dreary months at home in bed or in a reclining wheelchair after both operations. Her itinerant teacher became her home-school teacher during her recuperation, keeping Nora in touch with all that was going on in her classroom, sometimes arranging to bring a group of her friends to the house for lunch or recess. Thanks to her teacher's efforts and Nora's own dogged determination not to fall behind her peers, she was able to return to school without losing a grade. Nora is now doing well in every subject, although math is an ongoing challenge.

So far, the surgery has proved successful. Nora now wears a modified Milwaukee brace to support her back. She has a new set of hearing aids that are operated by a small hand-held computer that allows her to control volume and choose different settings programmed for party or traffic noise. We've had a hard time getting her to use the FM unit consistently at school. "It's just not cool, Mom!"

Nora loves to read. One Saturday recently, I drove Nora and two of her friends downtown to the main Vancouver Public Library. The three of them staggered out with 33 Nancy Drew novels! Nora's ambition is to become a writer—of mystery stories, of course—and a banker. When asked why a banker, she replied that she'd heard that writers don't make very much money, so, if she worked in a bank during the week, she could write at night or on weekends and still enjoy a steady income.

It is immediately obvious on meeting Nora for the first time that she has a profound disability. But people are invariably amazed when they learn she is also hearing impaired. "She just doesn't act or talk like she's deaf," they say. It's true. Nora argues with her sister Meg, giggles and gossips on the phone with her friends, and sings along with the Barenaked Ladies. We thank God for these not-so-small miracles!

Update

It's spring 2004, and re-reading the last postscript makes me feel it all happened far more than a decade ago.

As I write this, Nora is working furiously on a final paper for her fourth year class in Social Statistics, prior to completing her B.A. in Sociology at the University of British Columbia. She has two computers going: one, a laptop borrowed from me on which she can do her statistical analyses, and the other on which she can type her paper and use MSN messenger—so that she can stay in touch with her friends even while she's in the doldrums of paper writing. Nora is, like her father, adept with computers. She keeps her mouse on the left side, but otherwise is able to type reasonably quickly and is far more proficient in using most software applications than either me or her sister, Meg.

Nora's glasses are perched on the end of her nose, and she keeps her hearing aids turned off to help her concentrate. If I need to speak to her, I have to go downstairs to her basement suite, flick the light switch or stamp on the floor and shout to get her attention. Every once in a while she dashes across the welter of paper on the floor to snap on the TV to find the hockey score as the Canucks and the Flames battle it out in the last game of the play-offs.

Looking back over the last 10 years, I could not have imagined that anyone with Nora's challenges would come so far. Nora has had numerous surgeries, some very serious with protracted recovery times, and her back is still greatly

Nora McKellin and family today

curved despite the support of four Harrington rods along either side of her vertebrae. She is still a very small dwarfed person; no bigger, really, than a 3- or 4-year-old child, even though she will be 24 years old in May. She has such a good mind and a determined nature that people who know her don't think of her as being small. As a friend of mine says, Nora may be tiny but she has a very big aura. (This is the West Coast, after all, and people talk like that here.)

The fact that Nora is in university, despite her severe to profound hearing loss and her other disabilities, is a culmination of a number of decisions that we and she made years ago about her education. Many of her milestones have revolved around finding a school that would be right for her and finding ways to support her many physical needs. It has not been easy. When we first moved to Vancouver, I wondered whether our local primary school would accept her into their mainstream classroom and if they would offer the support services she would need to thrive there. We have had some uphill battles working with school boards and principals, as they coped with diminishing resources in an age of cutbacks. As Nora grew up, we tried to ensure that she participated in some of the decision-making around strategies for her care and support. Invariably, she would have a practical and do-able solution to the problems, and we all learned—parents, teachers, therapists—to let her have a say in these matters. If I could give any advice to professional caregivers of disabled children, it would be to learn to listen to what the kids say they need and respect their ideas about what will work best for them in their particular circumstances.

For the most part, we were lucky to find a sympathetic teacher in school, but the reality is that sometimes Nora was placed in a classroom with a teacher who looked upon her and her special needs as an unwelcome burden. But by and large, the public school system supported Nora as she moved successfully through elementary school, to secondary school, and finally to university. She had an itinerant teacher of the deaf for most of her elementary years. When she moved into high school, the local coordinator for special needs in the school district took Nora on as part of her own caseload and worked with her and her teachers to ensure she had the services needed to accommodate both her hearing impairment and her short stature.

My husband and I made an early decision early not to send Meg, Nora's twin sister, to the same school, mainly because we wanted Meg to attend a French immersion program. We kept Nora in an English-language program, rather than try too ambitiously to have her taught in French. Looking back, this decision was probably good for both of them. It allowed Nora to develop her own circle of friends and foster a healthy sense of independence from Meg, and it allowed Meg not to have to be Nora's caregiver and protector. In fact, Meg used to complain that Nora had more friends than she did. This was apparent whenever I drew up a list of invitees for their joint birthday celebrations.

As the parents of a child who is multiply disabled, my husband and I have had to discipline ourselves in hopeful blindness and deafness about the worries of the future. Quite simply, peering ahead into the murky unknown filled me with such terror that, at times I was incapacitated. I wondered what would happen to Nora without us there too look after her. What would she do with her life, how would she get on, who would help her?

The one thing that has been a kind of grace for us is that by recalling the past and dealing fully with the present, we are best able to keep the sense of hope and buoyancy that has characterized most of Nora's life thus far. She has triumphed and excelled where we least expected it, and it is her own hope and joy in life that sustains us when we allow ourselves to drift into anxiety about the future. We do plan ahead, set goals, and make decisions today that we think will serve Nora well in the future. But when I am with Nora and see all that she has accomplished and lived through so far, and all that she is accomplishing and overcoming today, I see no reason to be fearful of what will come.

Nora's desire to travel and see the world was a very great test of that resolve. In driving home from the airport after seeing her off on her first trip away—a high school exchange to Australia—I wept, thinking of all the things that could go wrong, and imagined her stranded or sick or in pain with neither Bill nor I there to make it all right. What if she lost her hearing aids or they stopped working? What if she slept through her alarm clock? What if she could not hear the announcements of her flight over the loudspeakers? How would she cope with different accents? How would she manage her rolling backpack on stairs with no elevators or escalators?

But Nora had the time of her life on that trip. After graduation she went to Europe with friends, traveled around haphazardly on the train, slept in youth hostels across France, Germany, and Italy, learned to get by on two meals a day with baguettes and cheese, and came home exhilarated by her adventures and her ability to move about independently.

I was less anxious when she went off to Australia a second time to attend the University of Queensland for 6 months on a student exchange. But I still worried about how she would cope for so long without all the supports of home. Again, she breezed through with very few of my anticipated problems. When she needed help she was not too shy to ask for it, and wonderful people came into her life at key times when she was lonely or just needed a friend.

When her sister got married in 2003, people asked how Nora was coping with the separation from her twin. Actually, it is Meggie who is having the greater trouble separating from Nora. Fortunately, Meg and her husband Andrew live not far away, and the twins see each other often.

Nora is getting ready to graduate from university in a few months, and the next milestone will be what she does after getting her degree. She is planning to move into an apartment with a friend after she graduates. I suppose the next challenge Bill and I will face will be life as empty nesters.

The University of British Columbia has done much to ensure that Nora had what she needed to succeed—providing paid note-takers for classes, giving her extra time to write tests, allowing her to use a computer for tests (it's difficult for her to write cursively for long periods of time), and advocating for her with individual professors. These accommodations were small but critical adjustments that have enabled Nora to do well in a large, sometimes impersonal, public Canadian postsecondary institution. She is getting A's and B's in her courses, and is even managing to do well in the dreaded statistics class that all sociology majors have to take in order to graduate.

Nora, who is majoring in sociology, understands only too well that our bureaucracies and institutions can and should alter their policies and programs to accommodate the needs of the disabled. The changes do not always have to be monumental; many can be done easily and paid for easily. Sometimes small, practical changes can make an inestimable difference. For example, having an academic advisor help Nora plan her classes so that she could move easily between them on the large campus took some time and attention, but enabled her to take more courses at a time.

When Nora first began Auditory-Verbal therapy at the Learning to Listen Foundation in Toronto, I couldn't imagine how the daily tedium of helping her learn to listen, comprehend, and talk was the steppingstone to what she has become today. Like other parents of children who are hearing impaired, my husband and I encountered moments of profound despair, weariness, anxiety, and stress as we tried to raise our daughter in the best way we could. I cannot claim that we don't experience some of those feelings of anxiety still. Over the years, we have found the will to persevere and the strength and determination to "keep on keeping on." But it is not just our strength that has helped us overcome challenges. Our children, as they grew and developed, have exhibited their own strength and determination. Ultimately, this is what makes it possible for us to look at Nora's future, for all that is unknown, without undue fear or trepidation. It is not my hope, determination, courage, or perseverance that will make a difference—it is hers. And as she has begun, please God, may she continue.

In 2006, Nora was studying for her master's degree in social work at the University of Toronto. She is a world traveler and a well-regarded motivational speaker on topics of accessibility and the disabled.

MARK

Tania Orr

Fifteen years ago, on a very cold night in January, I was terrified. My third son, Mark Lindsay Orr, was born prematurely by Caesarean section at North York General Hospital in Toronto. He was 3 months premature and weighed 1 pound, 12 ounces—the smallest baby ever born at the hospital. This event put us on a roller-coaster adventure of life and death. It has a happy ending; Mark might have died had it not been for a few miracle workers.

The next 4 months involved daily trips to Toronto's Hospital for Sick Children, carrying a 24-hour supply of breast milk. Even though Mark's weight fell to 480 grams—a little over 1 pound—he was determined to live. These were stressful "incubator" months filled with constant complications. Finally, one early spring day, Mark came home, where he continued to change our lives. At home, Mark progressed well with months of physiotherapy. By age 1, he weighed 13 pounds and could sit up. By 18 months, he was walking. Just as life was back to normal, I found to my surprise that I was pregnant again.

Mark Orr (center) and family, 1994

Timothy, our fourth son, was born 5 weeks premature weighing 4 pounds, 10 ounces, but was healthy. He was to have a profound influence on Mark's development. By the time Mark was 2 years old, he was still not speaking. Regular hearing tests and check-ups at the clinic showed no major problems, and his slow speech development was attributed to prematurity. The audiologist referred us to an ear, nose, and throat (ENT) specialist who ordered an auditory brainstem response test (ABR) to determine the reason for Mark's delay. The test revealed a permanent severe hearing loss in both ears due to the nerve damage in the brain caused by the constant amount of oxygen that Mark had required for his survival in the incubator.

By this time, my husband had already accepted a company transfer to Sarnia, Ontario. We soon left Toronto with two new hearing aids, no knowledge of deafness, the book *Learning to Listen*, and the ENT doctor's advice to educate Mark with children who could hear and to teach him to listen and talk. Soon after, we joined VOICE for Hearing-Impaired Children for support.

What were we to do in a small town with its limited resources, not to mention our lack of knowledge of deafness and all its problems? For the first 18 months, we were involved in a preschool home visiting program. At the same time, Mark attended a large nursery school. At the age of 4, Mark was barely talking and had difficulty making himself understood. As a family, we were determined that Mark not attend a residential school for deaf children.

Thanks to the kind concern of the ear specialist in Sarnia, Mark quickly began receiving speech therapy twice a week for the next 3 years. I received wonderful support from the speech therapist, who believed that Mark had great potential and would learn to talk. We exposed Mark to all sorts of new learning experiences, took trips, and read to him constantly. He played all the time with his youngest brother who, at 12 months of age, could not walk, but would talk in complete sentences! Mark also learned quickly from the older boys and from the constant flow of children in and out of our busy household.

Once Mark started kindergarten, I got involved by helping the teacher at his school. This enabled me to reinforce everything Mark learned at school. We worked aggressively with the school board in order to receive support services from an itinerant teacher of the hearing impaired. For 6 months, an Auditory-Verbal therapist sponsored by VOICE came to Sarnia once a month to provide 2 hours of therapy. We were thrilled at this wonderful opportunity!

At the end of that summer, we moved to Thornhill, Ontario, north of Toronto. Mark began therapy at the Learning to Listen Foundation. This consisted of weekly lessons with the auditory-verbal staff. Mark was entering 1st grade at age 7, and he found the auditory-verbal program demanding, challenging, and stimulating.

A typical lesson might start with a discussion about Mark's relationships with his mom, dad, and brothers. There was always new vocabulary to learn, and the fact that one word might have several meanings. Stumping the therapist was always a game that Mark loved to play. At home in advance of the lesson, Mark would ask one of his brothers for a difficult word that he could use with the therapist, such as "Zamboni." Even though the therapist usually got most of these difficult words, sometimes he didn't (he missed "Zamboni," the machine at an ice hockey rink that is used to clean the ice). Mark got a big kick out of this! Much of the lesson focused on speech development through listening, word comprehension, and articulation. We worked on idioms, current events, a diary, and poetry. Even today, Mark can still recite from memory his all-time favorite poem, "The Owl and the Pussycat."

An integral component of the Learning to Listen Foundation's program was 1 hour of daily reinforcement at home of the skills covered in the lesson that week. We, the parents, had to do it. The therapist taught us the techniques to use. We were asked to be very disciplined and focused at home, and the rest of the family learned not to disturb Mark during a home lesson. This pattern of daily work has continued with Mark to this day, and he now uses this study discipline on his own for his schoolwork.

During the years at the Learning to Listen Foundation, Mark developed a very strong bond with the therapist because of the therapist's caring manner, sensitivity, unbridled sense of humor, and his use of provocative and colorful materials. Mark loved the program and looked forward to every lesson. Afterward, he would get chocolate milk and cookies (Mom's treat) in the hospital cafeteria.

By the time he was in 8th grade, Mark was succeeding in school, largely as a result of two factors: our educational philosophy was supported by the school board, and we have given dedicated support to Mark at home. Mark has always been in a mainstream classroom at our local neighborhood school and has benefited from the following support services:

- Our school board provided an *itinerant teacher of the hearing impaired* who came to see him and his teacher in the classroom two to three times per week. The itinerant teacher would assist with classroom projects or work with Mark in a group of his classmates. Because Mark disliked being removed from the classroom for one-on-one work, this was rarely done. When Mark was in 8th grade, the itinerant teacher assigned to him was herself hearing impaired, and she effectively reinforced his wish to be more assertive in exercising his rights to hear and to learn.

- The *school principal* played a major role in ensuring Mark's placement in an appropriate classroom. For example, Mark would be assigned to a classroom teacher who operated a quiet, structured class. The principal also agreed that all of Mark's teachers should receive a one- to three-day special course on awareness and teaching of students who are hearing impaired. Usually, Mark was placed with several students from previous years who understood him and his needs.
- Mark benefited from exposure, over 8 years, to the *same teaching assistant* who came into the classroom for a portion of the day. She helped Mark interpret and reinforce concepts that he might not have understood otherwise. She also helped him organize his work and gave him special assistance with activities requiring fine motor skills, such as cutting with scissors. Mark gradually learned to become more independent, with less reliance on her, and he never felt that she was there solely for him.
- Mark initially received about 20 minutes of *speech therapy* every 2 weeks for 18 months. I was always present for this service, and we reinforced it at home. However, lessons were discontinued suddenly without notification. After we exerted much pressure, they were re-offered. The school board finally agreed to provide a properly qualified speech pathologist, although by this time we had already made private arrangements at our own expense. We learned that speech pathology services were difficult to get for school-aged children who are hearing impaired. Simply finding a private pathologist willing to work with our son took 6 months. Mark received this private service over a 30-month period, with 2-hour lessons given twice per month and daily reinforcement at home. We discontinued speech therapy when Mark began a 3-year orthodontic treatment program.
- The most critical factor in Mark's academic success was an *acceptable acoustical classroom environment.* This was a never-ending battle with school officials and auditory consultants. While they were willing to provide every other service, they usually overlooked the key element needed for him to succeed—classrooms with low background noise. Ventilation fans, noisy lights, uncarpeted floors, outside noise from trucks passing by, and children playing in the schoolyard create a great deal of ambient noise. The best way to deal with most of these factors was to carpet the classroom. The school board offered so much resistance to this simple request that it forced high-level reviews and tested our patience over the 2 long months that it took to accommodate Mark's needs.

On a number of occasions, school officials attempted to influence us in a way that contradicted our educational philosophy and that of the school board. For example, they recommended that Mark be placed in a segregated class with other students who are hearing impaired, outside our school area. They also recommended modifying his curriculum to fewer subjects, despite his academic success in a mainstream classroom with the standard curriculum. These measures were suggested to be in Mark's best interests and, coincidentally, would have saved the school system some money. We resisted these recommendations strenuously, and Mark continued to excel in the top half of his class. We have always considered low standards and expectations for special-needs students an abhorrent and constant challenge. Inside and outside school, Mark has accomplished much.

Mark is an easygoing, natural kid who is well liked by his peers. He tends to be popular at school but favors only a few close friends. We've always emphasized the need to develop good social skills. Since he doesn't hear well, he can easily become frustrated, and the impatience of some of his peers has been a barrier. His challenge with his gross motor skills and his lack of interest in sports restrict his ability to tap into the full circle of teenaged friends. On the other hand, Mark skis, swims with confidence, and has attended summer sleep-over camps. He has a particularly sensitive manner and an interest in helping children with special needs. Mark is a fanatic Star Trekkie who has memorized the details of episodes, mastered the technical vocabulary, and collects *Star Trek* memorabilia. Surprisingly, he also reads historical novels and newspapers, and loves to discuss Canadian politics. He plays the piano and has an active interest in home computers and gaming. He also assists weekly in our church as an altar boy, where he is learning dependability, acting out his religious beliefs, and helping others.

Mark has a good relationship with his family, largely because he has been treated no differently from anyone else. He is spontaneous in communication and freely provides details about school, friends, and interests. He is comfortable about seeking help from us. Mark respects his two older brothers and misses them deeply when they are away at university. His older brothers are patient and superb in teaching him athletic and computer skills. They tell him what is cool and how to display appropriate behavior. Mark's youngest brother, Tim, is his best friend. Tim looks out for Mark at school and lets him share in his many friendships.

Based on our experience, we offer some friendly suggestions to parents in similar circumstances:

- Persevere in working faithfully every day with your child, and definite progress will occur.
- Read to your child often.
- Do things together as a family and experience new adventures together.
- Get involved with parent association groups for support, encouragement, and advice.
- Get involved as a parent volunteer in your school and become a member of your local PTA. You will learn a lot about your school, teachers, and educational philosophy.
- Get involved in advisory groups to your school board that foster education, awareness, and understanding of hearing impairment.
- Raise your child as naturally as possible, without any favor over any of your other children.
- Always take control of ensuring that your child's education is tailored to his or her needs. Leaving this role to others is not in your child's best interests.

Mark has made tremendous progress, and I know that many years of hard work still lie ahead for us. As his family, we will continue to help him become a happy, productive, and caring individual who will listen and talk for himself.

Update

Our story continues with a major transition in Mark's life, from the small, close-knit local elementary school that he had attended since 1st grade to a very large local high school, attended also by his older brothers. This occurred after much discussion with his itinerant teacher. She had recommended that Mark attend a high school that had a class for students who were hearing impaired. That school was over an hour's drive away from home. Her rationale was that Mark would receive more support in such a class and would have a better opportunity to make friends. After much soul-searching and discussion with Mark, we followed our instincts about what we thought would be in his best interests, and enrolled him in the local high school with his brothers.

We also insisted that Mark be enrolled in a mainstream 9th grade academic program with academic French and a regular English program instead of the English literacy program typically prescribed for students who require special education. Mark also signed up for the well-established music program. He was assigned a special-education teacher with whom he interacted daily, and she became his liaison with the other teachers.

To help his transition further, Mark enrolled in a summer course to obtain a 9th grade academic credit in keyboarding skills. He enjoyed the experience, made friends, and passed the course in spite of his lifelong difficulties with coordination.

Throughout Mark's 5 years of high school, the special-education teacher was his major anchor. She is the person whom Mark considers the most influential in his academic success. She taught him self-advocacy skills; provided liaison with his other teachers; gave him the support and facilities to complete tests and examinations. His itinerant support, however, was limited to short sessions of 15 minutes twice per week. This happened because of Mark's refusal to leave his regular classroom for this support. He felt that being in the classroom was more important.

Mark's progress in high school appeared to be going smoothly until we received an urgent call from the

Mark Orr and family today

vice-principal a short 4 months into his freshman year. Mark had written in a journal entry to his English teacher that there were students in the school who were bullying him. Mark had never mentioned this to us. The school administration stepped in immediately and effectively dealt with this serious development. Mark received a number of sessions with the school psychologist on how to handle himself in such situations. The psychologist discussed the issue of his hearing impairment and how to cope with exclusion from peer groups.

Fortunately, Mark progressed well with a full load of academic courses. Throughout high school, he performed at an average level with an overall standing of 75%. To help with his coordination, the school provided a simple laptop computer, and there were always students who were happy to be note-takers. However, Mark always retyped those notes into his computer. By 11th grade, all hearing support was stopped, and Mark was monitored only by the special-education teacher. He also required very little parental support with his academic studies. I think this is because he had been taught at an early age through Auditory-Verbal therapy that he had to work hard to succeed.

After 11th grade, Mark was hired by a large children's summer camp, where he has worked for the past 8 years in roles of increasing responsibility. He has been in charge of the camp computer program, worked with children with special needs, and assumed administrative roles. The camp employment significantly influenced Mark's interest in working with young people.

Mark did the many things that most teenagers do in high school. At age 16, he obtained his beginner's driver's permit. This truly frightened us because of his poor coordination. However, he became an avid driver and to date has remained accident free. With his friends, he attended his 12th grade prom with all the trimmings. Mark developed a great interest in computers. At graduation, he received an award for community service.

We worked closely with Mark to plan a successful transition to university, spending many months in dialogue about his career interests. We helped him narrow down his choices, then visited several universities and made appointments with their disability offices. Mark's choice was St. Jerome's University, affiliated with the University of Waterloo in southwestern Ontario. The important advantages to us, beyond the quality of the institution, were its small size and proximity to home.

Mark spent the next 4 years in residence at St. Jerome's, with its small classrooms and excellent student networking. There were students who always volunteered to be note-takers. The disabilities office provided an FM system, liaison support to Mark's professors, and a place to write exams on a computer with extra time allotted. It also offered guidance and support as required.

Mark enrolled in a program of honors English and religion. He always took the full course load, which required a great deal of reading and writing. In his second year, the workload created so much stress that Mark's occasional stuttering escalated to the point of severe disfluency. His scheduled speech therapy did not help this at all. We enrolled him in a specialized stuttering clinic in Toronto, which helped him greatly.

In his last 2 years at university, Mark was successful and quite independent with his academic program, and was actively involved in both religious and campus social life. He helped younger students, particularly with computer work, and was even hired by the university to help set up its computer network.

At his graduation in May 2003, Mark received a service award for his involvement in the university community.

Mark decided that he wanted to become a teacher. He had applied to several faculties of education and was accepted at the University of Western Ontario. This was his opportunity to live on his own, not in residence, and to be far away from home. So far, he has done well in this program, particularly with practice teaching at the high school level. His students accept Mark's hearing impairment. Mark has high hopes of obtaining a permanent teaching position in Ontario upon graduation in April 2004.

This young man, our son, who was a little 1-pounder at birth, approaches life today with a positive attitude. He has certainly come a long way and surprised most of the people he has encountered, including his parents. We are extremely proud of Mark's hard work, perseverance, and accomplishments despite the many obstacles he has confronted throughout his life.

In 2006, Mark was working as an itinerant teacher with high school students who are deaf or hard of hearing. He is employed by the Dufferin–Peel Separate School Board in Ontario, Canada.

COLIN

Nancy O'Brien

This is not a success story. I remember reading all the positive stories in *Learning to Listen* (Vaughan, 1981) and feeling truly inspired—and overwhelmed. Could we do all that? Looking back, the answer was yes, but our story continues to be one of love and perseverance.

One of our most difficult challenges in raising our son, who is hearing impaired, was to determine an appropriate communication method. We heard many different viewpoints and conflicting opinions. We wanted Colin to be able to function in a hearing society, but we were also concerned about his confidence, well-being, and happiness. As a result of these concerns and of living in various communities with different services, we used a variety of communication strategies.

Fortunately, Colin's hearing impairment was diagnosed early through the Neonatal Follow-up Program at the Glenrose Hospital in Edmonton, Alberta. Colin was fitted with hearing aids at 11 months of age. My husband and I knew little about deafness. We didn't anticipate any problems; we thought the hearing aids would restore the hearing, and even anticipated that the need for them would be temporary until speech and language were established. I remember the day we came home with the body aids strapped on—I kept calling his name and Colin just crawled away. I thought he would respond to my voice immediately. It was evident we had some work to do.

Colin O'Brien (right) and family, 1994

We were funneled into an oral program at the Glenrose Hospital, beginning with home visits by a qualified teacher for the hearing impaired. I remember the teacher's first visit and being told to turn off the radio. There was to be no background noise. Consequently, music became my luxury during quiet times alone. We babbled with Colin constantly, starting at the beginning. "Do you hear that?... I hear that!" was a common phrase in our home as we called Colin's attention to meaningful sounds. We quickly discovered he would rather not wear earmolds! Eventually, non-allergenic tape over the molds provided a deterrent to their removal. Colin wore cumbersome body aids and, because of the unusual way he crawled, we were forced to strap them on his back. In retrospect, it was a very unusual, but necessary, place to begin auditory stimulation. I sewed colorful vests with pockets for the hearing aids and made them a part of dressing every day.

I set about to inform myself about deafness. There was no information package in Edmonton at the time (we later developed one). I wrote to the Canadian Hearing Society, VOICE for Hearing-Impaired Children, and the John Tracy Clinic. The last provided a free correspondence course to parents of children who are hearing impaired under the age of 5. The 12-month course included beginning lessons in sense training, lipreading, language, auditory training, and speech preparation. The course was a great addition to our Glenrose classes and was full of practical advice. Monthly reports on the lessons were shared through personal letters.

Through the Canadian Hearing Society, we received a parent sharing kit, and through VOICE, I ordered the *Learning to Listen* book. Through the hospital, we were involved in a parent group where thoughts, anxieties, and joys were shared. We were not alone. Another source of information was the Association for the Hearing Handicapped in Edmonton. We attended several meetings at which we met a number of deaf adults and discussed the merits of the Total Communication approach.

After the initial home visits, Colin received individualized oral instruction at the hospital two to three times weekly. I viewed the lesson behind a one-way mirror, often accompanied by Colin's older sister, Kathy. I used to pack up a special "fun bag" for her entertainment. It was important to us that Kathy's needs were not neglected and that she feel special.

Our home was full of pictures, and lesson words turned up in every room of the house. Books were plentiful, and drawing was a favorite pastime. Language! Language! Language! Repetition was the key. By the age of 3, Colin had a word list of about 40 words, many understood only within our family. It is a good idea to keep word lists to look back on. During this time of formal teaching, Colin also attended a mainstream preschool. This was a time when coordination between teachers and parents was very important.

Colin's oral teacher went to the preschool to observe, share information, and give helpful hints. I used to provide a mini-sheet of "To Do's" to help the teacher get Colin's attention. Colin received ear-level aids at age 3 years, 6 months. It was a whole new experience for him to receive auditory stimulation at ear level through something small enough to misplace if Colin chose to remove them. Sometimes, he inadvertently kept them on in the excitement of bath time. We dried them out with a hair dryer and placed them in a dry-aid pack more times than I care to remember. In later years, Colin recognized the importance of removing his hearing aids near water. Once he took them off and placed them carefully on a sandy beach—the ultimate camouflage. To diminish our anxieties, we put a rider on our household insurance policy to cover accidental loss and obtained an extended warranty on the hearing aids. These steps have saved us dollars and worry!

We moved to Victoria, British Columbia, on the Canadian West Coast. After getting settled in, we enrolled Colin at the G.R. Peakes Centre for Children, a Total Communication program with a strong emphasis on verbal and auditory components. Colin's vocabulary was very limited at this time, and his teacher suggested that sign language might be helpful. We agreed to the use of sign language, took classes ourselves, and used it at home along with speech. This helped overcome earlier frustrations in communicating with Colin, and his vocabulary seemed to expand. Success in communicating was important to build up Colin's self-confidence. When we felt that oral words were established, we stopped using sign language.

In July 1980, the teacher wrote that Colin was understanding the words "big" and "little" 100% of the time. These were difficult concepts for him to grasp. By the fall, he was expressing possession. Colin was 4 years old, and this was a milestone for him.

During the preschool years, we always kept a parent–teacher book to share progress and highlights from home and school. I assisted in classroom sessions and field trips. This participation allowed me to see Colin's progress and talk to teachers, and it provided focus for our teaching activities at home. We also obtained some private therapy for Colin from an Auditory-Verbal therapist in Victoria.

When it was time for Colin to enter the mainstream elementary school system, he attended an oral program with several other children who were hearing impaired. This meant taking a bus out of our neighborhood, a situation that has since been repeated. I wish we had had the foresight to buy our house exactly where the appropriate program was located! For half a day, Colin attended a mainstream kindergarten class, and the other half day he attended a self-contained oral program. That was a long school day for a 5-year-old! That school program used another communication method, Cued Speech. Cued Speech is an oral communication approach that uses hand and finger signs near the speaker's mouth to help distinguish between different sounds that have similar lip shapes. As parents, we never tried to master Cued Speech, but Colin's exceptional lipreading skills may have their origin here. Use of residual hearing was also required. During the latter part of kindergarten, Colin's teacher sent home a note to let us know he was beginning to make himself understood in class: "He has been saying a few sentences we all understand." I have held dear those memories, as they were wonderful encouragement that his speech was progressing.

In 1st grade, Colin continued in a self-contained setting but was integrated for non-academic subjects. In retrospect, we had been in a very sheltered school situation. The term "mainstream" was new. In July 1983, we moved to Toronto. The Metro Toronto Board of Education gave Colin a full assessment, and we were confident of the decision to mainstream him.

Based on Colin's varied educational background, it was also recommended that he be referred to the Learning to Listen Foundation. We were assigned to the waiting list. Colin was an older child, and admission was primarily reserved for infants and toddlers. Colin was, however, eventually admitted to the program. The wait was worth it! We attended a program weekly, and eventually biweekly. Colin enjoyed the sessions under the excellent guidance of the Auditory-Verbal therapist. Diligent work was also required at home. Colin's residual hearing was challenged, his listening skills improved, and there was a noticeable increase in language acquisition.

We did specific tasks in audition and speech. During the summer, our program included keeping a diary. As an auditory exercise, I would select a story, read it to Colin, and then ask him, through audition, to answer such questions as, "Who? What? Where? Why? How? When?" We worked on past verb tenses, sequencing skills, opposites, and plurals. Colin would often make up sentences or draw pictures to reinforce his understanding of a concept. We maintained an ongoing list of new vocabulary and practiced speech drills. Colin's speech improved tremendously when he was conscious of doing better. I reminded him of this as much as possible, and encouragement brought results. With Auditory-Verbal therapy, Colin was able to enter a highly sophisticated stage of speech and language development.

When Colin was 9, it was necessary to leave the Learning to Listen Foundation. It was important for newly diagnosed children to have first priority. We were disappointed to leave and missed the regular lessons. We recognized the long way that Colin had come and that it is never too late to be in such a program. Much hard work was behind us, but we knew we could always go back for help—which we did in time.

Within the school system, the itinerant program was excellent. An FM system was used in the classroom, and Colin required new hearing aids with direct audio input—another new concept! Our neighborhood school operated on the open plan, but Colin worked best one-to-one. Large group settings were difficult for him. Even though we had wonderful itinerant and resource help, Colin struggled, and so did we.

When Colin entered 6th grade, it was clear that he needed more structure. He attended a different school in our area but retained the same itinerant teacher to ease the transition. This arrangement provided a more organized school setting, as well as the presence of another child who was hearing impaired. However, because the other child was in 3rd grade, there was no particular bonding between the two children. Taxi service was provided, and Colin knew some of the children at this school. The game plan was for Colin to remain there for 7th and 8th grades. At the beginning of 7th grade, Colin was very unhappy as he watched neighborhood peers go to the local senior public school, and he wanted to transfer. We weighed the pros and cons, wrote them down, and talked to school personnel in the itinerant and mainstream sectors. Within a week, Colin was ensconced back in home territory at the senior public school with the same itinerant teacher. Amidst all of this, he appeared to be coping like any student.

Colin progressed into 7th grade with minimal passing grades and was "on rotation" in a large school of 500. Suddenly, everything was going too fast for him. We sought outside help and followed some practical suggestions. First, we discontinued French, a required course in Canada. We had not been aware that there was a special exemption available for students who are hearing impaired. (Later, in high school, Colin would have to substitute an alternative subject.) He was not enjoying music; this was discontinued, too, to enable him to get extra help during a resource period. Note-takers were instituted, and all teachers were made aware of Colin's needs. He had to pull his own weight, too! He successfully graduated from 8th grade, receiving a certificate of achievement—a special honor in recognition of effort, attitude, cooperation, and improvement in performance.

While Colin was in 7th and 8th grades, we put up the "help" flag again for speech therapy. We had been relying on incidental correction and casual lessons, but Colin needed more structured help. The program at the Learning to Listen Foundation was still full, but the clinical staff directed us to a therapist in private practice. She served as both mentor and teacher, giving Colin the boost of self-confidence he needed. Homework was Colin's responsibility now, including setting times to review listening skills, speech, language, and research.

In 1989, VOICE and Auditory-Verbal International, Inc. (AVI) held a conference in Toronto called Learning to Listen: Ten Years Later. It could not have been more timely. Colin attended several conference sessions and listened to other young adults telling their stories. One panelist remarked, humorously, that his mother "pushed him." Colin told me afterward that he was glad I had pushed him. He has always been positive about Auditory-Verbal therapy.

During these past years, as educational and social issues arise, our involvement with groups like VOICE has been of utmost benefit. Sharing with other parents is important; we never feel alone. Our involvement with local organizations has led to new friendships and a broader understanding about hearing impairment. My own involvement has included helping put together an information kit for parents in Edmonton, promoting May Hearing Awareness Month in Victoria, and serving on the VOICE executive committee. My husband serves as a VOICE representative for the Special Education Advisory Committee (SEAC) of our local school board. We are convinced that having an active voice in the educational system is a very positive vehicle for ensuring the best services.

Here are some friendly pointers that, as parents ourselves, we feel others will find helpful:

- Look at different points of view.
- Be flexible.
- Listen to your child's concerns.
- Remember that your child needs a parent first and a teacher second.
- Give lots of hugs.
- Work hard.
- Dedicate time to develop your child's listening skills. It is never too late to try something new; after a late start, Auditory-Verbal therapy became an integral part of our family's life.

We have learned all about special assistive devices for individuals who are hearing impaired, such as volume controls on the telephone, a vibrating alarm clock, and a closed-caption decoder. The last has opened a whole new realm of television viewing, and it is wonderful to hear Colin laugh heartily when he "gets" the punch lines. Prior to purchasing a decoder, we borrowed one from the public library.

We moved to Burlington, Ontario (near Toronto), where Colin started 9th grade. We chose this area carefully for the excellent school program offered for children who are hearing impaired. Colin continues to rely on residual hearing along with very fine speechreading skills, and he continues to receive private Auditory-Verbal therapy. Carrying on a conversation without slurring or mumbling is a challenge for my teenager, but Colin's desire to improve makes us very proud of him. We still have ups and downs, but Colin appears to be an independent and confident young man.

Update

How happy I am to write again about Colin and our family!

Let me first revisit my opening line of 10 years ago. The sentence, "This is not a success story" was a big mistake! I was using the word "success" based on a now-obsolete mental definition that I understood to mean a particular result or outcome. I now know that there are many unexpected kinds of success.

In February 1994, Colin passed his driver's license exam on the first try. With that new responsibility, he had more independence and freedom to travel farther afield when he got the family car. With that accomplishment also came fretting by his parents. But it was a great achievement for our son.

In June 1994, his remedial teacher wrote, "Colin continues to be unsure of his plans, possibly resulting in his inconsistent effort and work habits. His desire to achieve academically and his need for an active social life often come in conflict, producing a great deal of frustration and unfocused energy." Could this not have been written to describe any teenager in his almost-last year of high school at age 17? Colin remained under the watchful eye of this teacher all through those grades, and we welcomed the extra help and tutoring. However, as a growing teenager, he had little opportunity to go astray at school without our hearing about it!

This same teacher was instrumental in advising us about the educational opportunities that lay beyond high school, particularly at the Rochester Institute of Technology (RIT) in Rochester, New York. Colin took a school trip to RIT, and we subsequently visited the campus with him to investigate the courses and programs. RIT has eight colleges on campus, including the

Colin O'Brien and family today

National Technological Institute for the Deaf (NTID). With 1100 students who are deaf or hard of hearing and 14 000 counterparts with typical hearing, RIT/NTID offers students a unique opportunity to enjoy both worlds.

With flying colors and accolades from his family, Colin was accepted by RIT/NTID into its College of Imaging Arts and Sciences (CIAS) in January 1995. His sense of accomplishment and his excitement were keen. We all attended an orientation weekend during which we received much advice for both parents and students. We even met parents who had been in our parent support group in Edmonton. You can imagine our delight at connecting again as our sons started college together.

In August of the same year, Colin was off to college in Rochester. His remedial teacher sent him a note: "I wanted to wish you well as you begin your educational career at RIT. If you are like most students starting a new school, you will feel some apprehension and nervousness. You have certainly shown the potential and skills required to be successful. I hope you are not only successful but enjoy your years at RIT." For ourselves, we began yet another process of letting go.

When Colin started at RIT/NTID, it could be said he was in a dual minority: both deaf and gay. When he was 17, he came home one day and said he had something to tell us. I inquired innocently, "Oh. Did you get a speeding ticket?" Colin said, "No; I know I'm gay." This should not have been a surprise, but at that time I was sure he just needed a girlfriend. We supported Colin, of course, but the social path I had envisioned for him had taken a different turn. That was a time of growth and acceptance, especially for me! Throughout the process of "letting go" we want our children to be happy, independent, and successful. But they really become themselves when we stand off to the side and let them explore who they are. We did that, and offered our support when it was needed.

The transition from high school to university was exciting for Colin because he was on his own and had many new experiences ahead. Initial adjustments to residence were difficult, but he eventually found compatible roommates. Prior to attending RIT, he had no friends who were deaf. At college, he spent a lot of time learning about Deaf culture. He discovered a deaf identity by finding a support network that included friends who were deaf who had had the mainstream experience, and those who had attended schools exclusively for the deaf. Initially, he challenged us about our not sending him to such a school when he was young. He felt he might have been happier there. At this time, Colin learned to use sign language very quickly, and I subsequently took lessons through the Canadian Hearing Society in hopes of possibly bonding with new friends that he might bring home.

Colin flourished in the educational environment offered at CIAS under the direction of teachers who had experience in teaching students who were deaf and who understood the communication issues they faced. His four years there seemed to go quickly. Our parental involvement meant sharing happy times and sometimes anxious days, helping him move from residence to his apartment, his solo visits home and those he made with friends, sending him "care packages," making trips to Rochester, and providing financial help, of course. Colin also received financial aid from the Ontario Student Assistance Program (OSAP).

It was a proud day when we attended his graduation in May 2000. Colin received his Bachelor of Fine Arts degree (School of Design) and his Associate in Applied Science degree (School of Art) from the CIAS. He subsequently remained in Rochester, where he freelanced with design studios until July 2001. He then headed off to Tucson, Arizona with a friend to see new parts of the United States. Even though he found freelance work in the USA, he required permanent employment to stay there, so he returned home in November 2001.

In the months that followed, Colin adjusted to living at home again. His determination to find employment was commendable, and he worked at it daily. I came home one day the following March and asked, "How was your day?" to which he responded with a wide smile, "A lot better now that I have a job." He has since been working as a graphic designer for a company in Burlington, Ontario. He said that it was challenging to enter the working world where most people can hear normally, but he integrates well with fellow employees. He designs packaging for amenity products for retail stores and the high-end hospitality sector. On your next vacation, take a look at that wee bottle of shampoo in your room. Colin may have designed the label!

Colin has remained in touch with VOICE for Hearing-Impaired Children and participated at a VOICE conference a few years ago. The last hearing aids he got were steel gray in color. He said that people should notice that he is deaf, so, away with dull beige! Design and attitudes have come a long way since we first strapped those cumbersome body aids to Colin's chest.

Colin lives in the Greater Toronto Area with a wonderful hearing partner, Greg. They have a full social life with friends who are both hearing and deaf, and Greg has learned sign language a lot better than I did. Colin's sister, Kathy, graduated from Queens University in Kingston, Ontario in 1997 and spent some time teaching in Bogota, Colombia, where she met Henry, her terrific partner. They subsequently relocated to Toronto. Kathy and Colin and their respective partners get together frequently, and we see them quite often. Both our children are confident, creative, successful adults and have found respectful and caring partners in life.

To parents new to their children's diagnosis of hearing loss, please know that your children will succeed, too. All you can do is your best by giving them lots of love, consistency, and support. That is what we did, and I am proud to say that this really is a success story, 10 years later.

In 2006, Colin was living in Mississauga, Ontario with his partner. He won recognition of his graphic design work at the 2005 American Design Awards, and has achieved professional accreditation with the Association of Registered Graphic Designers of Ontario.

REFERENCES

Estabrooks, E. (Ed.). (1994). *Auditory-Verbal Therapy for Parents and Professionals.* Washington, DC: Alexander Graham Bell Association for the Deaf.

Luterman, D., with M. Ross. (1991). *When Your Child Is Deaf: A Guide for Parents.* Parkton, MD: York Press.

Vaughan, P. (Ed.). (1981). *Learning to Listen: A Book by Mothers for Mothers of Hearing Impaired Children* (rev. ed.). Washington, DC: Alexander Graham Bell Association for the Deaf/ Beaufort Books/VOICE for Hearing-Impaired Children.

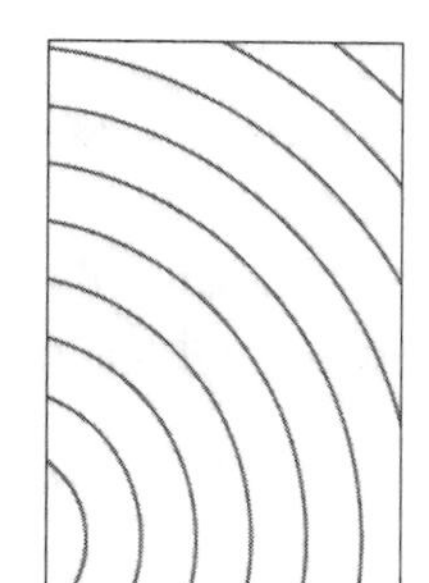

CHAPTER 10

Research in Auditory-Verbal Therapy

Alice Eriks-Brophy, B.A., B.Ed., M.Sc. (A), M.Sc., Ph.D.

The auditory-verbal approach has for some years been a popular intervention for children who are deaf or hard of hearing, yet few empirical studies have evaluated the communication and academic outcomes of those children who have participated in this approach. The focus of this final chapter is to discuss the standards of evidence-based practice and to examine the existing evidence that supports Auditory-Verbal therapy (AVT) as an intervention. The chapter will (a) categorize the various types of evidence in terms of the scientific strength they provide in favor of treatment approaches, (b) present the current evidence in support of AVT through a review of eight studies examining various outcomes associated with this intervention, and (c) consider a study-in-progress that takes into account the limitations of previous research examining outcomes of AVT. The chapter concludes with a discussion of the types of evidence that are still needed to support the outcomes of AVT, and a call for collaboration among parents and professionals in the generation of such evidence.

Surprisingly little empirical knowledge is available about the efficacy of various treatment approaches for individuals with communication difficulties. Many of the most commonly used clinical approaches in audiology and speech-language pathology have never been objectively evaluated, nor have their outcomes been empirically documented. In the current climate of cutbacks in healthcare, patient rights, quality-of-life issues, and pay-for-service, this situation has become untenable. It is no longer sufficient for clinicians to rely on their clinical training, knowledge, and experience to convince clients, other professionals, administrators, academics, and governmental agencies of the value of the services they provide. Provision of objective, quantifiable evidence regarding which treatments are effective and their likely outcomes is now essential to justify not only the approach adopted, but also the need to employ clinicians to supply these interventions. This attitude of accountability has contributed to the current emphasis on evidence-based practice in support of clinical treatment approaches and their associated outcomes.

As defined in earlier chapters, AVT is an intervention approach for children with hearing loss that emphasizes the development of spoken language through early identification of hearing impairment; optimal amplification, cochlear implant technology, or both; and intensive speech and language therapy (AVI,

1991). In this approach, parents serve as the primary language models for their children. AVT is based on the notion that most children with hearing losses ranging from mild to profound can learn to communicate through spoken language if provided with appropriate amplification or cochlear implant technology (or both), abundant language stimulation, and adequate opportunities to develop their hearing and listening potential.

Few empirical studies have evaluated the communication and academic outcomes of children who have participated in AVT. Furthermore, studies examining the social functioning, self-perception, and personal adjustment of children participating in AVT are virtually non-existent.

EVIDENCE-BASED PRACTICE

Evidence-based practice (EBP) in the fields of audiology and speech-language pathology typically consists of gathering outcome data related to a specific clinical approach. Treatment outcomes may be gathered for a variety of purposes, such as to document the effectiveness of a clinical program, to identify gains in specific domains of communication subsequent to having participated in a particular treatment, to determine whether treatments are cost-effective and resources are being well spent, and to monitor clinical effectiveness (Carney & Moeller, 1998; Coyte, 1992; Enderby, 1997; Enderby & Emerson, 1995; Frattali, 1998).

The measurement of outcomes associated with various treatment approaches in the field of speech-language pathology and audiology has traditionally concentrated on clinically observed changes in the speech and language deficits associated with a particular communication disorder (Carney & Moeller, 1998; Enderby, 1997; Frattali, 1998). In the past, such evidence typically consisted of the documentation of specific behavioral changes associated with participation in an intervention program as observed in a clinical setting. Clinicians, however, have always been aware that limiting the examination of outcome evidence only to observed behavioral changes in the context of the therapy session alone does not necessarily reflect the broader range of improvements associated with specific treatment approaches. In the present context, it has become clear that practitioners must also take into account outcomes that are defined by the needs or interests of individual clients at particular times and which may not be assessed within the therapy session alone.

Fortunately, the focus of outcome measurement has recently expanded to include not only traditional client-centered models, but also evaluation of the social, academic, and employment contexts in which clients regularly participate. As a result of this widening of focus in the description of outcomes, the effectiveness of intervention approaches can now be assessed not only in terms of improvements in specific communication skills, but also in terms of (a) changes in the ability of communicative partners to facilitate communication and interaction, (b) increased opportunities for clients to communicate and integrate into a variety of social contexts and activities, and (c) levels of client satisfaction with services received.

The categories for description of these broader domains of outcome measurement have been defined in terms of functional, administrative, financial, social, and client-defined outcomes related to communication (Coyte, 1992; Frattali, 1998). *Functional outcomes* of a treatment approach might include the ability to use the telephone or to communicate needs in a real-world environment. *Administrative evidence* is typically presented in terms of the productivity of a unit or department, the number of sessions a client misses, or the referral practices of a clinical program. *Financial evidence* examines issues related to the cost-effectiveness of a particular treatment approach. *Social outcomes* might include an individual's employability or integration into the community. Finally, *client-defined outcomes* might be described in terms of satisfaction with services received or in relation to quality-of-life issues (Enderby & Emerson, 1995; Frattali, 1998; Fougeyrollas, Cloutier, Bergeron, Côté, & Michel, 1998).

Clinicians and researchers currently emphasize EBP in clinical language intervention because it allows us to demonstrate to those outside our discipline that what we do works and therefore is worth doing. Another benefit of EBP is that it permits us to plan for clinical practice and to develop new and improved models and approaches to intervention and service delivery. Constant upgrading of current practices is expected to lead to improved outcomes for our clients. Finally, EBP enables us to make links with other fields, resulting in new applications of knowledge and new treatment approaches, thus continually advancing our discipline.

WHAT CONSTITUTES GOOD EVIDENCE IN FAVOR OF A CLINICAL APPROACH?

Until fairly recently, there was little consensus regarding the outcomes that provided the most solid evidence in favor of a treatment approach. Based on a classification system adopted from epidemiology, an outcomes measurement classification for communication intervention has recently been proposed (Frattali, 1998; Fineberg, 1990; Holland, Fromm, DeRuyter, & Stein, 1996). This classification system weighs the strength of evidence of a treatment based on the degree of scientific rigor of the methodology used to collect the evidence, and categorizes this evidence into three established classes (American Academy of Neurology, 1994). Thus, a high degree of scientific methodological rigor in conducting outcomes research contributes to the strength of the evidence it provides in support of a treatment approach through the use of controlled research designs that protect against bias and subjectivity in the interpretation of findings.

Methods resulting in *Class I* evidence consist of well-designed, experimentally controlled research studies. The most scientifically controlled of such studies are randomized control trials (RCTs), which typically involve large numbers of subjects randomly assigned to various treatment groups. Class I evidence provides the strongest empirical support for a treatment approach, and RCTs are considered the gold standard towards which outcome research should strive.

Indeed, the RCT is the only research design that permits clear inferences to be made regarding causal relationships between treatments and their associated outcomes—in other words, a statement that the treatment itself caused the observable effect.

Class II evidence is obtained from quasi-experimental designs, often in the form of cohort studies or program evaluations. Cohort studies are prospective studies in which a group of individuals with a common characteristic are evaluated at a particular time or are followed longitudinally to examine the particular outcome(s) under investigation. Such studies may involve a control group, allowing inter-group comparisons to be made on variables of interest to the research. Class II evidence is often cited in program evaluations, which are typically carried out to determine whether a program is meeting its goals. Program evaluations are systematic and include pre-established standards, or benchmarks, against which a program is judged. Studies resulting in Class II evidence are based on less methodologically rigorous research approaches than those of Class I, and therefore are seen by some as presenting less compelling evidence in favor of a particular treatment. Such studies are therefore considered potentially more open to the influence of extraneous factors that may bias the results of the investigation of an intervention's effectiveness, and are often limited in their generalizability owing to a limited number of participants and the lack of a control group.

Class III evidence is typically obtained through non-experimental research designs. Such designs are often retrospective in nature, and may include case studies, registries and database studies, group judgments, or expert opinions of performance. These designs lack experimental control or contain important flaws in research design, and are therefore often criticized for their subjective or anecdotal nature. Evidence from studies utilizing Class III research methods are deemed to provide the least compelling evidence in favor of a treatment approach.

The classification system described above is based on an epidemiological model. In clinical speech-language applications, for example, Class I evidence may be unattainable or even unethical. For this reason, Class II evidence is becoming widely acceptable as good evidence in favor of a treatment approach in clinical outcome measurement, while Class III evidence is considered useful in lending support to further experimental studies. Such evidence can help shape and inform the development of more methodologically rigorous research. Nevertheless, a primary goal of outcome-based research is to seek the strongest possible evidence in support of a clinical intervention.

THE EVIDENCE IN FAVOR OF AVT AS A TREATMENT APPROACH

Historically, research examining the performance of children who are deaf or hard of hearing in various domains of communication outcome has been fraught with methodological difficulties. Confounds in terms of groupings of children (based on mode of communication, intervention approach, degree of hearing loss, chronological age, amplification or cochlear implant technology, and cognitive status, among other variables) have made this research almost impossible to interpret.

Reports of the effectiveness of AVT as an intervention approach have not been immune to criticism and accusations of subjectivity and anecdote. A perception that outcomes of AVT were based on the performance of "AVT stars" who were not representative of the general population of children who are deaf or hard of hearing has led to a degree of skepticism towards the reported benefits of AVT from those outside the field.

Eight studies have specifically examined various treatment outcomes of AVT. These studies vary widely in the age of the participants involved, the geographical region implicated, and the form of evidence collected. Each study is presented below in light of the strength of evidence it provides in favor of AVT as a treatment approach. Studies appear in the chronological order in which they were published. Only those that have specifically examined domains of outcome associated with AVT are described.

Goldberg and Flexer (1993, 2001)

The earliest seminal outcome study of AVT is a survey conducted by Goldberg and Flexer in 1993. The study attempted to examine the efficacy of AVT practices and to document the status of graduates of a number of AVT programs in the United States and Canada. The research used a consumer survey approach to examine the question, "How do these now-grown-up recipients of AV practice and way of life describe themselves and their histories?" The data were collected in the form of a six-page survey, which provided descriptive information related to the degree and etiology of hearing loss, age of onset, amplification and cochlear implant technology, educational history, and employment history of the participants. One hundred fifty-seven individuals with hearing loss, who had obtained preschool AVT intervention and who ranged in age from 18 to 47 years, responded to the questionnaire. All responses were self-reports and included individuals' perceptions of their current levels of functioning. On the basis of these responses, the researchers concluded that the majority of respondents to the survey identified themselves as successfully functioning in their communities, local schools, and postsecondary institutions.

An updated version of this study conducted by the same authors was carried out in 2001. The authors made a concerted effort to contact all known AV centers and all certified AV therapists in the United States and Canada in order to obtain information about the status of their graduates. A survey approach was again taken to collect this information. Three hundred nineteen surveys were distributed, with a response rate of 36%. Results were similar to those reported in the 1993 study, and indicated that regardless of degree of hearing loss, children who are deaf or hard of hearing have the potential to become independent and contributing members of society. Early detection of hearing loss;

prompt audiological management; appropriate fitting with amplification devices, cochlear implants, or both; and early enrollment in AVT were proposed as key elements in achieving these outcomes.

The results of these two studies provide interesting insights into a self-selected group of graduates of various AV programs in North America. The participants are considered a self-selected group because they were willing to respond to the survey while other potential participants were not. Since all these data are descriptive and based on self-reports and self-perceptions, no cause–effect relationships related to AVT and subsequent outcomes can be inferred. The studies can thus be rated as providing Class III evidence in favor of AVT as a treatment approach. The 1993 research study was nevertheless a milestone in the examination of AVT, and delineated a number of crucial variables that have been utilized in subsequent survey-based examinations of the outcomes of AVT, including those used in the 2001 update.

Robertson and Flexer (1993)

These authors conducted a survey study requesting parents to provide standardized test scores of reading development for their school-aged children with prelingual hearing loss who were educated through AVT. Additional variables examined included age, etiology and degree of hearing loss, age at amplification or cochlear implantation, description of school placement, extracurricular activities, and early contact with reading. Questionnaires were distributed to parents through therapists known to have been practicing AVT in the United States and Switzerland. The survey consisted of such questions as, "What is your impression of your child's reading ability compared to the hearing children in his/her class?" Parents were also asked to submit standardized test scores of reading performance.

Results from 37 children who are deaf or hard of hearing who ranged in age from 6 to 19 years were used in the analysis. According to the authors, 30 of the 37 children scored at the 50th percentile or higher on a variety of reading tests that had been standardized using data from children with typical hearing. Performance on 17 different standardized measures of reading are reported in order to support the authors' conclusion that "[t]he children in this study, all of whom acquired language through the process of listening, developed reading ability comparable to their peers who hear normally" (p. 253).

While those parents who provided standardized reading test scores for their children who are deaf or hard of hearing indicated that these children had attained high levels of achievement, it is difficult to make comparisons across the various reading measures reported as well as across the ages of the children involved. Other than the fact that the questionnaires were distributed by AV therapists, no information is provided related to the comparability of the centers in which these children received their intervention. Results are anecdotal in that they rely on parental report, making it impossible to conclude that there is a causal relationship between participation in AVT and the reading scores attained by these children. The respondents again constitute a self-selected group of participants. While the study provides some interesting descriptive information related to a self-selected set of families of children who are deaf or hard of hearing, their children, and their home literacy practices, we are again presented with Class III evidence in support of AVT outcomes.

Roberts and Rickards (1994a,b)

In 1994, these authors conducted an extensive survey of graduates of an Australian integrated auditory/oral preschool. In addition to receiving intensive intervention focused on the development of speech and language through audition, the children enrolled in this program were integrated with their peers with normal hearing in preschool groups of 16 to 20 children with a ratio of children with hearing loss to children with typical hearing of 1:4. The authors utilized a 26-item descriptive self-report questionnaire to examine participants' perceptions of their usage of amplification and cochlear implant technology, communication practices, speech intelligibility, academic achievement, use of support services, and friendship patterns. One hundred graduates of this preschool AVT program, who ranged in age from 7 to 17 years, responded to the questionnaire. The survey contained such questions as, "Do you receive extra help in school? What sort of help? What sort of help would you like?" Based on the descriptive information provided by the participants, the authors concluded:

> The majority of students reported that they used hearing aids consistently, used speech as their major mode of communication, were less reliant on supplementary modes of communication than their deaf friends, and perceived themselves as better listeners than speakers. Eighty-three percent of children perceived their overall academic progress to be "average" to "above average" as compared to their class peers. Nearly all children received audiological support and over one third were supported by speech therapists and integration aides. Nearly two thirds of the children reported that most of their friends had normal hearing (p. 207).

The authors are careful in stating that their findings cannot be interpreted as causally related to the preschool AVT services received by the participants. Results presented in this study are again based on a self-selected sample of participants and are primarily retrospective in nature. Information related to these individuals' perceptions, experiences, and current levels of functioning present an interesting description of a sample of graduates of a specific AVT program, but provide only Class III evidence in favor of AVT as a treatment approach.

Wray, Flexer, and Vaccaro (1997)

These authors examined the classroom performance of children who are deaf or hard of hearing and who learned spoken language through the auditory-verbal approach. The goal of the study was to examine the efficacy of an early-intervention AVT program in preparing participants for educational placement in mainstream settings. A questionnaire was used to examine the classroom performance of 19 children with hearing loss who had attended a preschool AVT program at the University of Akron between the ages of 2 and 5 years and who were being educated in mainstream classrooms. These students ranged in age from 5 years, 5 months to 15 years, 2 months. Teachers completed the Screening Instrument for Targeting Educational Risk (SIFTER) (Anderson, 1989), which assesses teacher perceptions of student performance in the areas of academics, attention, communication, class participation, and school behavior through 15 questions rated on a Likert scale. Additionally, teachers provided reading-level and qualitative information about classroom and support services for individual children, while parents reported on involvement in community and school activities. Descriptive information regarding demographics, degree of hearing loss, and type and use of amplification and cochlear implant technology was also collected as part of the study. The authors concluded that 16 of the 19 children who had attended the program were fully included in their local schools and, according to their teachers, read at or above grade level.

In this study, a standardized tool, the SIFTER, was utilized in order to obtain information about students with hearing loss in integrated settings. The SIFTER is considered a screening tool, however, and does not provide any associated normative data other than a cut-off score indicating those students who may be experiencing difficulties in the classroom setting. Additional information obtained through the study is descriptive and based on parental and teacher reports and anecdotal information. It should be noted that the stated goal of this study was to examine the treatment efficacy of AVT rather than to document specific outcomes related to this treatment approach. Treatment efficacy studies are typically conducted to demonstrate that a program was able to produce a specific predicted outcome, a subtly different objective than studies that are conducted to examine broader domains of outcome. The study provides Class III evidence in favor of AVT as a treatment approach.

Rhoades and Chisholm (2000) and Rhoades (2001)

This was one of the few studies examining outcomes of AVT that can be classified as utilizing a true experimental design. It examined global language growth rates in children who had received intensive AVT for a period of 1 to 4 years. Participants in this study were children with moderate to profound hearing losses, 13 of whom wore hearing aids and 27 of whom had cochlear implants. These children ranged in age from 50 to 120 months. Participants were administered three measures of global language development normed on children with typical hearing. The language measures used were the Sequenced Inventory of Communication Development (SICD) (Hedrick, Prather, & Tobin, 1984), which measures overall language development in children from 0 to 4 years; the Preschool Language Scale—3 (PLS-3) (Zimmerman, Steiner, & Pond, 1992), which assesses language from 1 to 7 years; and the Oral–Written Language Scale (OWLS) (Carrow-Woolfolk, 1995), which measures language development in individuals from 3 to 21 years. All these measures have documented psychometric properties and are frequently used in assessing language development in preschool and school-aged children.

The research, which is reported in two parts, documented changes in receptive and expressive age equivalency scores over time and as a function of the number of years the child was enrolled in AVT. Results indicated that all children, regardless of amplification or cochlear implant technology used, showed some growth in expressive and receptive language development over time, a finding that might easily be explained through typical developmental maturation. Results from some of the graduates of the AVT program showed no gap between their chronological age and their receptive and expressive language age-equivalency scores, indicating age-appropriate language skills. The authors concluded:

> Group performances in receptive and expressive language for each year indicate that a reasonable overall expected average rate of growth should be 100% for each of the first 2 years of AVT, even for typical older preschool children. Furthermore, performance of the "graduates" in this study shows that the gap between CA and LA was closed—these children essentially attained linguistic competency at levels commensurate with peers who have normal hearing. (Rhoades & Chisholm, 2000, p. 5)

The authors are careful with respect to implying that a direct cause–effect relationship exists between AVT and the achievement of high degrees of language skills in the participants. They do not imply that AVT alone led to the outcomes reported in their study. The authors conclude only that AVT is a "highly viable communication option" (p. 24) for children who are deaf or hard of hearing. The study did not utilize a control group, represented a relatively small sample size, and recruited participants from a single AVT program. Results are therefore limited in terms of their generalizability to other children who are deaf or hard of hearing enrolled in AVT. Through use of an experimental design and the administration of standardized test measures, this research provides solid Class II evidence in favor of AVT as an intervention option, and is the only study of its kind to date that examines outcomes utilizing a prospective, objective research methodology.

Duncan (2001)

This was another study using an experimental design that highlights positive outcomes associated with enrollment in AVT. This study examined discourse skills of children who are deaf or hard of hearing who had been enrolled in AVT programs as compared to typically hearing peers in an integrated kindergarten setting. Eleven children with prelingual, severe to profound hearing loss and 11 age-matched peers were compared on their use of a variety of conversational discourse features. Each paired dyad was videotaped for 10 minutes while playing with Lego™ blocks in a small tutorial room. These videotaped interactions were transcribed and coded using an organizational framework adapted from the Social Organization of Discourse Checklist originally developed by Beattie (1990). The checklist was used to code the children's abilities in initiating, maintaining, and shifting topics, and terminating conversations within a semi-naturalistic play setting. Transcription and coding reliability in the analysis of the videotaped interactions was very high. Nonparametric statistical analyses were carried out on the coded data to examine differences in social discourse strategies between the children with and without hearing loss.

Results of the study showed very few significant differences between the children who are deaf or hard of hearing and their age-matched peers with typical hearing in the four domains of discourse ability captured by the checklist. The author concluded that an important component of these children's development of such a high degree of conversational competence is their immersion in an intensive AVT program at an early age, along with ongoing audiological management and inclusion in integrated educational and social environments from time of diagnosis.

While the goal of Duncan's research was to examine conversational abilities of children who are deaf or hard of hearing in naturalistic conversation with their peers with typical hearing, her study provides convincing Class II evidence in favor of AVT as an intervention approach. The matched-pairs research design allowed inter-group comparisons to be made on the discourse variables of interest to the research. Objective criteria for the coding of the discourse data were derived from a checklist with sound empirical characteristics, and a high degree of reliability was obtained between coders prior to conducting statistical analyses on the coded data. While use of a matched subject research design is in many ways equivalent to using a control group, the study results are based on a very small sample size recruited from a single AVT program in South Australia. As was the case in the study by Rhoades and Chisholm (2001), results are limited in terms of their generalizability to other children who are deaf or hard of hearing enrolled in AVT. The author makes no claims regarding any cause–effect relationship between the intervention approach in which the children who are deaf or hard of hearing were enrolled and their documented competence in conversational discourse. She does state, however, that children with profound hearing loss who are provided with (a) early amplification, cochlear implant technology, or both, (b) an intervention approach that facilitates the development of communicative competence, and (c) opportunities for inclusion are able to develop oral language abilities equivalent to their peers without hearing loss. These recommendations are consistent with the primary principles underlying AVT.

Durieux-Smith, Eriks-Brophy, Olds, Fitzpatrick, Duquette, and Whittingham (2001)

These authors' research consisted of a retrospective follow-up study of young adults who are deaf or hard of hearing who had received preschool AVT at a regional pediatric hospital in Ontario, Canada. The study examined current levels of communicative, academic, and psycho-social functioning of these young people, identified facilitators and barriers to the integration of young people with hearing loss, and developed a set of recommendations to enhance the integration of students with hearing loss in educational, family, and social settings. In order to participate in the study, these young adults had to:

- have a permanent hearing loss requiring hearing aids,
- have been enrolled in preschool AVT at the pediatric center in question,
- have no developmental or cognitive disability that might affect communication ability,
- use English as their primary language of instruction, and
- be of high school age or older.

Information was gathered in three phases. First, questionnaires were distributed to the young people and their parents in order to collect demographic information, information regarding the young people's hearing loss, educational history, and family characteristics. In phase 2, standardized assessments in the areas of communicative competence, academic functioning, and self-perception were administered to all participants who agreed to be tested. In phase 3, focus groups were conducted with the young adults with hearing loss, their parents, and professionals in the education of children who are deaf or hard of hearing. All standardized measures had excellent psychometric properties and had been standardized on individuals with typical hearing. A total of 43 young people participated in the questionnaire phase of the study; 24 participated in the standardized testing phase, and 16 participated in the focus groups. Participants with hearing loss had a mean age of 18.9 years and an average PTA of 74.4 dB HL. They had spent an average of 24.5 months in AVT. Seventeen of the 24 participants in the standardized testing phase had been fully integrated in classrooms with their hearing peers throughout their educational history.

Results of the standardized testing phase showed that participants achieved levels of performance comparable to their hearing peers in all the domains tested. These domains included receptive vocabulary, speech intelligibility, listening comprehension, oral expression, written expression, word attack skills, reading comprehension, numerical operations, spelling, and self-perception. The authors concluded that children who received early AVT could grow up in mainstream learning environments, could function effectively and successfully in integrated school and community environments, and could achieve at average or above average levels on measures of communication, academics, and self-perception compared to their peers with typical hearing.

While the use of standardized measures allowed comparisons to be made between individuals with hearing loss and their peers, no control group was used in the study. The research was primarily retrospective rather than prospective in nature, and again involved a self-selected sample of participants. An additional limitation to the research included the relatively small number of young adults who participated in the standardized testing, all of whom had received AVT at the same pediatric center in their preschool years. While these limitations affect the generalizability of the findings, the study nevertheless presents reasonably strong Class II evidence in favor of AVT as an intervention approach.

SUMMARY: EVIDENCE IN SUPPORT OF AVT

The combined observations regarding the studies reviewed above allow a number of conclusions to be drawn about research examining the outcomes of AVT and the types of existing evidence to support this intervention approach. This evidence would be classified as providing only limited support in favor of AVT as a treatment approach owing to a number of significant problems related to research design. These issues are summarized below:

- First, the majority of research examining the outcomes of AVT is retrospective, anecdotal, or both. A number of the studies reviewed relied on questionnaires, expert opinions, and data contained in student files. Such information is deemed to provide only the lowest level of evidence in favor of a treatment approach.
- Second, research examining outcomes of AVT has often been based on a small participant pool or a self-selected or convenience sample of participants rather than a sample population enrolled at the beginning of a particular study. In most of these studies, no clear inclusion criteria, other than the child's previous enrollment in a particular AVT program, are cited as eligibility criteria for participation. None of the studies utilized a control group for comparison purposes in their documentation of outcome. Only two of the studies used standardized measures whose normative data were based on scores from children with typical hearing at the same chronological age. These normative data provided a point of comparison for the performance of the students with hearing loss but do not replace the use of a control group in the documentation of outcomes.
- Third, comparison of results across studies is difficult, as a wide variety of communication skill outcomes have been examined using many different measures. The studies reviewed above concentrated on differing domains of communicative competence—including speech intelligibility, reading, and academic achievement—using a variety of research tools and approaches. Only one of the studies reported on these children's levels of functioning across multiple domains. Furthermore, the validity of using social development and psycho-social functioning of children who participated in AVT as a domain of outcome remains largely unexplored.
- Finally, much of the reviewed research contains methodological problems. Combined results are often presented from children with widely differing degrees of hearing loss, age of diagnosis, chronological and hearing ages, and type of amplification or cochlear implant technology. While intervention approach is assumed to be constant across the studies reviewed, few details are provided regarding the specific teaching principles used in the various treatment centers that might support the categorization of the intervention approach as AVT.

What Evidence Is Still Needed to Support AVT As a Treatment Approach?

The scientific evidence reviewed above demonstrates that children who are deaf or hard of hearing who are enrolled in AVT are able to make substantial progress in the development of speech, language, and reading skills in spite of their hearing difficulties. Some of these children have reportedly been able to achieve levels of language and literacy development that are commensurate with those of their hearing peers. It thus appears that AVT intervention for children who are deaf or hard of hearing may have a substantial positive effect on oral communication and literacy skill development. Nevertheless, based on the evidence, it is not possible to conclude that a direct cause–effect relationship exists between AVT and the documented outcomes reported by the researchers, because the research methodologies utilized in these studies provide primarily Class III evidence in support of AVT as an intervention approach.

There is currently an urgent need for more sophisticated and controlled research examining the outcomes of AVT that incorporates the high standards associated with scientific evidence required to illustrate intervention effectiveness. Class III evidence is no longer considered sufficient to justify intervention approaches, particularly in the current atmosphere of government cutbacks to healthcare and pay-for-service health insurance plans. It is therefore crucial that we move towards the collection of data that are methodologically sound and provide the best possible class of evidence in favor of AVT as an intervention approach. The danger of not having such evidence is illustrated in the recent criticisms leveled against universal newborn hearing screening by the United States Preventative Services Task Force (Agency for Healthcare Research and Quality, 2001), where the lack of prospective, controlled studies examining outcomes of newborn hearing screening and early intervention was cited repeatedly as grounds for the conclusion that there is insufficient scientific evidence to make recommendations either for or against routine neonatal hearing screening. As the basis for its conclusions, the report utilized available research results in two central domains, both of which have implications for outcomes documentation in AVT: evidence of the effectiveness of existing universal hearing screening programs, and evidence that early identification and treatment of hearing loss result in better speech and language outcomes.

Clearly, similar criticisms regarding the lack of sound scientific evidence can be leveled against the existing research examining outcomes of AVT as well as other communication options used with children who are deaf or hard of hearing. It is unlikely that Class I evidence generated through randomized, controlled trials will ever be obtainable to support AVT outcomes, as it is parents, not clinicians and researchers, who make decisions related to the adoption of a communication approach for their children who are deaf or hard of hearing. Nevertheless, it is imperative that future research studies examining outcomes of AVT apply the highest possible degree of scientific rigor in their research designs in order to provide the strongest possible Class II evidence in favor of this intervention approach. In order to accomplish this, such designs should be minimally expected to:

- administer objective assessments utilizing assessment tools with well-validated psychometric properties,
- incorporate an appropriate comparison group,
- be prospective and longitudinal rather than retrospective in nature,
- delineate specific predictor variables for the outcomes it proposes to assess, and
- provide the opportunity for conducting correlational statistical analyses of the variables proposed to be predictive of outcome results.

A large, multicenter study is currently underway in Ontario, Canada that takes into account many of these recommendations in its research design (Durieux-Smith, Eriks-Brophy, Olds, Fitzpatrick, Clifford, Gaines, Moran, & Scram, in progress). The goal of the study is to examine outcomes of a recently implemented provincial neonatal hearing screening program through documenting prospectively a wide range of outcomes of screened and unscreened children from the ages of 12 months to 5 years. In addition to examining the different routes to identification of permanent hearing loss in children in Ontario, the study will:

- determine whether children who are identified early demonstrate better oral communication development and social and adaptive functioning than children identified later;
- compare the development of children with hearing loss to a control group of hearing children in the areas of speech, language, social, and cognitive functioning; and
- examine those factors that may predict positive outcomes in children who are deaf or hard of hearing.

The study combines parent questionnaires and standardized testing and incorporates a well-defined control group. All participants are enrolled in programs that are clearly identified as AVT and are being tested prospectively at 12, 18, 24, 36, 48, and 60 months using a set of standardized measures with well-established psychometric properties. The research is being carried out in two large urban centers in Ontario and is supported by numerous partner agencies that provide AVT intervention to the participating children and aid in the recruitment of participating families. A total of 150 children who are deaf or hard of hearing and 75 control children will be recruited to participate in the research. Intervention approach is a well-controlled variable in the inclusion criteria, ensuring that the findings with respect to outcomes will be generalizable to a wide range of children who receive AVT. This study should provide the strongest and most convincing Class II evidence in favor of AVT of any research carried out to date.

Methodological Challenges

There are numerous methodological challenges to conducting outcomes research that can generate sufficiently high levels of evidence in favor of AVT as an intervention approach. These include, among others, the small number of children who are deaf or hard of hearing enrolled in an AVT program in any given geographical area; the variety of factors that influence intervention outcomes, including family involvement, the cultural and language background of the family, and the skill of the individual therapist; and individual variables related to the children themselves, such as degree of hearing loss, level of cognitive functioning, and temperament. Designing research studies examining the outcomes of AVT that can control for such variables is therefore an enormously difficult task.

To overcome these limitations, the development of collaborative, multicenter research projects may be the most effective method of obtaining the high degree of scientific rigor required for strong outcome evidence. In order to accomplish this, it may be advantageous to engage in a discipline-wide discussion regarding the aspects of functioning that might constitute the strongest possible evidence in favor of AVT and the methods through which these data might be collected. A preliminary list of such issues is presented in Figure 10.1. This discussion could include the various skill domains that should be comprised in the assessment of outcome, the child and family variables that might need to be controlled in order to reduce potential bias in the findings, and the importance of acknowledging cultural, language, and socio-economic factors as significant potential variables in the examination of outcomes of AVT. A preliminary list of specific questions to consider in conducting such research is provided in Figure 10.2.

We have a responsibility to document that AVT works, not only to satisfy the demands of policy makers, employers, health insurance agencies, and the children and families we serve, but also for ourselves. The debate regarding the effectiveness of our work has raged for too long. The pressures and demands to demonstrate objective, scientifically rigorous outcomes related to AVT are

Figure 10.1 Issues for Discussion

- The aspects of functioning that might provide the strongest possible evidence in favor of AVT
- The skill domains to be included in assessment of outcome
- The measures that might most effectively be used to assess outcome in children across a wide range of ages and language abilities
- The child and family variables that might need to be controlled to reduce bias in the findings
- The importance of recognizing cultural, second-language, and socio-economic factors as potential influences in the examination of outcome
- The establishment of collaborative, multicenter research projects to circumvent the limitations of previous research and to obtain the highest degree of scientific rigor possible for strong outcome evidence in favor of AVT

Figure 10.2 Questions to Consider

- Which domains are essential to measure?
- How do we want to measure outcome?
- Standardized assessments allow comparisons to peers without a hearing impairment. Do we want to specify which standardized tests to use to facilitate collaboration and comparison of results across centers? (See, e.g., discussion in Rhoades, 2003.)
- How do we deal with cultural bias in standardized assessments?
- What do we do for children whose language levels do not yet permit the use of standardized measures?
- Are standardized assessments enough? Questionnaires allow collection of a range of information not available from the standardized tests but are not objective, do not generally permit statistical analysis, and are more difficult to summarize. Nevertheless, not all domains are measurable through standardized assessment tools.
- Are there tools that do not yet exist that are needed in order to examine outcomes of AVT?
- How do we deal with the impact of individual variables that we believe have an impact on outcome, such as:
  - access to services (e.g., rural, urban)
  - parental involvement
  - technological advances (e.g., cochlear implants)
  - multicultural issues
  - school factors, including resource support
  - socioeconomic factors

increasing. It is time we take a proactive approach to resolving the issues, by organizing, participating in, and conducting objective, empirical research that will demonstrate categorically and definitively that AVT is a viable and effective communication option for children who are deaf or hard of hearing.

REFERENCES

Agency for Healthcare Research and Quality. (2001, October 23). "US Preventive Services Task Force reviews evidence on newborn hearing screening." Press release. Retrieved September 3, 2005. <www.ahrq.gov/news/press/pr2001/newbornpr.htm>.

American Academy of Neurology, Therapeutics and Technology Assessment Subcommittee. (1994). "Assessment: Melodic intonation therapy." *Neurology, 44,* 566–568.

Anderson, K. (1989). *Screening Instrument for Targeting Educational Risk (SIFTER).* Little Rock, AR: Educational Audiology Association Products Manager.

Auditory-Verbal International (AVI). (1991). "Auditory-verbal position statement." Alexandria, VA: Author.

Beattie, R. (1990). *Pragmatic Language Competencies of Hearing-Impaired Preschool Children.* Unpublished doctoral dissertation. Edmonton: University of Alberta.

Carney, A., & Moeller, M.P. (1998). "Treatment efficacy: Hearing loss in children." *Journal of Speech, Language, and Hearing Research, 41,* S61–S84.

Carrow-Woolfolk, E. (1995). *Oral and Written Language Scales.* Circle Pines, MN: American Guidance Service.

Coyte, P. (1992). "Outcome measurement in speech-language pathology and audiology." *Journal of Speech-Language Pathology and Audiology, 16*(4), 275–286.

Duncan, J. (2001). "Conversational skills of children with hearing loss and children with normal hearing in an integrated setting." *The Volta Review, 101*(4), 193–211.

Durieux-Smith, A., Eriks-Brophy, A., Olds, J., Fitzpatrick, E., Clifford, T., Gaines, R., Moran, L., & Scram, D. (In progress). "The impact of screening and case finding on the functional status of children with a hearing impairment." Research study supported by the Canadian Language and Literacy Research Network and the Masonic Foundation.

Durieux-Smith, A., Eriks-Brophy, A., Olds, J., Fitzpatrick, E., Duquette, S., & Whittingham, J. (2001). "Facilitating the integration of children and youth with hearing loss." *The Listener.* Toronto: The Learning to Listen Foundation.

Enderby, P. (1997). *Therapy Outcome Measures.* San Diego: Singular Publishing.

Enderby, P., & Emerson, J. (1995). *Does Speech and Language Therapy Work?* London: Whurr Publications.

Fineburg, H. (1990). *The Quest for Causality in Health Services Research. Research Methodology: Strengthening Causal Interpretations of Nonexperimental Data.* Rockville, MD: Agency for Health Care Policy and Research, US Department of Health and Human Services.

Fougeyrollas, P., Cloutier, R., Bergeron, H., Côté, J., & Michel, G. (1998). *Classification québécoise: Processus de production du handicap.* Lac St. Charles, QC: Réseau international sur le processus de production du handicap.

Frattali, C. (1998). "Outcomes measurement: Definitions, dimensions, and perspectives." In C. Frattali (Ed.), *Measuring Outcomes in Speech-Language Pathology* (pp. 1–27). New York: Thieme.

Goldberg, D., & Flexer, C. (1993). "Outcome survey of auditory-verbal graduates: A study of clinical efficacy." *Journal of the American Academy of Audiology, 4,* 189–200.

Goldberg, D., & Flexer, C. (2001). "Auditory-verbal graduates: Outcome survey of clinical efficacy." *Journal of the American Academy of Audiology, 12,* 406–414.

Hedrick, D., Prather, E., & Tobin, A. (1984). *Sequenced Inventory of Communication Development.* Seattle: University of Washington Press.

Holland, A., Fromm, D., DeRuyter, F., & Stein, M. (1996). "Efficacy of treatment for aphasia: A brief synopsis." *Journal of Speech and Hearing Research, 39*(5), S27–S36.

Rhoades, E.A. (2001). "Language progress with an auditory-verbal approach for young children with a hearing loss." *International Pediatrics, 16*(1), 1–7.

Rhoades, E.A., & Chisholm, T.H. (2000). "Global language progress with an Auditory-Verbal therapy approach for children who are deaf or hard of hearing." *The Volta Review, 102,* 5–25.

Roberts, S.B., & Rickards, R.W. (1994a). "A survey of graduates of an Australian integrated auditory/oral preschool. Part 1: Amplification usage, communication practices and speech intelligibility." *The Volta Review, 96,* 185–204.

Roberts, S.B., & Rickards, R.W. (1994b). "A survey of graduates of an Australian integrated auditory/oral preschool. Part 2: Academic achievement, utilization of support services and friendship patterns." *The Volta Review, 96,* 207–236.

Robertson, L., & Flexer, C. (1993). "Reading development: A parent survey of children with hearing impairment who developed speech and language through the auditory-verbal method." *The Volta Review, 95,* 253–261.

Wray, D., Flexer, C., & Vaccaro, V. (1997). "Classroom performance of children who are deaf or hard of hearing and who learned spoken language through the auditory-verbal approach: An evaluation of treatment efficacy." *The Volta Review, 99,* 107–119.

Zimmerman, I., Steiner, V., and Pond R. (1992). *The Preschool Language Scale—3.* San Antonio, TX: Psychological Corp.

APPENDIX A

Recommended Protocol for Audiological Assessment, Hearing Aid Evaluation, and Cochlear Implant Monitoring*

The following protocol is intended to support programs for early detection of hearing impairment, which should include medical evaluation/clearance for hearing aid use for infants and children. It is also a guide to appropriate ongoing audiology services in Auditory-Verbal therapy programs. This protocol can be used to achieve and maintain optimal use of residual hearing to access spoken language. The test battery approach to audiological assessment is well recognized and is recommended in this protocol. This means that no single test should be used in isolation to define and describe the nature and extent of a hearing loss. Ideally, every auditory-verbal program will have on-site audiological services, but, regardless of setting, close collaboration of audiologists, therapists, and parents is essential. Parents should be present and participate in all assessments as well as in Auditory-Verbal therapy sessions. The Auditory-Verbal therapist should also be present at audiological assessments whenever possible or send a report identifying his/her questions or concerns regarding the child's hearing and amplification.

Procedures to be included in all assessments regardless of child's age:

- Medical/Developmental History
- Parent Observation Report
- Otoscopic Inspection
- Acoustic Immittance, including tympanometry with high-frequency probe tone and acoustic reflex tests

Audiological Diagnostic Assessment:

I. Auditory Brainstem Response (ABR) Assessment

a. Threshold search to click stimulus in 10 dB steps with a 0 dB (no stimulus) comparison

b. Comparison of ABR by rarefaction clicks and condensation clicks presented at 80–90 dB nHL using a click rate >30 seconds to rule out auditory neuropathy

c. Threshold search to a 500 Hz and 3000 Hz tone pip

d. Bone conduction ABR using click stimuli

ABR should not stand alone for diagnostic purposes. Absence of a detectable ABR does not necessarily indicate an absence of usable residual hearing. Special imaging (CT scan and/or MRI) may be required to rule out absence or abnormality of the cochlear structures, such as a Mondini dysplasia or enlarged vestibular aqueduct.

II. Otoacoustic emissions (TEOAE and/or DPOAE).

III. Behavioral Observation Audiometry (BOA) using speech as well as 500–2000 Hz warbled tones and/or narrowband noise, by air conduction and bone conduction to identify minimum response levels and to obtain startle response.

IV. Evaluation of auditory skill status and tests of speech perception.

V. Discussion of results, questions, and recommendations with parents.

VI. Written report of all tests and results, including:
   a. Descriptions of test procedures, conditions of testing, and reliability estimate
   b. A complete audiogram with symbol key, calibration, and stimuli identified, as well as plotting results on a "Familiar Sounds" audiogram to support parent/teacher counseling
   c. Identification of hearing device, including manufacturer, model, output and response, compression or special feature settings, earmold specifications, and quality of fit
   d. Copies to parents, primary care provider, Auditory-Verbal therapist and other health/education providers as requested in writing by parents

VII. Referral to medical, otolaryngological, or other resources (genetic counseling, social services, psychology, occupational therapy, etc.) as appropriate.

Amplification Assessment:

I. Electro-acoustic analysis of hearing aids
   a. On day of fitting
   b. Every 30 days at user volume as well as full volume
   c. Upon return from repairs
   d. If parental concerns arise from behavioral observation or listening check

II. Real-Ear-to-Coupler Measures (e.g., Desired Sensation Level [DSL])
   a. To establish fitting parameters for hearing aids using prescriptive methods
   b. To verify instrument settings in order to achieve target gain and output

III. Probe Microphone Measures
   a. To document hearing aid performance at initial fitting
   b. Upon return from repairs
   c. To assess changes in earmold style

IV. Sound Field Aided Response
   a. To demonstrate response to speech for parent education purposes

b. To assess speech perception at average and at soft conversational levels in quiet and in the presence of noise to evaluate the effectiveness of amplification technology
c. Assessment of distance hearing using the Ling Six-Sound Test to demonstrate the range of audibility provided by the technology

NOTE: Functional gain measure is an appropriate verification procedure for bone conduction hearing aids, cochlear implants, and vibrotactile aids only. Verification of amplification requires a real ear to coupler (RECD) measure appropriate for children.

Audiological Monitoring:

- Initial diagnosis and confirmation should be completed as soon as possible but, at the latest, within the first 3 months of life in order to ensure that habilitation is underway by age 6 months.
- Routine evaluation should occur ideally at 4- to 6-week intervals during the first 12–18 months of life and at 3-month intervals through age 3, although new earmolds may need to be obtained more frequently.
- Assessment at 6-month intervals from age 4 is appropriate if progress is satisfactory.
- Immediate evaluation should be undertaken if parent or caretaker concern is expressed or if behavioral observation by parent, therapist, or teacher expresses concern, or if behavioral observation suggests a change in hearing or device function.

More frequent evaluation is appropriate when middle ear disease is chronic or recurrent or when risk factors for progressive hearing loss are present.

Cochlear Implant Monitoring:

- When a child does not achieve optimal access to spoken language through conventional amplification by age 9 months, information should be provided regarding cochlear implant technology, including benefits and risks as documented in published, peer-reviewed literature along with referral to a cochlear implant center.
- Following initial mapping of a cochlear implant, re-mapping should be conducted on the schedule recommended by the cochlear implant team given the child's age, device implanted, number of electrodes activated, and additional individual considerations.
- Even if a map can be programmed to achieve optimal access to the speech spectrum within the first 3 months of use, ongoing evaluation at 6-month intervals for at least 3 years after initial stimulation is recommended.
- Routine assessment of cochlear implant performance should occur at 6- to 12-month intervals if progress is satisfactory.
- Immediate evaluation is recommended if parent, caregiver, and/or therapist observe behavior suggesting a change in performance or express concern regarding device function.

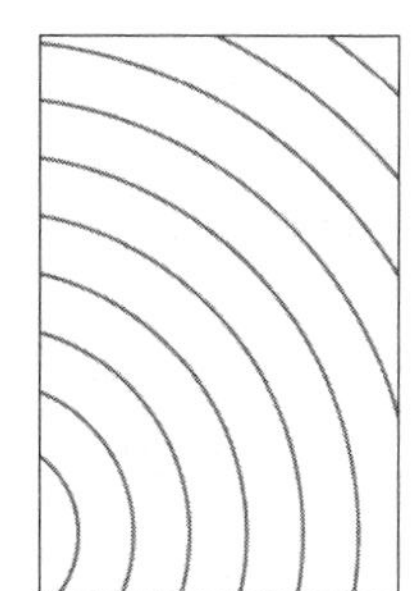

APPENDIX B

Professional Code of Ethics*

PREAMBLE

The AG Bell Academy for Listening and Spoken Language® (Academy) is dedicated to the purpose of ensuring that all children with hearing impairment who have the potential to develop speech and language through the optimal use of amplified residual hearing have the opportunity to do so. Establishing the highest standards of professional integrity based on accepted ethical principles and practice is vital to the fulfillment of this purpose.

This **Professional Code of Ethics** applies to those members who are responsible for the proper delivery of (re)habilitative services to such clients. The **Professional Code of Ethics** also seeks to protect persons served and to ensure the integrity of recognized auditory-verbal practices. Professional conduct of a member that is in violation of the spirit and purpose of this Code shall be considered unethical. Failure to specify any particular responsibility or practice in this Code should not be construed as denial of the existence of such responsibilities or practices. Professional members are hereinafter referred to as "individuals."

The fundamentals of ethical conduct are described by **Principles of Ethics and Rules of Ethics** as they relate to responsibility to persons served, to the public, and to the professions engaged in the provision of auditory-verbal services.

Principles of Ethics, aspirational and inspirational in nature, form the underlying moral bases for the **Professional Code of Ethics**. Individuals shall observe these principles as affirmative obligations under all conditions of professional activity. **Rules of Ethics** are specific statements of minimally acceptable professional conduct or of prohibitions and are applicable to all individuals.

Principle I:

Individuals shall agree with the purpose, philosophy and working principles of the Academy. Individuals shall honor their responsibility to make fully available to all children with hearing impairment those aspects of auditory-verbal practice that encourage habitual and maximal use of amplified residual hearing, and are known to have positive effects upon the human auditory system and the subsequent development of verbal communication.

---

* Reprinted with permission from the AG Bell Academy for Listening and Spoken Language®.

Rules

- Individuals shall support programs for the early detection and identification of hearing impairment and the auditory management of infants, toddlers and children so identified.
- Individuals shall seek to provide the earliest possible use of the most appropriate technology in order that their clients obtain the maximum auditory benefits possible.
- Individuals shall seek to instruct primary caregivers in ways to provide optimal acoustic stimulation within meaningful contexts and support the development of the most favorable auditory learning environments for the acquisition of spoken language.
- Individuals shall seek to integrate listening into the child's total personality.
- Individuals shall support the view that communication is a social act and seek to improve verbal (spoken) interaction within the typical social dyad of infant/child and primary care-giver(s). Parents are viewed as the primary models for the development of a child's spoken language with the provision that one-to-one teaching is critical to communication development.
- Individuals shall work to ensure that the child's emerging speech will be self-monitored through audition to the greatest possible extent.
- Individuals shall use natural sequential patterns of auditory, perceptual, linguistic and cognitive stimulation to encourage the emergence of listening, speech and language abilities.
- Individuals shall make ongoing evaluation and prognosis of the development of listening skills an integral part of the (re)habilitative process.
- Individuals shall support mainstreaming/integration of children with hearing impairment into regular education classes with appropriate support services and to the fullest extent possible.

Principle II:

Individuals shall honor their responsibility to hold paramount the welfare of persons served professionally.

Rules

- Individuals shall maintain high standards of professional competence in rendering services, providing only those professional services for which they are qualified by education and experience.
- Individuals shall provide professional services with honesty and compassion and shall respect the dignity, worth, and rights of those served.
- Individuals shall use every resource, including referral when appropriate, to ensure that the highest quality service is provided.
- Individuals shall not discriminate in the delivery of professional services on the basis of race, sex, religion, national origin, or sexual orientation.
- Individuals shall provide accurate information about the nature and management of hearing impairment and about the services and products offered.

- Individuals shall evaluate the effectiveness of services rendered and of products dispensed and shall provide services or dispense products only when benefit can reasonably be expected.
- Individuals shall maintain adequate records of professional services rendered and products dispensed and shall allow access to these records when appropriately authorized.
- Individuals shall not reveal, without authorization, any professional or personal information about the person served professionally, unless required by law to do so.
- Individuals may make a statement of prognosis, but shall not guarantee results, mislead, or misinform families or person served.
- Individuals shall recognize the right of parents to select the type of (re)habilitative, communicative or educational system or program they wish for their child.
- Individuals shall charge only for services rendered. They shall not misrepresent, in any fashion, services rendered or products dispensed.

Principle III:

Individuals shall honor their responsibility to achieve and maintain the highest level or professional competence.

Rules

- Individuals engaging in any aspect of the professions shall perform within the scope of their competence, education, training and experience.
- Individuals shall maintain professional competence, including participation in continuing education.
- Individuals shall provide appropriate supervision and assume full responsibility for services delegated to their staff.
- Individuals shall ensure that all equipment used in the provision of services is in proper working order and is properly calibrated.

Principle IV:

Individuals shall honor their responsibilities to the public through providing information and education and the development of services for unmet needs.

Rules

- Individuals shall not misrepresent their credentials, competence, education, training or experience.
- Individuals shall not participate in professional activities that constitute a conflict of interest.
- Individuals shall not misrepresent diagnostic information, services rendered, or products dispensed or engage in any scheme or artifice to defraud in connection with obtaining payment or reimbursement for such services or products.

- Individuals' statements to the public shall provide accurate information about the nature and management of hearing disorders, about the professions, and about professional services.

Principle V:

Individuals shall honor their responsibilities to their own professions, and maintain good relationships with, among others, AVI colleagues, members of allied professions, parents and students. Individuals shall uphold the dignity and autonomy of the professions, maintain harmonious interprofessional and intraprofessional relationships, and accept the professions' self-imposed standards.

Rules

- Individuals shall honor their responsibilities to professional colleagues by sharing, through workshops and other professional activities, information, techniques and strategies which stimulate the development of residual hearing and verbal communication.
- Individuals shall inform colleagues and the public in a manner consistent with the highest professional standards about products and services they have developed.
- Individuals shall assign credit to those who have contributed to a publication, presentation, or product.
- Individuals shall not use professional or commercial affiliations in any way that would mislead or limit services to persons served professionally.
- Individuals shall provide professional services by exercising independent professional judgment, regardless of referral source or prescription.
- Individuals shall not violate these Principles and Rules, nor attempt to circumvent them.

Amplified residual hearing is the auditory potential which can be accessed in the child with hearing impairment. For the purpose of this Code of Ethics, the term "amplified residual hearing" refers to any and all means: mechanical, electrical, or other, that can be employed to give meaning to sound.

For the purposes of The Code of Ethics, misrepresentation includes any untrue statements or statements that are likely to mislead. Misrepresentation also includes the failure to state any information that is material and that ought, in fairness, to be considered.

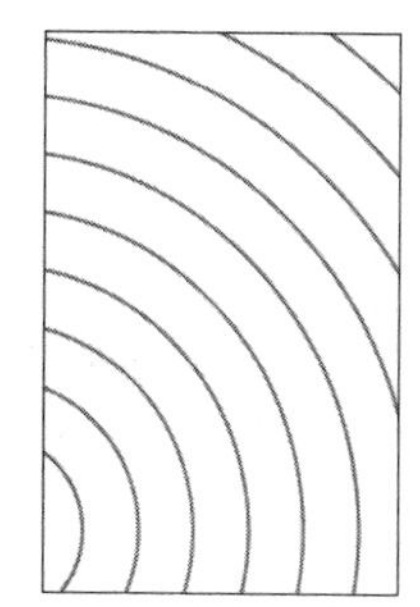

APPENDIX C

Genetic Counseling and Deafness: What Is It and How Can It Help Me?

Wendy S. Meschino, M.D., FRCPC, FCCMG

Individuals with hearing loss and their families are referred to genetics clinics in two common situations. The first occurs when parents of a child with severe to profound deafness wish to know the risks of recurrence in their future children. In the second scenario, a couple who are deaf may want to know the chances of hearing loss in their offspring.

Often prior to or during the first appointment in the genetics clinic, important information about the affected individual is collected. This might include family history, pregnancy history, audiological records, and hospital and medical records. During the session, a physical examination by the geneticist and possible laboratory testing may be necessary before definitive genetic counseling session can be provided.

Perhaps the best definition of genetic counseling is given by the well-known geneticist, Peter S. Harper (1998):

> Genetic counseling is the process by which patients or relatives at risk of a disorder that may be hereditary are advised of the consequences of the disorder, the probability of developing and transmitting it and of ways in which this may be prevented, avoided or ameliorated.

WHAT CAUSES DEAFNESS?

Although a large portion of deafness in children is inherited, it is important to realize that in a sizable proportion, the cause is environmental and is associated with a low risk of recurrence in future children. It is therefore important to search for external factors that may have caused the hearing loss. These include viral infections during pregnancy, such as rubella (German measles), and cytomegalovirus (CMV), a common viral infection in young women. Prematurity, severe jaundice, birth injury, and lack of oxygen at birth are also predisposing causes. Other causes of acquired hearing loss after birth include meningitis, head injury, middle ear disease, and exposure to certain medications.

DEFINING THE NATURE OF THE HEARING LOSS

Other factors to help differentiate the type of hearing loss and the possible inheritance pattern include:

- *Is the hearing loss congenital (present at birth) or did it develop later in life?* Inherited hearing loss is usually present at birth, but some forms develop in childhood or adulthood.
- *Is the hearing loss primarily conductive (problem in the external or middle ear), sensorineural (affecting the cochlea or nerve), or a mixed pattern?*
- *Is the hearing loss complete or is it present in a milder form? Does it affect one ear or both?*
- *Does the hearing loss remain at a constant level or is it progressive?*
- *Are there any other features in the affected individual?* (i.e., birth defects; developmental handicaps; growth, skin, eye, thyroid, heart, or kidney problems)
- *Are other family members affected? Are the parents blood relatives?* (e.g., cousins)

After an assessment of these factors, the geneticist will attempt to provide the patient and his or her family with an understanding of the probable pattern of inheritance.

HOW IS DEAFNESS INHERITED?

In severe to profound, congenital, sensorineural deafness, half of all cases have been estimated as due to genetic causes. Environmental causes, such as meningitis and prenatally acquired infections, account for 25%. In the remaining quarter, the cause is unknown. Of the genetic cases, the majority are due to a recessive pattern of inheritance. This means that the deaf child inherits one copy of the altered gene for deafness from each parent.

The parents, who have normal hearing, are called carriers; each has one gene for hearing loss and one normal gene arranged in a pair. Carrier parents face a 25% risk of having a child who is hearing impaired in each pregnancy (Figure 1).

A smaller proportion of genetic cases are inherited in a dominant pattern. This means that a deaf parent, who has one altered copy of a deafness gene, faces a 50–50 chance of passing on the condition to his or her children in each pregnancy (Figure 2).

In partial nerve deafness or late-onset forms of hearing loss, genetic causes are also important, with a higher proportion due to dominant inheritance. Importantly in this group, the severity of the hearing loss can vary markedly among family members. Therefore, careful audiological testing is helpful to rule out subtle hearing loss in relatives of an affected individual.

Rarely, deafness may follow a different pattern of inheritance. For example, an altered gene may be passed on from a hearing mother to her sons. On average, half of the sons will be deaf and half will be hearing (X-linked inheritance). In mitochondrial inheritance, only the mother can pass on the altered gene to children of either sex.

A number of special features or investigations may be helpful in detecting genetic conditions in which deafness is one component. These include:

- patches of white hair or eyes of different colour (Waardenburg syndrome);
- severe short-sightedness, cleft palate, and arthritis (Stickler syndrome);
- night blindness and vision loss (Usher syndrome)—eye examination;
- goiter (enlarged thyroid) and Mondini malformation (Pendred syndrome)—CT scan of temporal bone in the skull;
- fainting episodes (Jervell and Lange-Nielsen)—electrocardiogram;
- kidney disease (Alport syndrome)—urinalysis;
- diabetes, followed by deafness (mitochondrial gene)—DNA test.

Other studies may be warranted, depending on the clinical picture.

Figure 1 Autosomal Recessive Inheritance

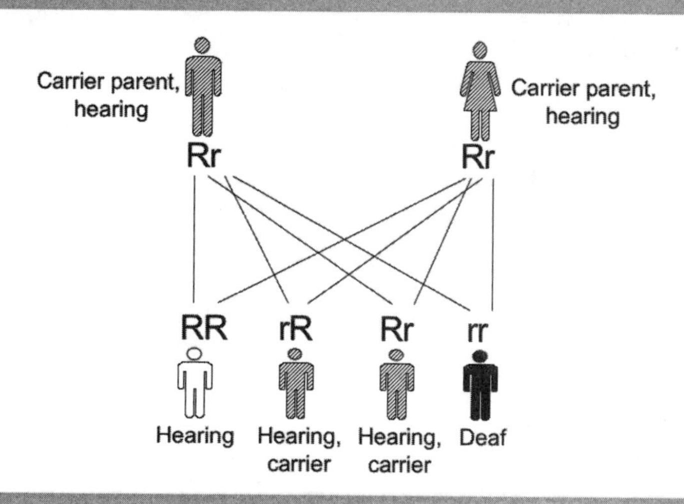

Figure 2 Autosomal Dominant Inheritance

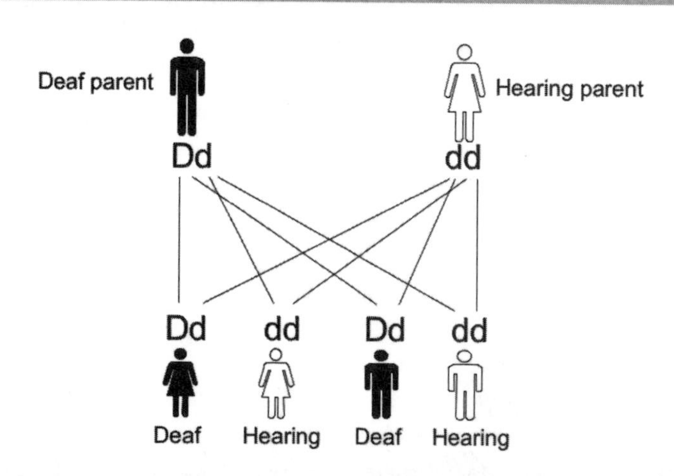

It is estimated that several hundred genes are implicated in causing deafness. In recent years, remarkable progress has been made in discovering many of these genes. Seventy percent of genetic cases are not associated with other medical problems; in this group a gene known as GJB2 accounts for half of all cases. Testing in specialized DNA laboratories is available for this gene and a related gene called GJB6. DNA testing is most often ordered through a genetics clinic following a full evaluation of the individual.

In summary, evaluation of an individual in a family for genetic forms of hearing loss is complex and may be time consuming. Nevertheless, the information obtained may be of major importance to the individual or family and may have implications for future family planning.

REFERENCES

Harper, P.S. (1998). *Practical Genetic Counselling* (5th ed.). London: Butterworth–Heinemann.

FURTHER READING

ACMG statement from Genetic Evaluation of Congenital Hearing Loss Expert Panel. (2002). "Genetics evaluation guidelines for the etiologic diagnosis of congenital hearing loss." *Genetics in Medicine* 4, 162–171.

Smith, R.J.H., Green, G.E., & Van Camp, G. (2003). "Hereditary hearing loss and deafness overview." In GeneReviews at GeneTests: Medical Genetics Information Resource (database online). Retrieved December 1, 2005. <http://www.genetests.org>.

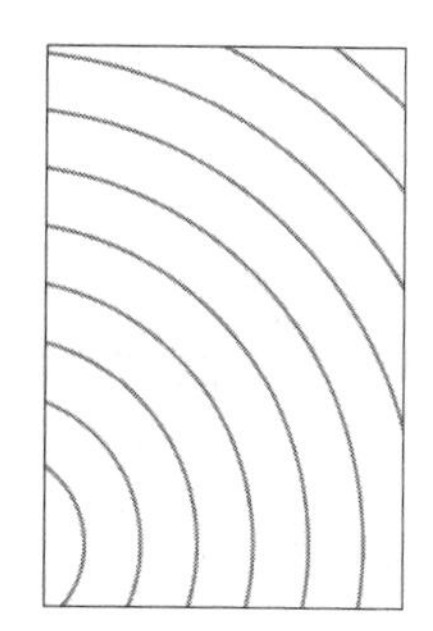

APPENDIX D

Sensory Integration

Ellen Yack, B.Sc.O.T.

The theory and practice of sensory integration, as developed by occupational therapist A. Jean Ayres, has contributed to the understanding of sensory motor development in all children. It also has had a significant impact on the assessment and treatment of children with a variety of special needs, including children who are hearing impaired.

WHAT IS SENSORY INTEGRATION

Sensory integration is a process controlled by the central nervous system that allows the brain to take in, sort, and organize sensory information from the environment. The flow of sensory information to the brain needs to be well organized and integrated to allow natural development. Sensory information about the body and gravity, for example, allows the toddler to conquer gravity and walk independently. The basic functions of sensory integration are mature by 8 to 10 years of age, but are constantly being refined (Ayres 1972, 1979). Sensory integration dysfunction occurs when the brain is not effectively processing or organizing the flow of sensory information from the body and environment.

Most human beings experience sight, sound, smell, taste, touch (pressure, temperature, pain, texture), proprioception (sensory information from muscles, tendons, and joints, which is vital for development of fine and gross motor skills), and vestibular sensations (information about movement, gravity, and changing head positions, which is critical in motor development). The organization of touch, proprioception, and vestibular sensations are the primary foci of sensory integration theory.

SENSORY INTEGRATION DYSFUNCTION AND CHILDREN WHO ARE HEARING IMPAIRED

The efficiency of the central nervous system to integrate sensory information varies greatly among individuals. Sensory integration dysfunction occurs when the brain is not efficiently processing or organizing sensory information. Definitive diagnosis of sensory integration dysfunction is not possible, but hypotheses are made based on standardized tests of vestibular, tactile, proprioceptive, and motor function; observations of quality of movement and interaction with the environment; and review of developmental history.

Children who are hearing impaired have an increased incidence of sensory integration dysfunction. This is likely because the hearing mechanism is so closely linked to the vestibular system (Horak, Shumway-Cook, Crowe, & Black, 1988; Potter & Silverman, 1984). It is estimated that 49% of children with mixed etiology (sensorineural or conductive hearing impairments) have some form of vestibular dysfunction, and the incidence is 95% in children with acquired hearing loss (Arnvig, 1955).

Some children who are hearing impaired may have some form of sensory integration dysfunction that has no relation to their hearing status, but has a significant impact on the development of communication skills. A child who is sensitive to light tactile stimulation may have great difficulty accommodating hearing aids. A child who has impaired proprioception may exhibit poor coordination and poor motor planning skills.

SIGNS OF SENSORY INTEGRATION DYSFUNCTION

The following are motor and behavioral signs that may suggest a child is experiencing some form of sensory integration dysfunction:

- avoidance of balance-related activities, such as unnatural fear of falling or heights, difficulty walking on uneven surfaces, or dislike of having head upside down;
- discomfort with movement-related activities, such as swings;
- delayed gross motor skills and/or fine motor skills, with difficulty learning new motor tasks. Motor skills may vary daily. The child often requires an excessive amount of energy and concentration to complete motor tasks and may become easily frustrated when presented with new motor tasks;
- difficulty judging physical space, such as being unable to walk down center of hall;
- avoidance of light touch, especially around face; the child may be distressed about haircuts, being washed and dressed, or certain textures of clothing and food. May become aggressive when frequently touched;
- floppy or awkward appearance;
- fatigue with physical activity and difficulty attending to tasks;
- dislike and avoidance of messy play or being barefoot, especially in sand and grass.

INTERVENTION

An occupational therapy assessment may help determine whether a child is experiencing sensory integration dysfunction. Depending on the degree of dysfunction, regular treatment sessions may be recommended. Treatment attempts to provide controlled sensory motor experiences aimed at enhancing the processing and organization of sensory information. Management strategies for home and school use are also provided and depend upon the nature of the dysfunction. Knowledge of some of these management strategies may be beneficial for professionals and parents of children who are hearing impaired.

STRATEGIES TO USE WITH CHILDREN WITH SENSORY INTEGRATION DYSFUNCTION

1. Light touch excites any individual and can be particularly uncomfortable for a child who is tactile defensive. When touching a child during therapy, light touch needs to be avoided to allow for enhanced concentration on tasks.
2. When a child is very excited, physically restless, or is having difficulty concentrating, deep touch pressure on the head or shoulders can help to relax the nervous system.
3. When seated to work at a table, the child needs to be well supported, with feet firmly on the floor or on some form of foot rest.
4. A desensitization program around the ear areas may be required during introduction of hearing aid wear.

REFERENCES

Arnvig, J. (1955). "Vestibular function in deafness and severe hardness of hearing." *Acta Otolaryngological, 4,* 283–288.

Ayres, A.J. (1972). *Sensory Integration and Learning Disorders.* Los Angeles: Western Psychological Services.

Ayres, A.J. (1979). *Sensory Integration and the Child.* Los Angeles: Western Psychological Services.

Horak, F., Shumway-Cook, A., Crowe, T., & Black, F. (1988). "Vestibular function and motor proficiency of children with impaired hearing or with learning disability and motor impairments." *Developmental Medicine and Child Neurology, 30,* 64–79.

Potter, C., & Silverman, L. (1984). "Characteristics of vestibular function and static balance skills in deaf children." *Physical Therapy, 64,* 1071–1075.

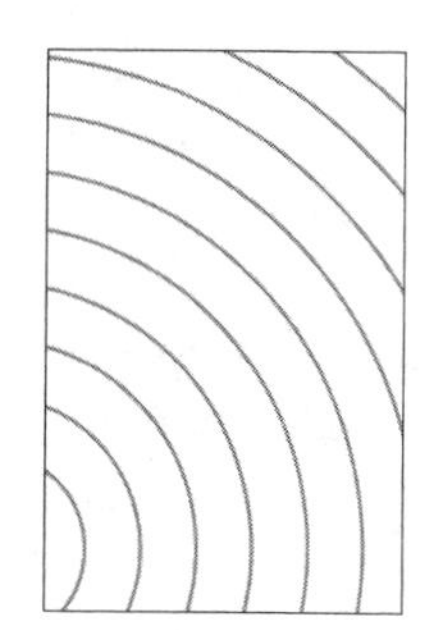

APPENDIX E

The Six-Sound Test*

Daniel Ling, O.C., Ph.D.

The reason for this test, to which children can learn to respond in less than a minute, is that parents and professionals need to determine whether a child's audition is at least minimally adequate hearing for speech. Hearing aids and cochlear implants should elevate the intensity levels of sounds across the complete frequency range of speech. They should provide comfortable and effective listening levels so that as many as possible (preferably all) of the cues involved in speech perception and speech production are audible to most children who are hearing impaired. This is not always the case. Hearing aids frequently fail to provide optimal amplification and cochlear implants are sometimes inappropriately mapped.

I devised *The Six-Sound Test* to provide a speedy and face-valid check on children's ability to *detect* sounds across the whole frequency range of speech. The test can also be used to check whether they are able to *identify* each of the six sounds. The test checks the integrity of all levels of the child's auditory system, beginning at the microphone of the hearing aid or cochlear implant and ending at the brain.

Both forms of the test involve a professional or a parent saying the six speech sounds, one at a time in random order. The test can be administered either by a male or by a female. The children should be able, in real life, to hear both equally well. While the pitch of voices may differ, the components of the sounds that permit the identification and comprehension of speech sounds are sufficiently close for the purpose of this basic test. (If they were not closely similar, males and females would not be able to understand each other's spoken language. Whatever difficulty men may have in understanding women or *vice versa*, it is unlikely to relate to the acoustics of speech.)

In the *detection* form of the test, the sounds are presented at a conversational level from different distances as described below. Young children can respond by playing a "go game"—placing an object in a box or putting a ring on a stick as soon as they *detect* the speech sound presented. In the *detection* form of the test, care must be taken to avoid presenting the sounds rhythmically, because children are then likely to respond in time with the presentation and thus provide false positive responses. Older children can respond when they *detect* the sound presented by raising a hand or saying "yes." In the *identification* form of the test, children who have adequate speech simply imitate the sound presented when they hear it.

The focus of the test is on perception in the different regions of the speech frequency range from the lowest voiced sounds to the highest unvoiced sounds. The sounds selected, from low to high, are /**m**/ as in *me,* /**oo**/ as in *two,* /**ah**/ as in *aha!,* /**ee**/ as in *she,* /**sh**/ as in *fish,* and /**ss**/ as in *us.* To control for duration, we use continuant sounds—those that can be made as long or as short as the tester finds necessary. To control for intensity, the test is administered in a normal conversational level from either one meter (the average distance normally maintained between adult and child in one-on-one interaction) and three meters (the average distance for interactions in a group). Sounds in an acoustically treated room vary in intensity by about 6 dB each time distance between talker and listener is doubled (they are quieter) or halved (they are louder). To use the test at different distances is important, because results obtained at one meter says nothing about what the child hears at greater distances, for example, in a classroom. At no time should the six sounds be presented at levels that are louder or quieter than the tester uses in real life, during normal conversations. To do so invalidates the test.

So, six sounds can be used to check children's ability to detect and to identify the basic speech patterns that occur over the frequency range of speech. Only if voice levels and distance are carefully controlled can the results of this test be valid.

Why these six sounds? Our voices as we speak and sing are among the lowest sounds we produce. So, too, are the resonances associated with the nasal sounds */m/, /n/, and /ng/,* and the low vowels in words such as *shoe* and *toe.* If we can't hear a sound like */m/,* then we are unlikely to be able to hear enough of the other low frequency sounds to develop speech with normal prosody (tune) without vowel errors through hearing.

So, we use the sound /m/ to check whether hearing for low frequencies is adequate. If /m/ cannot be heard at three meters or so, then poor prosody and nasalized speech are likely to develop.

Vowel sounds are very complex. They consist of fundamental voice (the sound made in the larynx when we vocalize) and some higher resonances (called formants) created in the mouth cavity that change in frequency as we move our tongues. Unless the first two of these formants is audible, a listener will not be able to identify the vowel with certainty. The two main formants of /oo/ are both in the low frequency range. The two main formants of /ee/ are at very different frequencies—one is low and the other is high. If the low one cannot be detected, then abnormal sounding voice and inability to hear tunes and sing songs will result.

So, we use the /oo/ vowel to check whether the low end of the vowel formant range can be detected. It also lets us ensure, in tests of identification, that sounds in the frequency range of /oo/ and /m/ are recognized and not confused. If they are, greater emphasis should be placed on listening skills.

The formants in the vowel /ah/ as in the exclamation "Aha!" are at the center of the vowel range, indeed the center of the whole speech range. Central vowels are louder than others because the mouth is wider open in their production. If the /ah/ is inaudible, or inadequately amplified, then unstressed words, particularly those that fall in the center of the speech range, are likely to be missing. Thus instead of hearing all the words in a sentence such as "I went to the park" a child may hear only *"I went park"* and, as a result, develop several grammatical problems. A child who uses hearing aids and has substantial low-frequency hearing can usually detect the vowel /ah/. If this same child can detect the /ah/ but not the /m/ and /oo/ sounds, then either sounds in the low frequency range are under-amplified or sounds in the mid-frequency range are over-amplified. In either case, the hearing aids require adjustment to ensure that all vowels are equally detectable. Over-amplification of the mid-frequency range is suggested when such a child can detect a stage whispered /ah/ at six meters or so. For several reasons, the /ah/ is rarely confused with other vowels in tests involving identification.

So, we present /ah/ to check that the central vowels are audible and neither under- nor over-amplified.

The vowel /ee/ may be detected through the audibility of either the low first formant or the high second formant, which is at the upper end of the frequency range of vowels. Thus, children may respond to /ee/ because they detect either the low formant, the high-formant or both. Their response to the /ee/ must therefore be interpreted by comparing it to their response to other sounds in the test that have components in the same frequency range. It follows that the deductions that can be made relative to the /ee/ are:

1. No response indicates that neither formant can be detected.
2. A response indicates the detection of only the low frequency formant if /oo/ and /m/ can be detected but /sh/ cannot.
3. A response indicates detection of only the high frequency formant if /sh/ can be detected but /m/ and /oo/ cannot.
4. The response indicates the detection of both formants if the /sh/, /oo/ and /m/ can also be detected.
5. It is likely that the /ee/ and possibly other vowels will be nasalized if the /sh/ and /oo/ can be heard but the /m/ cannot be detected.

So, the vowel sound /ee/ is used to check a range of possible problems.

The high and very high sounds in speech are mainly unvoiced plosives or stops like *p, t,* and *k* and the unvoiced fricatives like *sh* and *s, f* and *th.* All of these are relatively quiet sounds. Also, children's hearing loss for high sounds is usually greater than for low sounds. For these reasons high frequency sounds are the most likely to be missed by children who have severe or profound hearing impairment and whose hearing aids or cochlear implants are not well selected and well adjusted (mapped). The test, remember, measures the effectiveness of the transmission of sounds from the microphone of the hearing aids or cochlear implant to the brain. The root of a problem in detecting or identifying sounds could, therefore, be with any link in the auditory chain, for example, in a temporary middle ear infection, a loss of fluid in the cochlea or to the auditory devices that are used. The reasons for any such failure requires further audiological evaluation and, if it persists, perhaps modification of strategies used in teaching or therapy. The high sounds of speech carry most of the information required for the discrimination, identification and comprehension of speech, so ability to detect them is of the utmost importance.

So, the sound /sh/ is used to check whether the moderately high sounds are audible and the unvoiced sound /sss/ to check whether the very high sounds can be detected.

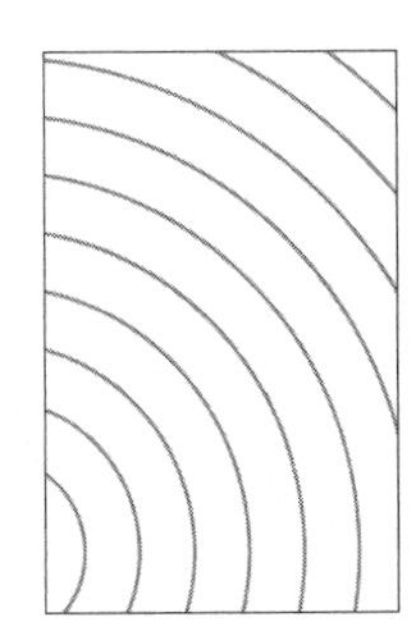

APPENDIX F

Save the Auditory-Verbal Session*

What to do when the session is falling apart and you want to save it from going down the drain.

1. Get up and dance
2. Do some magic tricks
3. Put on some costume jewelry
4. Play with a box of buttons
5. Open a present
6. Eat a cookie
7. Play some music and make some noise
8. Turn out the lights
9. Play with some stickers
10. Have a little party
11. Drop things in colored water
12. Draw a picture
13. Put on some funny hats
14. Read from the "Blank Book"
15. Watch an imaginary TV show
16. Find something in a Feely Bag
17. Open your "treasure chest"
18. Play "Look What I Found"
19. Get out the playdough
20. Go "Fishing"
21. Sit under the table and "do the session"
22. Go on a treasure hunt
23. Make something (arts and crafts activity)
24. Go through a purse full of goodies
25. Play a video or a CD of musical games
26. Put on make-up

---

* Collected from certified Auditory-Verbal therapists worldwide.

27. Paint fingernails
28. Wash toys in warm, soapy water
29. Organize a messy toy box
30. Make a thank-you or birthday card
31. Look at the pictures in a magazine
32. Do a "power point" session
33. Make funny faces and talk with funny voices
34. Play bowling
35. Play some musical instruments or make some
36. Make a mask and decorate it
37. Do a puppet show
38. Blow bubbles
39. Spin a top
40. Play with wind-up toys
41. Go "shopping"
42. Bring out the scotch tape. "Accidentally" tear a piece of "important" paper and fix it before continuing
43. Your dolly or favorite animal is sick, remember? You have to check on it, so get out the band aids and the doctor kit
44. Pretend you are VERY tired and fall asleep. Parent and child will have to wake you up and keep you awake
45. Bring out the flashlights. Pretend it is night
46. Go camping
47. Take out a favorite toy/activity with gusto and conspiratorial excitement. Put it just out of reach. Complete the tasks at hand and THEN play with the toy
48. Spray a little perfume into the air
49. Look out the window. When you have no window, walk to the front door, look outside, see the sun shining on the snow, put your boots on, trudge over the road to the loonie store… and use a coupon you "won" in your last session to buy a treat!
50. Chew some gum and ponder your future

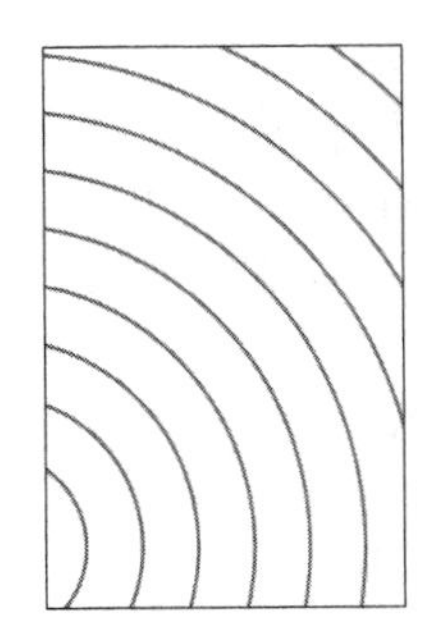

APPENDIX G

A Position on Auditory-Verbal Therapy (AVT) for the School-Aged Child

Ellen A. Rhoades, Ed.S., Cert. AVT®

Given the guiding principles of the auditory-verbal approach (Goldberg, 1997), we know that Auditory-Verbal therapy (AVT) is about primary caregivers taking the principal responsibility for helping their child, who is deaf or hard of hearing, to learn to develop spoken language primarily through listening and to become linguistically competent. The major goal is full assimilation into the mainstream of family, school, and community. Assimilation denotes full inclusion in a "regular" learning environment in which children who are deaf or hard of hearing would not receive support services over and above those typically provided for children with typical hearing, with the exception of assistive listening systems. Full inclusion, then, is an attitude whereby the student who is deaf or hard of hearing is an integral part of the hearing community, and pull-out services are not warranted (Hyde & Power, 2004).

Full inclusion is more than just integration, which is simply the initial, physical process of ensuring that children with and without disabilities are mixed together in the same school. Full inclusion is also more than mainstreaming, which occurs when the child must receive supportive services while being educated within regular learning environments (Rafferty, Piscitelli, & Boettcher, 2003; Hyde & Power, 2004). Full inclusion, then, occurs when the child "fits in" within the typical social and academic life; the child feels engaged and has peers with whom he or she appropriately interacts; and the child functions well within the social context of learning.

Clearly, for assimilation to occur, AVT must also be about creating independent learners who know how to learn by themselves. It seems logical to assume that when the child demonstrates a solid foundation of listening skills and linguistic competency, the professional's role as a certified Auditory-Verbal therapist is complete. According to widely published data (e.g., Boysson-Bardies, 1999; Crystal, Fletcher, & Garman, 1978; Juszcyk, 1998; Pinker, 1994; Rhoades & Chisolm, 2001), linguistic competency is developed when a child attains a language-age equivalency of approximately 4 years. Consequently, it stands to reason that AVT should be provided for the young child who is deaf or hard of hearing for approximately 3 to 5 years (Rhoades, 2003).

Therefore, for the child with a severe to profound hearing loss who has access to soft conversational sound (at approximately 30 dB HL) and for whom auditory-verbal intervention has occurred during the first 3 years of life, AVT can be completed prior to 1st grade. For example, the typical 2-year-old who just begins to learn language through listening can attain a 4-year level of language by 6 years of age. Some children, particularly those not initiating AVT until age 3 or 4, might delay entry into 1st grade to provide time for the child to become linguistically successful enough to cope with 1st-grade instruction.

It is true that a child in Auditory-Verbal therapy, like other children who are hearing impaired, may encounter some difficulties understanding speech over distance and in noise, although to a lesser degree. And, like other children who are hearing impaired, the average child in Auditory-Verbal therapy can benefit immeasurably from using assistive listening systems within the educational environment, perhaps to an even greater degree. Even with all this, the child may still miss some verbal asides or incidental information, again perhaps to a lesser degree than other children who are hearing impaired. However, children in Auditory-Verbal therapy typically learn to read well and, indeed, read frequently. Thus, through the written word, such children often have an advantage over a child with typical hearing. Moreover, as a result of AVT, children have learned how to ask appropriate questions when something is not understood, just as family members have learned the strategies of routinely including the child in conversations.

Like the child with normal hearing, the typical child who "graduates" from AVT will continue to learn language beyond the minimal linguistic competency level. Just as any child eventually becomes communicatively competent by expanding knowledge of complex sentences, by broadening semantic networks, and developing a more sophisticated understanding of pragmatics, so does the child who is in Auditory-Verbal therapy. Such growth occurs over time, as long as expectations remain high and caregivers continue to facilitate independent learning. In fact, for anyone with typical hearing, vocabulary grows continually until at least 90 years of age (Dunn, 1996).

Finally, as with any child, the listening skills of a child in Auditory-Verbal therapy become more sophisticated over time, again, developing well beyond minimal linguistic competency. Listening to multistep directions, figure-ground auditory discrimination, auditory closure, auditory blending, and various types of complex auditory analyses are skills that must be developed as the child matures and is repetitively exposed to these tasks in school. The process of learning these skills is the same process experienced by children with typical hearing; the journey to true communicative competency occurs only after basic linguistic competency is attained. The child who is in Auditory-Verbal therapy can and, indeed, does learn these skills simply because early on there are high expectations from the parents, and the child internalizes these.

Typically, children in Auditory-Verbal therapy learn to own their deafness (Rhoades, 2004). They advocate for themselves, are intrinsically motivated, develop internal discipline, effectively use repair strategies, develop the power of cogent thought processes, and learn to learn. By taking the responsibility for hearing and learning, they effectively adjust to reality. During the first stage of therapy, the Auditory-Verbal therapist as quickly as possible relinquishes ownership of the child's deafness to the primary caregiver. By the time spoken language has been well learned during the final stage of AVT, the primary caregiver, in turn, relinquishes ownership of the child's deafness to the child.

Continuing AVT beyond the preschool years, for the linguistically competent child, can (a) create learned helplessness in families, including both caregivers and child; (b) undermine the family's sense of control and competency; and (c) undermine the child's self-esteem and facilitate dependency on others. It is imperative that auditory-verbal professionals avoid creating these conditions or else they will be accused of adopting, at worst, a "savior complex" or, at best, "convenient compassion."

When a child in Auditory-Verbal therapy becomes a passive learner, it may be because adults have repeatedly rescued or permitted him or her to be mollycoddled in less than ideal learning conditions. Perhaps the child was pre-taught academic concepts that are typically learned within the classroom school day. The passive-learning child may not have experienced failure constructively, and so has yet to suffer the consequences of such. Failure can and should be instructive.

Children in Auditory-Verbal therapy learn to take responsibility for failures as well as successes, and learn how to learn independently. They can listen throughout the school day, even when not hearing their own name called by the teacher who is asking questions of the class. They know how to use a dictionary, how to deduce the meaning of words from context, and how to ask questions when a task or linguistic element is not understood. Children in Auditory-Verbal therapy understand what to do when a task is not understood and make use of effective conversational repair strategies learned during the early years of AVT.

However, for the atypical child in Auditory-Verbal therapy who has co-occurring disorders, or whose deafness was identified later, or who used sign language prior to receiving a cochlear implant, AVT most likely was not implemented during the early years of life. The family with an atypical child can still benefit from the services of Auditory-Verbal therapists, but the services provided will not necessarily be AVT. Instead, the services may be auditory-based with many accommodations made to fit the child's unique needs. Perhaps there will be greater use of the "auditory sandwich" strategy (Koch, 1999) to facilitate listening, or perhaps the child will benefit from daily one-on-one therapy sessions that don't necessarily include the primary caregivers, or perhaps a wider variety of effective multisensory strategies will be employed for facilitating the development of speech and language skills.

Services provided directly to the atypical child are often academic and may include reading assistance, vocabulary enrichment, resource or itinerant teaching, language therapy, speech therapy, aural rehabilitation, auditory training, or listening therapy. These support services may warrant the pull-out model by appropriately trained personnel. For example, an educational audiologist can help classroom teachers provide an educational environment where students who are hearing impaired will have optimal auditory access to information in order to maximize their educational achievement. A professional other than an Auditory-Verbal therapist may also be needed to take some ownership of hearing technology problems, particularly for the atypical child in Auditory-Verbal therapy who is not able to report accurately on the status of the equipment.

Another example is that of the child with a cochlear implant whose other ear is subsequently implanted (sequential bilateral cochlear implantation). This child may greatly benefit from listening therapy so that maximum binaural hearing can develop as a result of bilateral hearing. Regardless, the use of appropriate terminology in service delivery is highly recommended, particularly since there may be well-qualified rehabilitation professionals already providing these various support services in many communities.

While there is ample justification for these services for many children (Galvin, Sarant, & Cowan, 1997; Hull, 1992; Koch, 1999; Rhoades & Jovanovic, 2002; Stout & Windle, 2001; Tye-Murray, 1993), a caveat should always be kept in mind: avoid making sweeping generalizations. Stereotypes are neither recommended nor practiced by experienced and highly-qualified auditory-verbal professionals. Some children who are in AVT do not need or want special or support services. A wise parent comes to understand that more is not necessarily better.

That said, it is understood that children in Auditory-Verbal therapy need to be made aware of all possible support services and delivery models, including collaboration, pull-out, and co-teaching, that can be offered by competent itinerant teachers and other personnel (Hyde & Power, 2004), in addition to assistive listening system options. The critical factor is that the child should make the request, if for no other reason than that he or she owns the deafness.

It is sometimes thought that even children who are progressing in Auditory-Verbal therapy are "at risk" for not reaching full potential, perhaps because they are missing some information each day. One must ask: Just exactly what information is the child missing? How important is the missed information? Is the child aware that some information is missed? If so, are repair strategies being used? If not, why not? Who is abrogating responsibility, and for what? Is the missed information placing the child at risk for failure? Do children with typical hearing always reach their full potential? At what cost do we strive to enable the child who is hearing impaired to attain full potential? Do we continue spoon-feeding the child so that no information is "missed"? What is the trade-off in that child's life? Sometimes sacrifices must be made for the greater good, i.e., enabling the child to become an independently effective learner so that he or she is integral to the mainstream of life.

Certified Auditory-Verbal therapists practice a specialty within the profession of audiology, teaching, or speech-language pathology. Like any area of specialization, certain tenets of knowledge characterize its uniqueness. Auditory-verbal professionals embrace a variety of therapeutic strategies that emphasize primary dependency on audition. Such strategies are improved over time, particularly as research findings yield additional information about the development of auditory-verbal communication. When Auditory-Verbal therapists provide auditory-based therapy rather than AVT, it can be viewed as more traditional auditory training in the hope that the process will evolve into AVT.

On the other hand, auditory training, listening therapy, speech-language therapy, or aural rehabilitation is what it is, without intending to evolve into something else. Just like certified Auditory-Verbal therapists, other professionals should continually learn new skills that will improve their delivery of services. Unfortunately, some public school systems provide neither adequate support services nor appropriately trained personnel for children who rely primarily on their use of audition in learning. Consequently, some certified Auditory-Verbal therapists can and do assist children within those school systems, and no fault can be found with this practice. But this type of assistance is not AVT and should not be called such.

It is hoped that an increasing number of teachers, speech-language pathologists, and audiologists will seek certification in Auditory-Verbal therapy. Increased knowledge can only benefit our children. However, because many professionals are unable to obtain all the AVT hours needed for certification, it is at least hoped that more audiologists, speech-language pathologists, and teachers will learn about the auditory-verbal approach, so that highly effective auditory-based strategies can be incorporated into their own model of service delivery.

AVT is currently facing several far-reaching changes and has areas of controversy. Given the widespread implementation of universal newborn hearing screening, more auditory-verbal professionals are increasingly working with primary caregivers who have very young children, from birth to 3 years of age. As a result, auditory-verbal professionals need to differentiate clearly between the delivery of services that are developmental and those that are remedial (Fey, 1986). An increasing number of auditory-verbal professionals (Rhoades, 2004) are arguing that we should not lay claim to the practice of AVT for most of our grade-school children. The effectiveness and efficiency of Auditory-Verbal therapists who seem to need significantly more than 5 years to guide each primary caregiver in the "creation" of a linguistically competent child, particularly if that child does not manifest significant developmental delays, is being called into question.

The 21st century heralds a new era for the child who is born deaf or hard of hearing. In westernized countries, early identification, early amplification/implantation, and early family-focused intervention are much more evident today. This welcome evolution has dramatically changed the face and future of AVT. The confident auditory-verbal professional embraces these long overdue changes, and this necessarily affects the perception and delivery of auditory-verbal services for the child who must wear the ownership mantle of deafness, so that ultimately, and deservedly so, he or she can become a self-actualized human being.

The Chinese philosopher Lao Tzu said, "Give a man a fish and you feed him for a day. Teach him how to fish and you feed him for a lifetime."

REFERENCES

Boysson-Bardies, B. (1999). *How language comes to children: From birth to two years.* Cambridge, MA: The MIT Press.

Crystal, D., Fletcher, P. & Garman, M. (1978). *The grammatical analysis of language disability.* London, UK: Edward Arnold.

Dunn, L.M., & Dunn, L.M. (1997). *Peabody Picture Vocabulary Test-III.* Circle Pines, MN: American Guidance Service.

Fey, M. (1986). *Language intervention with young children.* Western Ontario: Allyn & Bacon.

Galvin, K.L., Sarant, J.Z., & Cowan, R.S.C. (1997). Habilitation: School-aged children. In G.M. Clark, R.S.C. Cowan, & R. Dowell (Eds.), *Cochlear implantation for infants and children* (pp. 191-204). San Diego, CA: Singular Publishing.

Goldberg, D. (1997). Educating children who are deaf or hard of hearing: auditory-verbal. *ERIC Digest #E552.*

Hull, R. H. (1992). *Aural rehabilitation: Serving children and adults.* San Diego, CA: Singular Publishing.

Hyde, M.B., & Power, D.J. (2004). Cochlear Implants in deaf children: A review of research. The Encyclopaedia of Disability. Chicago: Sage Publishers.

Juszcyk, P.W. (1998). *The discovery of spoken language.* Cambridge MA: MIT Press.

Koch, M.E. (1999). *Bringing sound to life: Principles and practices of cochlear implant rehabilitation.* Bethesda, MD: York Press.

Pinker, S. (1994). *The language instinct: How the mind creates language.* New York: HarperCollins.

Rafferty, Y., Piscitelli, V., & Boettcher, C. (2003). The impact of inclusion on language development and social competence among preschoolers with disabilities. *Exceptional Children, 69,* 467-479.

Rhoades, E.A., & Jovanovic, S. (2002, June). *Auditory learning and telephone training for teens and adults with cochlear implants.* Workshop presented at the 2002 Convention of the Alexander Graham Bell Association for the Deaf and Hard of Hearing, St. Louis, MO.

Rhoades, E.A. (2004). Learning to listen while coming of age. *ASHA Division 9: Perspectives on hearing and hearing disorders in childhood, 14*(2), 4-8.

Rhoades, E.A. (2003). Lexical-semantic and morpho-syntactic language assessment in auditory-verbal intervention: a position paper. *The Volta Review, 103*(3), 169-184.

Rhoades, E.A. (2001). Language progress with an auditory-verbal approach for young children with hearing loss. *International Pediatrics, 16*(1), 41-47.

Rhoades, E.A. & Chisolm, T. (2001). Global language progress with an auditory-verbal approach for children with hearing loss. *The Volta Review, 102*(1), 5-24.

Stout, G.G., & Windle, J.V.E. (2001) *Developmental approach to successful listening-II.* Englewood, CO: Resource Point.

Tye-Murray, N. (1993). *Communication training for children and teenagers: Speech, listening, speechreading, and using repair strategies.* Austin, TX: Pro-Ed.

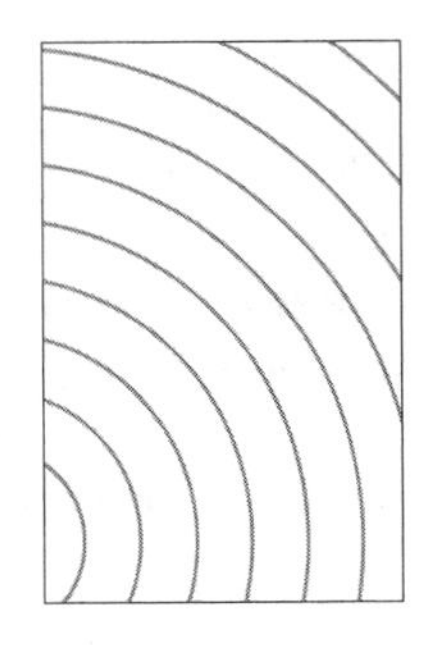

Contributors

Anne Beiter, M.S., FAAA, CCC-A, SLP, is an audiologist and speech-language pathologist who has worked for Cochlear Ltd., where she is currently global clinical director, since 1986. She has managed clinical support services and professional education for Cochlear Americas and also has been involved with cochlear implant adult and pediatric clinical trials. Beiter has presented papers at numerous conferences and published in professional journals and books.

Anita Bernstein, B.A. (Hons.), Dip. Spec. Ed., M.Sc. (A), Cert. AVT®, is director of therapy services for VOICE for Hearing-Impaired Children in Ontario, Canada. She is a course director at York University in the Deaf and Hard of Hearing Program. Bernstein has been a member of the Certification Council for Auditory-Verbal International, Inc., and was the recipient of the Alexander Graham Bell Association Professional of the Year Award in 2000. She continues to contribute to the literature.

Dorothy Boothroyd-Turner, B.A., M.E.D., coordinated the mainstream support program for the Toronto District School Board for almost 20 years prior to her retirement. She has conducted research and reported on Integration Support Units as an alternative service delivery model and (with Dr. Arthur Boothroyd) on the characteristics and attainment of children with cochlear implants. She is a founding director of the provincial organization of VOICE for Hearing-Impaired Children and was active in the development of the Auditory-Verbal Program at North York General Hospital 25 years ago. Currently she is an educational consultant, fulfilling special-education contracts for the Ontario Ministry of Education.

Teresa H. Caraway, Ph.D., CCC-SLP, Cert. AVT®, is clinical education director of the Hearing Enrichment Language Program (HELP) in Oklahoma City, Oklahoma. She is president of the AG Bell Academy for Listening and Spoken Language®. Caraway is an accomplished consultant and workshop presenter who blends research into clinical practice.

Teresa Caruso-Peters, M.Sc. (A), Aud. (C), Cert. AVT®, currently provides a full range of audiological services in private practice. She is the former clinical director of the Central Speech and Hearing Clinic in Winnipeg, Manitoba, Canada. Her areas of expertise include pediatric audiology, Auditory-Verbal therapy, cochlear implant programming, and (re)habilitation and mentorship.

Maria Emilia (Mila) De Melo, M.Fga., S-LP, Aud. (C), Reg. CASPLO, Cert. AVT®, is a speech-language pathologist, audiologist, and certified Auditory-Verbal therapist. She is the coordinator of research and development at the Learning to Listen Foundation (LTLF), North York General Hospital in Toronto, Canada. De Melo presents at many conferences and continues to train professionals worldwide. Her contributions to the literature include *Listen to This, Volume 1* (2004) and *Listen to This, Volume 2* (2006).

Carolyne Edwards, M.Cl.Sc., M.B.A., is director of Auditory Management Services, a private educational audiology practice that provides consultation in acoustical and auditory issues related to the education of school-aged children to many school districts in southwestern Ontario. She is the author of a number of publications and book chapters in the area of educational audiology and lectures throughout North America. She is also a member of faculty at the Gestalt Institute of Toronto.

Alice Eriks-Brophy, B.A., B.Ed., M.Sc. (A), M.Sc., Ph.D., is an assistant professor in the Graduate Department of Speech-Language Pathology at the University of Toronto. Her current research examines the role of parental involvement in early intervention for children who are deaf or hard of hearing, as well as outcomes of early identification and intervention. Formerly, Eriks-Brophy worked as an itinerant teacher for the Montreal Oral School for the Deaf and as an elementary classroom teacher on several First Nations reserves in northern and southern Québec.

Donald M. Goldberg, Ph.D., CCC-SLP/A, FAAA, Cert. AVT®, is currently co-director of the Hearing Implant Program (HIP) at the Head and Neck Institute of the Cleveland Clinic Foundation. He also maintains a private practice in auditory-verbal intervention in Brecksville, Ohio. Goldberg is former executive director of the Helen Beebe Speech and Hearing Center in Pennsylvania and is a co-author of *Educational Audiology for the Limited-Hearing Infant and Preschooler: An Auditory-Verbal Program* (Pollack, Goldberg, & Caleffe-Schenck, 1997).

K. Todd Houston, Ph.D., CCC-SLP, Cert. AVT®, is executive director and chief executive officer of the Alexander Graham Bell Association for the Deaf and Hard of Hearing in Washington, DC. As a certified Auditory-Verbal therapist and a speech-language pathologist, Houston has experience serving children with hearing loss in residential, public school, and clinical settings; he has also held positions as a cochlear implant program director, researcher, and professor. Houston continues to lecture both nationally and internationally, presenting workshops, scientific papers, and keynote addresses on a variety of topics related to childhood hearing loss.

Lisa Katz, M.H.Sc., S-LP (C), Reg. CASLPO, Cert. AVT®, is an Auditory-Verbal therapist and coordinator of professional education at the Learning to Listen Foundation in Toronto, Canada. Katz is actively involved in providing leadership in the training of professionals in Auditory-Verbal therapy. She has contributed to the literature and has presented papers and seminars at a number of national and international conferences.

Daniel Ling, Ph.D., was one of the most famous educators of children who are deaf or hard of hearing. He made hundreds of contributions to the literature, was a sought-after speaker, and revered by students, colleagues, and families. His landmark publication *Speech and the Hearing-Impaired Child* is still widely considered the classic in its field. Ling received many awards including the prestigious Order of Canada.

Karen MacIver-Lux, M.A., Aud. (C), Reg. CASLPO, Cert. AVT®, is coordinator of clinical services and an Auditory-Verbal therapist at the Learning to Listen Foundation in Toronto, Canada. She has a congenital, severe-to-profound hearing loss. MacIver-Lux has been honored by *Maclean's* magazine as one of the Top 100 Young Canadians and received the Who's Who in Students of American Colleges and Universities Award. She has contributed to several publications (*The Listener, 50 FAQs About AVT, Songs for Listening! Songs for Life!, Listen to This*) and continues to train professionals and lecture internationally.

Wendy S. Meschino, M.D., FRCPC, FCCMG, is a clinical geneticist and associate chief of the genetics program at North York General Hospital in Toronto, Canada. She is an assistant professor at the University of Toronto and has authored numerous scientific papers. Her interests include communication of genetic information to health care professionals, patients, and the public.

Tina Olmstead, M.Sc., Cert. AVT®, is a certified Auditory-Verbal therapist and a teacher of children who are deaf or hard of hearing. She works with school-aged children and their families in the Ottawa–Carleton District School Board in Ottawa, Ontario, Canada. She lectures internationally, contributes to the professional literature, and has served as a member of the board of directors for VOICE and Auditory-Verbal International, Inc.

Ellen A. Rhoades, Ed.S., Cert. AVT®, is an international consultant who has been recognized with many awards. She has written many papers for peer-reviewed publications and served as director on the boards of Auditory-Verbal International, Inc., the Alexander Graham Bell Association for the Deaf and

Hard of Hearing, and non-profit auditory-verbal centers. In addition to having founded an AV center and directed it for 25 years, her experience includes university instructor, Auditory-Verbal therapist, classroom teacher, supervisor, parent–infant coordinator, adult rehabilitation clinician, and grant writer/fundraiser/marketer. Owing to bilateral congenital sensorineural deafness, she uses binaural cochlear implants.

Ariella Blum Samson, M.A., is a parent and grandparent of children who are deaf or hard of hearing. She currently resides in Toronto, where she is on the board of directors of the Learning to Listen Foundation. A long time member of the Alexander Graham Bell Association for the Deaf and Hard of Hearing, Samson has contributed to the literature in *Do You Hear That?* and *Auditory-Verbal Therapy for Parents and Professionals.* She also contributed to the video, *Jacob's Journey,* which can be obtained in several languages from Cochlear Americas.

Wendy Sheppard, B.A., B.Ed., has worked with students who are deaf or hard of hearing in mainstream programs for 20 years. Her experience includes extensive work with cochlear implant users, students at all school levels, and families in the Parent Guidance Program. Currently, she coordinates sthe Special Education – Hearing Itinerant Program for the Toronto District School Board.

Judith I. Simser, O.Ont., B.Ed., Dip. Ed. Deaf, Cert. AVT®, is an international consultant in childhood hearing impairment. She has trained many therapists and established auditory-verbal centers in Taiwan and Singapore, where she also trained professionals. Simser is a past president of Auditory-Verbal International and has received many awards and honors for her work. She is a frequent contributor to the literature and the parent of an adult son who is profoundly deaf.

Pamela Steacie, M.Sc., Cert. AVT®, obtained a master's degree in aural habilitation from McGill University in 1980. She is a certified Auditory-Verbal therapist who has worked for most of the last 25 years at the Children's Hospital of Eastern Ontario. She has lectured and published about Auditory-Verbal therapy in both English and French.

Sally Tannenbaum, M.Ed., C.E.D., Cert. AVT®, is a certified educator of the deaf and a certified Auditory-Verbal therapist in private practice in Chicago, IL. Tannenbaum has made many presentations worldwide and served on the board of directors of Auditory-Verbal International. She has worked as part of many professional teams and contributed to the literature in *Cochlear Implants for Kids* (Estabrooks, W. (Ed.), 1998).

Beth Walker, M.Ed., C.E.D., Cert. AVT®, is an Auditory-Verbal therapist on the cochlear implant team at East Alabama Ear, Nose and Throat in Opelika, Alabama. She has been teaching and learning from children who are deaf or hard of hearing and their families for over 25 years. She has served as an educational consultant to programs in the United States and abroad.

Ellen Yack, B.Sc.O.T., is the president of Ellen Yack and Associates Pediatric Occupational Therapy Services in Toronto, Canada. As an expert in sensory integration, Yack has made many presentations around the world and has contributed substantially to the literature, including *Auditory-Verbal Therapy for Parents and Professionals* (Estabrooks, W. (Ed.), 1994).